Advances in

CONTROL SYSTEMS

Theory and Applications

Volume 8

CONTRIBUTORS TO THIS VOLUME

KENNETH B. BLEY
L. F. BUCHANAN
THOMAS S. FONG
R. R. IYER
C. T. LEONDES
A. V. LEVY
A. MIELE
S. NAQVI
F. E. NORTON
C. E. SEAL
KURT SIMON
EDWIN B. STEAR
ALLEN STUBBERUD
C. H. WELLS
D. A. WISMER

ADVANCES IN

CONTROL SYSTEMS

THEORY AND APPLICATIONS

Edited by

C. T. LEONDES

Department of Engineering
University of California
Los Angeles, California

VOLUME 8 1971

ACADEMIC PRESS New York and London

ACADEMIC PRESS, INC.
111 Fifth Avenue, New York, New York 10003

United Kingdom Edition published by
ACADEMIC PRESS, INC. (LONDON) LTD.
24/28 Oval Road, London NW1 7DD

LIBRARY OF CONGRESS CATALOG CARD NUMBER: 64-8027

PRINTED IN THE UNITED STATES OF AMERICA

Contents

Discrete Stochastic Differential Games

Kenneth B. Bley and Edwin B. Stear

Optimal Control Applications in Economic Systems

L. F. Buchanan and F. E. Norton

Numerical Solution of Nonlinear Equations and Nonlinear, Two-Point Boundary-Value Problems

A. Miele, S. Naqvi, A. V. Levy, and R. R. Iyer

Advances in Process Control Applications

C. H. Wells and D. A. Wismer

Contributors

Numbers in parentheses indicate the pages on which the authors' contributions begin.

KENNETH B. BLEY, Hughes Aircraft Company, El Segundo, California (89)

L. F. BUCHANAN, General Dynamics Corporation, Electro Dynamic Division, Pomona Operation, Pomona, California (141)

THOMAS S. FONG,* University of California, Los Angeles, California (1)

R. R. IYER, Department of Mechanical and Aerospace Engineering and Materials Science, Rice University, Houston, Texas (189)

C. T. LEONDES, University of California, Los Angeles, California (1)

A. V. LEVY, Department of Mechanical and Aerospace Engineering and Materials Science, Rice University, Houston, Texas (189)

A. MIELE, Department of Mechanical and Aerospace Engineering and Materials Science, Rice University, Houston, Texas (189)

S. NAQVI, Department of Mechanical and Aerospace Engineering and Materials Science, Rice University, Houston, Texas (189)

F. E. NORTON, Graduate School of Business Administration, University of California, Los Angeles, California (141)

C. E. SEAL, TRW Systems Group, Redondo Beach, California (23)

KURT SIMON, TRW Systems, Inc., Redondo Beach, California (53)

EDWIN B. STEAR, School of Electrical Engineering, University of California, Santa Barbara, California (89)

ALLEN STUBBERUD, School of Engineering, University of California, Irvine, California (23, 53)

C. H. WELLS, Systems Control, Inc., Palo Alto, California (217)

D. A. WISMER, Systems Control, Inc., Palo Alto, California (217)

* Present address: Research and Development Division, Hughes Aircraft Co., Culver City, California.

Preface

The eighth volume of *Advances in Control Systems* continues the purpose of this serial publication in bringing together diverse information on important progress in the field of control and systems theory and applications as achieved and presented by leading contributors. The growing emphasis on application to large scale systems and decision making is increasingly evident in this volume.

The contribution by T. Fong and C. T. Leondes treats the important issue of an effective algorithm for dynamic system optimization with state variable constraints. Since the early important work of the application of steepest descent or gradient techniques to dynamic optimization problems some ten years ago, convergence difficulties were noted in that steepest descent techniques were very slow to converge. One of the contributions by D. E. Johansen in Volume 4 noted the fundamental reason for this, and efforts were made to develop algorithms for dynamic systems optimization with improved convergence rates. This first contribution presents an algorithm based on the conjugate gradient method extended to include bounds on the state variable which has proven to be most effective in various applications studies.

Final value control systems problems arise in a number of problems. The contribution by C. Seal and A. R. Stubberud addresses these issues and lists a number of fundamental problems in this important area. A number of effective techniques for the analysis and syntheses of final value control systems will be found in this contribution.

Since Kalman's pioneering work on filtering techniques, a number of significant problems associated with the practical application of Kalman Filter techniques have been identified, and methods dealing with these have evolved. The paper by K. Simon and A. R. Stubberud is a comprehensive and unified treatment of the subject of Kalman Filtering, expounding on a number of fundamental difficulties. Methods for treating these are included. Users of Kalman Filter methods will find this contribution to be indispensable.

Over the past several years a considerable amount of research and applications interest has been generated in the broad area of differential games. Techniques for two-sided differential games have proved especially difficult to develop. What usually has been done by research workers in the field is to start out with a difficult and meaningful differential game problem and successively introduce simplifying constraints until the problem could become tractable. The article by K. B. Bley and E. B. Stear presents new and significant techniques for discrete stochastic differential games. The techniques presented are quite effective in themselves, but will no doubt inspire further efforts by workers interested in this field.

The applications of control techniques in the forties were to rather simple problems. The problems grew in complexity in the fifties, but were still somewhat simple. Now that control technology has matured considerably the applications are to much more difficult problems. One of the most difficult areas of application and yet, potentially, clearly one of the most significant, is to large-scale economic problems. The contribution by L. F. Buchanan and F. E. Norton is viewed here as being most significant in this regard. Hopefully, the passage of time will see a greater utilization of the techniques and methods presented in this paper on optimal control applications in economic systems to problems on the national and international scene.

Professor A. Miele and his associates at Rice University are doing some of the most significant and fundamental work on the international scene in the development of effective algorithms for dynamic system optimization. In this volume we have the first of two very important contributions by this group, including A. Miele, S. Naqvi, A. B. Levy, and R. R. Iyer. The next volume will contain another contribution on their significant results which will no doubt find widespread practical application.

This volume concludes with a comprehensive treatment by C. H. Wells and D. A. Wismer of the application of modern control methods to complex industrial process control problems. This rather unique contribution on the international scene identifies all of the basic problem issues identified to date in this broad area and presents techniques for dealing with them. To illustrate the many important notions, a rather comprehensive industrial process drawn from the steel industry is treated in depth. It is probably fair to say that the contribution by Wells and Wismer could be a standard and important reference item in this field for years to come.

C. T. Leondes

August 1971

Contents of Previous Volumes

Volume 1

Volume 2

Volume 3

Volume 4

Volume 5

Volume 6

Volume 7

Advances in

CONTROL SYSTEMS

Theory and Applications

Volume 8

Method of Conjugate Gradients for Optimal Control Problems with State Variable Constraint[1]

THOMAS S. FONG[2] AND C. T. LEONDES

University of California
Los Angeles, California

I. Introduction

The past decade has seen considerable progress in techniques for optimization of nonlinear dynamical systems. The development of large digital computers coupled with the interest in optimal control theory,

[1] This work was supported by the Air Force Office of Scientific Research under AFOSR Grant 699-67.

[2] *Present Address:* Research and Development Division, Hughes Aircraft Co., Culver City, California.

particularly in optimizing of spacecraft trajectories, has inspired a large volume of literature devoted to both the mathematical theory of optimal processes and the methods for obtaining solutions to these problems. Nevertheless, from the computational standpoint, the class of control problems with constrained state variables has scarcely been considered, although these types of problems often occur in engineering practice. For example, the velocity of a vehicle may be limited by structure breakdown, or a motor may be overloaded to prevent safety and reliability of operation. Bryson, Denham and Dreyfus (*1*, *2*) and Starr (*3*) have treated this class of problems using the steepest descent technique and a suitable combination of various nongradient techniques, respectively. Others (*2*, *4*) have reduced the constrained problem to unconstrained status by introducing the penalty function in place of the constraints on the state variables.

Whereas the method of steepest descent is excellent for finding an approximate solution quickly, it often exhibits very slow convergence. Other techniques frequently face the problem of computational stability in the solution of the two-point boundary value problem. It is hoped that the method of conjugate gradients will offer an improved and more efficient computational method, which is the objective of this study.

The method of conjugate gradients, an iterative technique, was originally developed for solving linear systems of algebraic equations independently by Hestenes and Stiefel (*5*, *6*) in 1952. Further extensions of this method have been done by Hayes (*7*), Antosiewicz and Rheinboldt (*8*), and Daniel (*9*). On application of this technique to optimal control, Lasdon, Mitter, and Waren (*10*), and Sinnott and Luenberger (*11*) have treated unconstrained problems with considerable success. In the field of antenna theory, Fong (*12*) has applied this technique in pattern synthesis where nonlinear integral equations were to be solved.

In the following, a problem with state variable constraint of moderate difficulty is considered in order that the features of the method can be observed with greater clarity, although this technique has been applied to a problem with state variable constraint of greater complexity (*13*).

II. The Conjugate Gradient Algorithm

Let E be a convex performance functional defined on the set Q. Let $\nabla E(u)$ and $F(u)$ be the gradient and Hessian of the performance functional evaluated at the point u, respectively. The algorithm of the conjugate gradient method for solving nonlinear operator equations of the form $\nabla E(u) = 0$, i.e., minimizing E, is given below. For detailed development, the reader is referred to reference (*9*). To obtain u^*, the solution to the operator equation, let u_0 be arbitrary, and $p_0 = -\nabla E(u_0)$. Having obtained u_n, p_n, and $\nabla E(u_n)$, the iteration is continued according to the expressions below:

$$u_{n+1} = u_n + \alpha_n p_n \tag{1}$$

where α_n is the value of α that minimizes $E(u_n + \alpha p_n)$, $u_n + \alpha p_n \in Q$.

$$\beta_n = \frac{\langle \nabla E(u_{n+1}), F(u_{n+1}) p_n \rangle}{\langle p_n, F(u_{n+1}) p_n \rangle} \tag{2}$$

$$p_{n+1} = -\nabla E(u_{n+1}) + \beta_n p_n \tag{3}$$

Since $F(u)$ depends on u in general, if we generate conjugate directions p_n with respect to $F(u)$, we can at most assert that any two consecutive p_n elements are $F(u)$-conjugate, while the other elements are approximately $F(u)$-conjugate depending on how near u is to the solution u^*.

III. The Class of Control Problems to Be Considered

Our ultimate goal is to apply the conjugate gradient technique to solve the class of control problems which we formulate below. Suppose that the dynamical system is governed by the differential equation

$$d\mathbf{x}/dt = f(\mathbf{x}, u) \tag{4}$$

where $\mathbf{x}$ is a real n-vector for each t, called the state of the system; u is a real m-vector for each t, called the control variable of the system. Let $\mathbf{x}(t_0)$ be the initial state of the system, and let it be desired to transfer the system from the given initial state to some final state lying on a smooth hypersurface

$$\psi[\mathbf{x}(t_f)] = 0 \tag{5}$$

where the terminal time t_f is not fixed, while the states are confined to within a closed region in an n-dimensional Euclidean space E^n given by the inequality

$$g(\mathbf{x}) \leqslant 0. \tag{6}$$

where g is an N-time continuously differentiable function of $\mathbf{x}$. We will call a control u an element in the space of piecewise continuous functions on $[t_0, t_f]$ admissible, if the corresponding trajectory in E^n does not violate the state constraints above for all $t \in [t_0, t_f]$, and denote this set of controls by Q. Let the performance functional be

$$E(u) = w[\mathbf{x}(t_f)] + \int_{t_0}^{t_f} L(u, \mathbf{x})\, dt \tag{7}$$

or alternatively as in the formulation of Mayer,

$$E(u) = \phi[x(t_f)] \tag{8}$$

a function of end values of the states, where $x(t_f)$ is an augmented $(n+1)$-vector. In the following, x will be used to denote either the n-vector or the augmented $(n+1)$-vector without further specifying whenever the situation is clear from the context.

The problem's objective is to find the control u in Q that minimizes the performance functional while satisfying the conditions (4), (5) and (6). We will make an assumption that there exists a unique solution to this minimization problem.

IV. Computational Considerations

A. Nomenclature

For each control u in Q, there corresponds a trajectory in E^n. It may consist of two types of arcs. The portion of a trajectory in which the states satisfy

$$g(x) < 0 \tag{9}$$

will be called an interior arc, and the portion that satisfies

$$g(x) = 0 \tag{10}$$

will be called a boundary arc. The trajectory corresponding to the control $u^* \in Q$ that minimizes the performance functional is termed the optimal trajectory. The smallest value of t, say t_1, for which $x(t_1)$ lies on the constraining surfaces $g(x) = 0$ is called entering time, and $x(t_1)$, the entering corner. The largest t, say t_2, for which $x(t_2)$ lies on the constraining surface $g(x) = 0$ is called exit time, and $x(t_2)$, the exit corner. We will consider only the cases in which the optimal trajectory enters the constraining surface at most once. (See Fig. 1.)

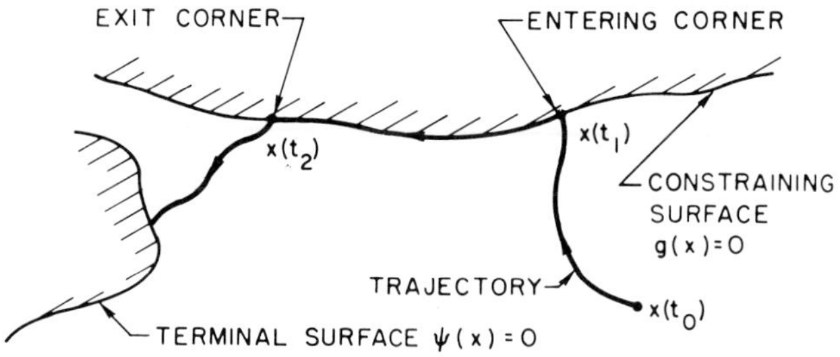

FIG. 1. Illustration of a typical trajectory.

B. Control on the Boundary Arc

For the period $t \in [t_1, t_2]$ along the boundary arc, the states are interrelated by

$$g(x) = 0 \tag{11}$$

It follows from the fact that along the boundary arc, the constraint function must vanish identically, which implies that

$$d^j g/dt^j = 0, \qquad j = 1, 2, \ldots \tag{12}$$

The first time derivative of g has a very simple geometric interpretation. It states that the boundary arc is normal to the gradient of g. That is,

$$dg/dt = \langle \nabla g, dx/dt \rangle = 0 \tag{13}$$

The control u will be determined according to (13), if u appears explicitly in the expression. If it does not, we may consider the second derivative or higher derivatives so that u will appear explicitly in $d^N g/dt^N = 0$. If the system is controllable, the existence of a smallest integer N, the order of the derivative of g for which u appears explicitly is assured. From (11) and (12) in particular for $t = t_1$, we have

$$g[x(t_1)] = 0 \tag{14}$$

$$(d^j g/dt^j)[x(t_1)] = 0 \qquad j = 1, \ldots, N-1 \tag{15}$$

It is worthy to note that Eq. (14) and (15) along with the control u satisfying

$$d^N g/dt^N = 0 \tag{16}$$

imply that

$$d^j g/dt^j = 0 \qquad j = 0, 1, \ldots, N \tag{17}$$

for all $t \in [t_1, t_2]$.

We will make the necessary assumptions, such as g has no singular point, i.e., $\nabla g(x) \neq 0$, to permit a possible unique solution for u in terms of the states in (16).

C. The Frechet Differentials of the Performance Functional

Let $\lambda(t)$ be the costate vector and $H(x, \lambda, u,) = \langle \lambda, f(x, u) \rangle$ be the Hamiltonian of the system. Treating the conditions (4), (5), (14) and (15) as constraints, consider the performance functional E at u,

$$E(u) = \phi[x(t_f)] + \nu\psi[x(t_f)] + \langle \mu, S[x(t_1)] \rangle + \int_{t_0}^{t_f} \left[H(x, \lambda, u) - \left\langle \lambda, \frac{dx}{dt} \right\rangle \right] dt \tag{18}$$

where ν is a constant, μ is a constant N-vector and

$$S[x(t_1)] = \begin{bmatrix} g[x(t_1)] \\ \dfrac{dg}{dt}[x(t_1)] \\ \vdots \\ \dfrac{d^{N-1}g}{dt^{N-1}}[x(t_1)] \end{bmatrix} \tag{19}$$

The first Frechet differential is

$$\langle \nabla E, h \rangle = \int_{t_0}^{t_1} \frac{\partial H}{\partial u} h\, dt + \int_{t_2}^{t_f} \frac{\partial H}{\partial u} h\, dt \tag{20}$$

where h denotes the perturbation on the control, and consequently the gradient of the performance functional is

$$\nabla E(u) = \frac{\partial H}{\partial u}(x, \lambda, u) \tag{21}$$

for $t \in [t_0, t_1)$ or $t \in (t_2, t_f]$ with the following conditions satisfied by the costate λ:

(i) $$\frac{d\lambda}{dt} + \frac{\partial H}{\partial x} = 0^{3} \qquad \text{for } t \in [t_0, t_1) \quad \text{and} \quad t \in (t_2, t_f]. \tag{22}$$

(ii) On the boundary arc, for $t \in (t_1, t_2)$,

$$\frac{d\lambda}{dt} + \frac{\partial f}{\partial x}\lambda + \left\langle \frac{\partial f}{\partial u}, \lambda \right\rangle \left[\frac{\partial}{\partial u}\left(\frac{\partial^N g}{\partial t^N}\right)\right]^{-1} \frac{\partial}{\partial x}\left(\frac{\partial^N g}{\partial t^N}\right) = 0^{3} \tag{23}$$

λ on the boundary arc is not unique, and this is one of the choices.

(iii) At t_1, t_2, and t_f,

$$\lambda(t_1^-) = \lambda(t_1^+) + \left.\frac{\partial S}{\partial x}\right|_{t1} \mu \tag{24}$$

$$\left\langle \lambda, \frac{dx}{dt} \right\rangle_{t_1^-} = \left\langle \lambda, \frac{dx}{dt} \right\rangle_{t_1^+} \tag{25}$$

$$\lambda(t_2^-) = \lambda(t_2^+) \tag{26}$$

$$\left\langle \lambda, \frac{dx}{dt} \right\rangle_{t_2^-} = \left\langle \lambda, \frac{dx}{dt} \right\rangle_{t_2^+} \tag{27}$$

[3] The quantities $\partial H/\partial u$, $\partial f/\partial x$, etc., are to be evaluated along the optimal trajectory.

$$\lambda(t_f) = \frac{\partial \phi}{\partial x}(t_f) + \nu \frac{\partial \psi}{\partial x}(t_f) \tag{28}$$

$$\left\langle \lambda, \frac{dx}{dt} \right\rangle_{t_f} = 0 \tag{29}$$

Equations (25) and (27) indicate that the Hamiltonian is continuous at the entering and exit corners, and Eqs. (26) and (24) show that the costate is continuous at the exit corner and discontinuous at the entering corner with a jump equal to $\partial S/\partial x|_{t_1}\mu$.

Let z be the solution of the linearized perturbation of (4) in the unconstrained regions, i.e.,

$$\frac{dz}{dt} = \frac{\partial f}{\partial x} z + \frac{\partial f}{\partial u} h \tag{30}$$

Then

$$z(t) = \Phi(t, t_j)z(t_j) + \int_{t_j}^{t} \Phi(t, \tau) \frac{\partial f}{\partial u}(\tau)h(\tau)\, d\tau \tag{31}$$

where Φ is the fundamental matrix and $t_j = t_0, t_2^+$. Writing (31) as $z = Th$ and letting $W = [^T_I]$ where I is the identity operator, the second Frechet differential is given by

$$\langle h, F(u)h \rangle = \left\langle h, T^\dagger \frac{\partial^2 \phi}{\partial x^2} Th \right\rangle_{t_f} + \left\langle h, \nu T^\dagger \frac{\partial^2 \psi}{\partial x^2} Th \right\rangle_{t_f} + \left\langle h, T^\dagger \frac{\partial^2 S}{\partial x^2} Th \right\rangle_{t_1}$$

$$+ \int_{t_0}^{t_1} + \int_{t_2}^{t_f} \left\langle h, W^\dagger \begin{bmatrix} \dfrac{\partial^2 H}{\partial x^2} & \dfrac{\partial}{\partial u}\left(\dfrac{\partial H}{\partial x}\right) \\ \dfrac{\partial}{\partial x}\left(\dfrac{\partial H}{\partial u}\right) & \dfrac{\partial^2 H}{\partial u^2} \end{bmatrix} Wh \right\rangle dt \tag{32}$$

(where † denotes adjoint) from which we can obtain the Hessian of the performance functional. Because the computation for the Hessian is quite involved in general in addition to the uncertainty about the optimal trajectory which introduces error in (32), the estimated Hessian may, or at least in the first few iterations, be approximated by $\partial^2 H/\partial u^2$, since the term $\langle h, (\partial^2 H/\partial u^2)h \rangle$ is the "most" dependent on h in Eq. (32)(*14*).

D. Computation for the Costate

In order to obtain the Hamiltonian at the nth iteration on which the gradient and Hessian are based, we must have the state variable and the costate in addition to the control u_n chosen for that iteration. Since the state variable is continuous and the initial condition is given, solving Eq. (4) is a straightforward problem, provided that the estimated quantities t_1, t_2, and t_f are settled. We will elaborate upon this point in the next subsection. On the other hand, the determination of the costate requires more considerations. Since the boundary condition for the costate is specified at the terminal time t_f and the costate is continuous at the exit corner, thus $\lambda(t)$ for $t \in (t_1{}^+, t_f]$ may be determined simply by solving the differential Eq. (22) and (23) backward in time using the latest estimated control and state variable. At the entering corner, when $t = t_1$, the costate may be discontinuous. In principle, it is possible to determine $\lambda(t_1{}^-)$, μ, t_1, a total of $N + n + 1$ unknown quantities, from Eqs. (24), (25), (14), and (15) as long as these equations are independent. Since in any stage of the iteration process, the time at which the trajectory reaches the constraint surface t_1 is in general not equal to $t_1{}^*$, the optimal time, an exact solution to the above quantities is not really essential if some means are taken to improve the estimates of these quantities as the process progresses. Initially, a trial and error technique may be used to obtain an approximation to these quantities. Depending on the problem at hand, examination of the Hamiltonian for $t \in [t_0, t_1]$ often provides a way to improve the estimates at each step. This is the most difficult part of the computation and also one of the most time-consuming portions of the iteration process.

After the estimate of $\lambda(t_1{}^-)$ is selected, the costate in the remaining portion for $t \in [t_0, t_1]$ may again resort to solving the differential equation (22).

E. Entering Time and Exit Time

Since the control program is updated at each step according to

$$u_{n+1} = u_n + \alpha_n p_n \tag{33}$$

the new trajectory may reach the constraint surface sooner or later than the previous iteration. In other words, the entering time in general varies with each iteration, and it is dictated by the control chosen. If t_1^{n}[4] is larger than $t_1^{(n+1)}$, there is no problem. However, when the opposite is true, then some extension on u_{n+1} must be made for the time interval $[t_1^{(n)}, t_1^{(n+1)}]$ such as

$$u_{n+1}(t) = u_n[t_1^{(n)}] \tag{34}$$

[4] $t_1^{(m)}$ denotes t_1 for the mth iteration.

or some convenient extrapolation based on $u_n[t_1^{(n)}]$ and the rate of change of u_n near $t_1^{(n)}$. When the estimated solution is near the optimum, signify by relatively small values of $\nabla E(u_n)$, a more accurate determination for the entering time and the entering corner being desirable (also the terminal time and terminal state), some refinement in step size "dt" in solving the differential equation near t_1 is necessary in order to minimize rounding errors.

Concerning the exit time, as it was observed by McIntyre and Paiewonsky (*15*), the conditions for leaving the constraint surface cannot be translated into mathematical statements that can be used conveniently in a computing process. Again, t_2 must be estimated and an improvement made in the estimation according to some means such as to increase t_2 when the new control causes the trajectory to violate the constrained surface and decrease t_2 otherwise. The amount of suitable change involved depends on the problem at hand. Often too large a change may cause the trajectory and some subsequent trajectories to deviate greatly from the optimal, while making too small changes would waste unnecessary computing time.

F. Determination of Optimum α_n

It is convenient to divide the state variable constrained problem into three parts in the following discussions, and designate them as Region I for $t \in [t_0, t_1)$; Region II for $t \in [t_1, t_2]$; and Region III for $t \in (t_2, t_f]$. For Region II, the computation for the optimum α_n, the value of α that minimizes the performance functional, or step size in the search, is not involved since the control on the boundary arc is not free to vary. For Region III, the optimum α_n may be determined by using

$$\alpha = \frac{\langle \nabla E(u_n), p_n \rangle}{2\langle p_n, F(u_n) p_n \rangle} \tag{35}$$

the optimum α for the case in solving linear operator equations as a guide for the search (5) and to compute the performance functional for selected values of α. A quadratic interpolation may be employed to improve the effectiveness of the search and to reduce the number of values of α needed to be considered. The computation for the optimum α_n for Region I needs further attention. First of all, due to the presence of the constrained conditions (14) and (15), the values of α to be considered must be selected in such a way that $u_n + \alpha p_n$ are admissible controls. This is a one-dimensional minimization problem subject to some side conditions. It is desirable to limit the number of values of α to be considered so that the computational time is reasonable while maintaining a tolerable accuracy on the approximating solution for each iteration. Second, the evaluation of the performance functional is not as simple as in the case for Region III since the value of $\phi[x(t_f)]$ will not be known until the complete trajectory is computed which includes Region III where the trajectory is as yet to be evaluated. Some equivalent condition at $t < t_f$ instead of $\phi[x(t_f)]$ sometimes may be used to great advantage. For the cases that an explicit equivalent condition is not possible, α_n may be taken to be the one that is nearest to the value of α computed by (35) while satisfying the condition that $u_n + \alpha_n p_n$ is an admissible control.

From the computational viewpoint, it is sometimes advantageous (especially when $N \geqq 1$) to relax the requirement that the estimated control u_k for each iteration be admissible. That is, associated with each iteration, a set of admissible controls Q_k such that $Q_{k+1} \subset Q_k$ and $Q_k \to Q$ as $k \to \infty$. In other words, computational time may be considerably reduced if the optimal control u^* is approached along a "path" whose intermediate "points" may be nonadmissible conceptually as shown in Fig. 2.

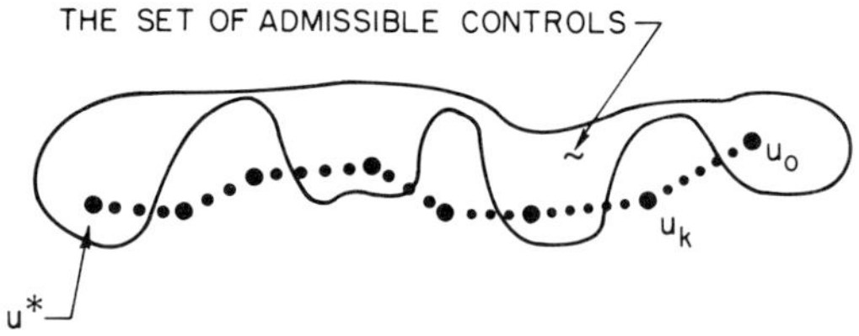

FIG. 2. Illustration of the path leading to optimal control u^*.

G. Summary of Computational Steps

The flow diagram of Fig. 3 shows the steps in the computational process. Because of the lack of advanced knowledge of the initial values for α_0, β_0, and p_0, some convenient values such as zeros may be used.

H. Substitution of Penalty Function for Constraints

In the state variable constraint control problems, most of the hardships in computation arise from the constraint requirements (14) and (15). The penalty function technique is designed to alleviate these difficulties. Instead of attacking the problem directly, it reformulates the control problem with state variable constraint into an unconstrained problem

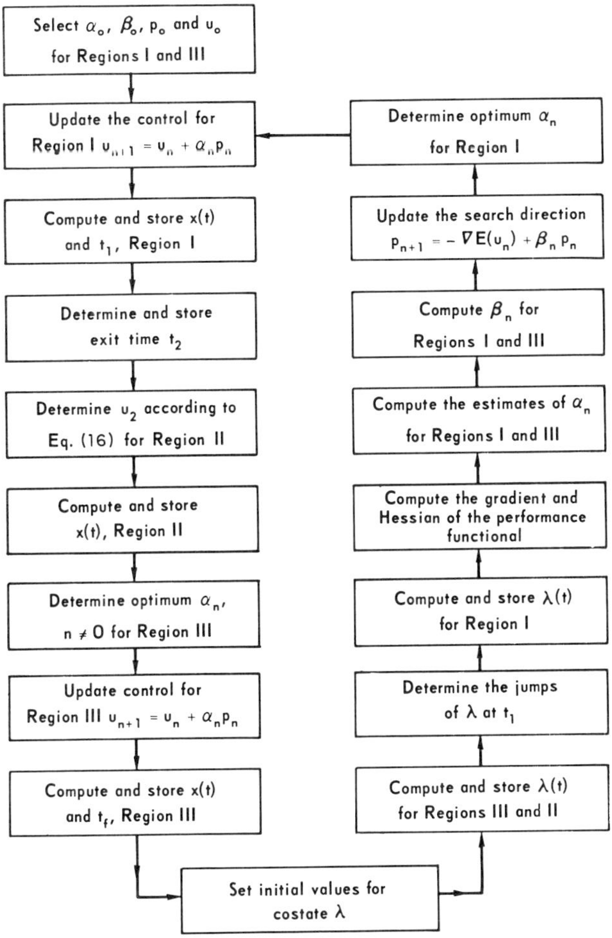

FIG. 3. Flow diagram for the computational process.

wherein the original performance functional is augmented by a nonnegative penalty term, a function of the state variable x which increased in value with trajectories that violate the state variable constraints. By selecting a suitable sequence of nonnegative penalty functions in the iteration process, it is conceivable that in many cases the desired solution for the original problem would be achieved as the limit of the sequence of approximating solutions obtained in the iteration. Indeed, this technique has been given rigorous justifications by various investigators, Moser [see (*16*)], Russell (*17*), and Okamura (*18*), just to mention a few. For most penalty functions, the intermediate trajectories usually violate the constraints. That is, some portion of the boundary arc is approached from outside of the constrained set.

An adaptation of this technique to suit the conjugate gradient computational method is as follows. A new performance functional is given by

$$\begin{aligned} E'(u_n) &= E(u_n) + \int_{Cn} \pi(x, n)\, ds \\ &= \phi[x(t_f)] + \int_{Cn} \pi(x, n)\, ds \end{aligned} \tag{36}$$

where C_n is the trajectory under the control u_n, and the nonnegative penalty function π as a function of x has the properties that for x within the constrained set π has small values relative to $\phi[x(t_f)]$, and for x outside of the constrained set π has large values that increase with the distance away from the constrained surfaces. And as a function of n for a given x, π is a monotonically increasing function for x outside of the constrained set and conversely for x within the constrained set. The gradient of E' in general does not approach zero as the optimum solution is near, due to the added penalty term $\int_{Cn}\pi(x, n)\, ds$. Therefore, some other means must be used to signal that the optimum solution is near in the iteration process. Comparison of the values for $\phi[x(t_f)]$ in consecutive iterations often fail whenever the performance functional has a "flat bottom" feature. Often direct comparison of u_{n+k} with u_n is necessary, such as evaluating the quantity

$$\|u_{n+k} - u_n\|^2 \simeq \sum_{j=1}^{k} \alpha_{n+j-1}^2 \langle p_{n+j-1}, p_{n+j-1} \rangle \tag{37}$$

To avoid instability in computation which causes the intermediate trajectories to swing far from the optimal trajectory and may sometimes cause the approximating solutions to diverge, the penalty function cannot be too "harsh." On the contrary, the solution may have a very slow convergence rate which would make the computation inefficient. Some compromise must be made so that each iteration brings the approximating solution closer and closer to the optimum at some reasonable rate. After the selection of the penalty function, the computational steps are the same as the one given above in Fig. 3 for the constrained problem except for the removal of the blocks concerning Regions II and III and some obvious modifications.

V. An Example: A Minimum Distance with Forbidden Region Problem

Let us now consider a problem of moderate computational difficulty so that the features of the conjugate gradient method can be observed with greater clarity. Suppose that among the planar curves joining the point (4, 1/4) and some point on the parabola with its vertex at the origin while avoiding a circular region, as shown in Fig. 4, it is desired to find one that minimizes the length of the curve. The control version of this problem would be to find the time-optimal control for a piecewise smooth path satisfying the specified conditions traversed at a constant speed, where the control variable u is taken as the angle formed by the tangent to the path and the negative x_1 axis (see Fig. 4).

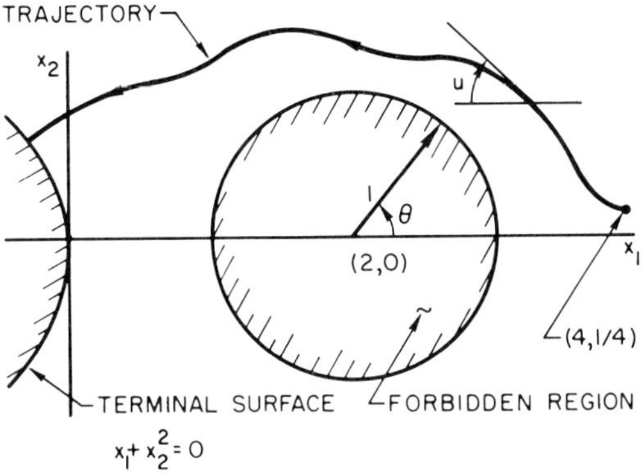

FIG. 4. Geometry of the minimum distance problem.

This problem will be solved using the conjugate gradient method in two ways. First, the computation will be carried out considering the constraints directly and then employing a penalty function to convert the constrained problem to an equivalent unconstrained one. Finally, another computational technique, the popular steepest descent, is studied with the same considerations as those given in the first case of the conjugate gradient method.

The performance functional to be minimized is

$$\begin{aligned} E(u) &= \phi[x(t_f)] \\ &= x_3(t_f) \\ &= \int_{t_0}^{t_f} dt \end{aligned} \tag{38}$$

The system dynamics can be written as

$$\begin{aligned} dx_1/dt &= -k \cos u \\ dx_2/dt &= k \sin u \\ dx_3/dt &= 1 \end{aligned} \tag{39}$$

where the constant k will be taken as unity in the sequel for simplicity. Letting $t_0 = 0$, the initial conditions are

$$\begin{aligned} x_1(0) &= 4 \\ x_2(0) &= 1/4 \\ x_3(0) &= 0 \end{aligned} \tag{40}$$

A. Computation Using Constraints Directly

The Hamiltonian associated with this problem is

$$H(x, \lambda, u) = -\lambda_1 \cos u + \lambda_2 \sin u + \lambda_3 \tag{41}$$

and therefore, the costate equation along the interior arcs, or Regions I and III, is

$$d\lambda/dt = 0 \tag{42}$$

In view of Eq. (28) and that $\phi(x) = x_3$ and $\psi(x) = x_1 + x_2{}^2$, at the terminal time t_f

$$\begin{aligned} \lambda_1(t_f) &= \nu \\ \lambda_2(t_f) &= 2\nu x_2(t_f) \\ \lambda_3(t_f) &= 1 \end{aligned} \tag{43}$$

where ν may be determined from Eq. (29). According to Eqs. (21) and (32), we have for the gradient and Hessian of the performance functional, respectively,

$$\nabla E(u) = \lambda_1 \sin u + \lambda_2 \cos u \tag{44}$$

$$F(u) = \lambda_1 \cos u - \lambda_2 \sin u \tag{45}$$

On the boundary arc, or Region II, the control is required to maintain the trajectory so that is will lie on the circle $(x_1 - 2)^2 + x_2{}^2 = 1$, hence

$$u(t) = \cos^{-1} x_2(t)$$

or

$$u(t) = \sin^{-1} [x_1(t) - 2] \tag{46}$$

Using Eq. (22), the costate equations for Region II are

$$\begin{aligned} d\lambda_1/dt &= -\cos u(\lambda_1 \sin u + \lambda_2 \cos u) \\ d\lambda_2/dt &= \sin u(\lambda_1 \sin u + \lambda_2 \cos u) \\ d\lambda_3/dt &= 0 \end{aligned} \tag{47}$$

By Eqs. (24) and (25), the jumps of the costate at the entering corner are governed by

$$\begin{aligned} \lambda_1(t_1^-) &= \lambda_1(t_1^+) + \mu 2[x_1(t_1^+) - 2] \\ \lambda_2(t_1^-) &= \lambda_2(t_1^+) + \mu 2x_2(t_1^+) \\ \lambda_3(t_1^-) &= \lambda_3(t_1^+) \end{aligned} \tag{48}$$

$$\lambda_1(t_1^-)\frac{dx_1(t_1^-)}{dt} + \lambda_2(t_1^-)\frac{dx_2(t_1^-)}{dt} = \lambda_1(t_1^+)\frac{dx_1(t_1^+)}{dt} + \lambda_2(t_1^+)\frac{dx_2(t_1^+)}{dt}$$

and from which

$$\mu = \frac{\lambda_1(t_1^+)[-x_2(t_1) + \cos u(t_1^-)] + \lambda_2(t_1^+)[x_1(t_1) - 2 - \sin u(t_1^-)]}{2\{[x_1(t_1) - 2]\cos u(t_1^-) - x_2(t_1)\sin u(t_1^-)\}} \tag{49}$$

It is worth observing that in the iteration process, precaution must be taken to avoid overflows in computation because the denominator of (49) may vanish when the approximating trajectory is tangent to the circle at t_1. When this occurs, the numerator vanishes also. In view of the limiting processes involved in leading to Eq. (24), we may therefore apply L'Hopital's rule to Eq. (49) and obtain

$$\mu = \tfrac{1}{2}[-\lambda_1(t_1^+)\sin u(t_1^+) - \lambda_2(t_1^+)\cos u(t_1^+)] \tag{50}$$

After a control is chosen, and the initial conditions (40) are given, the differential equations (39) can be solved in a straightforward manner. In order to evaluate the gradient and the Hessian of E, the costate in Regions I and III is needed. The values of the costate in Region III are clear from (42) and (43). By solving (47) backwards from t_2 to t_1, we have $\lambda_j(t_1^+)$, $j = 1, 2, 3$. Through Eq. (48), $\lambda_j(t_1^-)$, $j = 1, 2, 3$ may be determined, and consequently the values of the costate are for Region I obtained.

B. Computation Using Penalty Function

Let us now examine what modifications must be made when the penalty function is introduced, so that the problem with state variable constraint becomes an unconstrained problem. Let

$$\pi(x, n) = 0.01[(x_1 - 2)^2 + x_2^2]^{-A(n)} \tag{51}$$

where

$$A(n) = \begin{cases} 3 + n & 1 \leqslant n < 10 \\ 14 + 2(n - 10), & 10 \leqslant n < 20 \\ 34 + 4(n - 20), & n \geqslant 20 \end{cases}$$

As n becomes large, the contribution to the performance functional along the trajectory exterior to the circle is small, and $\pi(x, n)$ is positive everywhere. Hence π possesses the desired characteristics stated in the previous section.

The new performance functional to be minimized is

$$\begin{aligned} E(u) &= x_3(t_f) \\ &= \int_0^{t_f} dt + \int_0^{t_f} \pi(x, n)\, dt \end{aligned} \tag{52}$$

The equations describing the system dynamics (39) remain the same except for the last expression which becomes

$$dx_3/dt = 1 + \pi(x, n) \tag{53}$$

The initial conditions for the states are again given by (40). The new Hamiltonian is

$$H(x, \lambda, u) = -\lambda_1 \cos u + \lambda_2 \sin u + \lambda_3[1 + \pi(x, n)] \tag{54}$$

and the costate equations are

$$\begin{aligned} \frac{d\lambda_1}{dt} &= -\lambda_3 \frac{\partial \pi}{\partial x_1} \\ \frac{d\lambda_2}{dt} &= -\lambda_3 \frac{\partial \pi}{\partial x_2} \\ \frac{d\lambda_3}{dt} &= 0 \end{aligned} \tag{55}$$

with the terminal conditions as given by (43). The gradient and the Hessian are again given by (44) and (45). Since there are no constrained conditions involved, the computer program becomes considerably simpler.

C. Computational Results

Treating the problem as a constrained problem, the following initial estimates are used

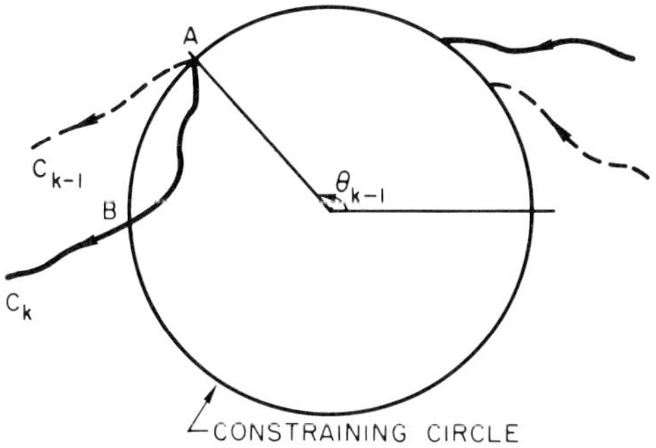

FIG. 5. Trajectory C_k violating constraining circle.

$$\begin{aligned} u_0(t) &= -\tfrac{1}{3}t, && 0 \leqslant t \leqslant t_1 \\ u_0(t) &= 0.1 + 0.05 \sin 10t, && t_2 \leqslant t \leqslant t_f \\ \theta_0 &= 2.8 && \text{(see Fig. 5)} \end{aligned}$$

The change in θ, $\Delta\theta$ is made according to the following:

(i) If the trajectory under the new estimated control does not violate the constraining circle in the kth iteration, then

$$\Delta\theta = \begin{cases} -0.1 \quad , & k < 8 \\ -0.01 \quad , & 8 \leqq k \leqq 15 \\ -0.0005, & k > 15 \end{cases}$$

(ii) If the trajectory under the new estimated control violates the constraining circle as shown above, where A is the point where the trajectory leaves the circle in the $(k-1)$st iteration and B is the last intersection of the trajectory C_k under the new control and the circle, then

$$\Delta\theta = \text{length of arc } AB$$

Treating the problem as an unconstrained problem, the initial estimate was

$$u_0(t) = 1 - 0.4t$$

The computed results are shown in Figs. 6 to 11. Comparisons are made between the different approaches to the solution whenever possible. Whenever there is no mention of whether the solution is obtained by using constraints directly or by using a penalty function, it is understood that the first is used. Figures 6 and 7, respectively, show the approximating controls $u_n(t)$ for various n computed by the conjugate gradient method

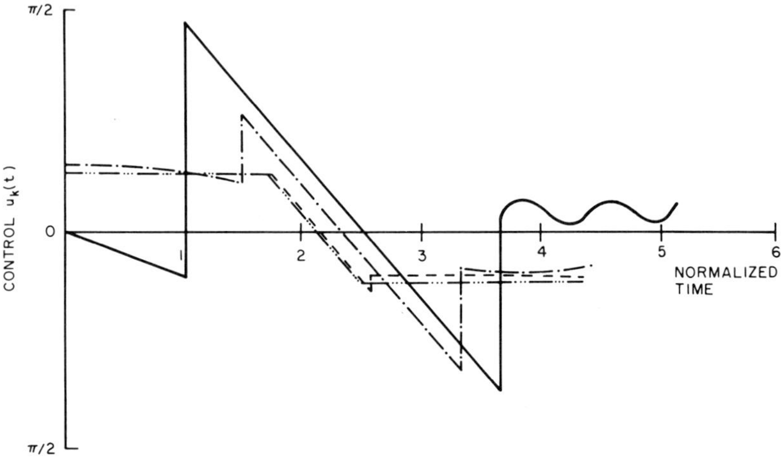

FIG. 6. Approximating controls computed by method of conjugate gradients. ——Iteration 1, –·–· iteration 2, –––– iteration 5, —···— iteration 9.

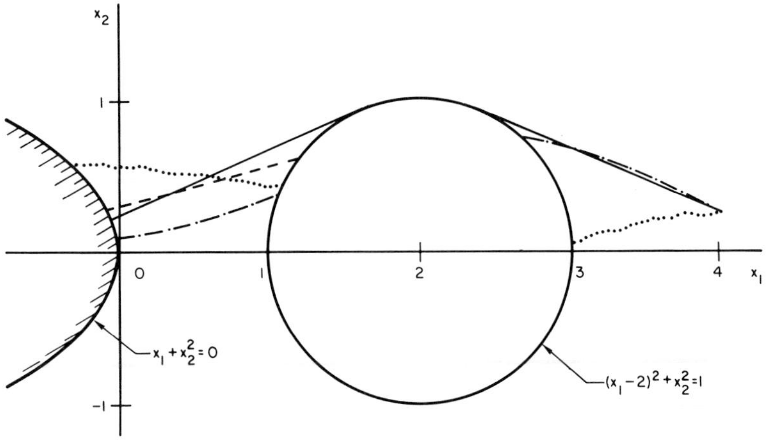

FIG. 7. Trajectories computed by method of conjugate gradients. —— Iteration 21, –––– iteration 5, –·–· iteration 2, ····· iteration 1.

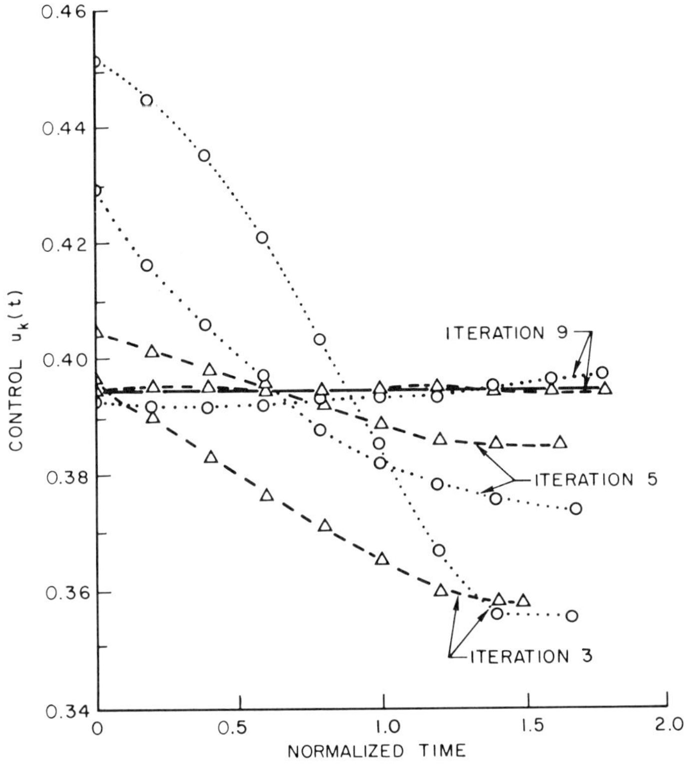

FIG. 8. Comparison of approximating control sequences in Region I by method of conjugate gradients (△ -- △) and method of steepest descent (O ··· O). —— Optimal solution.

and the corresponding trajectories. Figures 8 and 9 provide some comparisons of the conjugate gradient and steepest descent methods. Since the convergence characteristics of the approximating controls and the corresponding trajectories in Region III depend mainly on the choice of θ_n or the exit corner, only their convergence characteristics in Region I are considered. Figures 10 and 11, respectively, show the approximating controls $u_n(t)$ for various n computed using the penalty function approach and the corresponding trajectories.

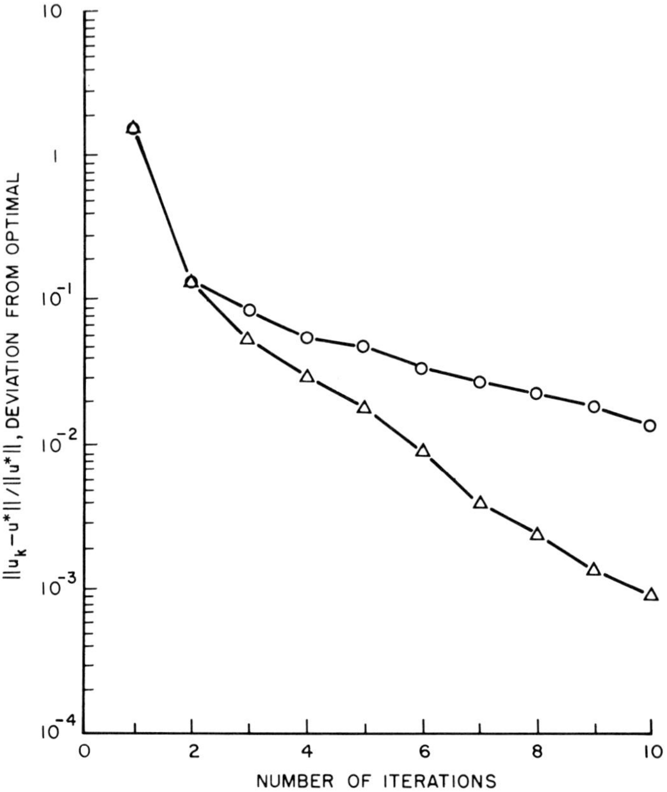

FIG. 9. Deviation of approximating controls from optimal by method of conjugate gradients (△—△) and method of Steepest descent (○—○).

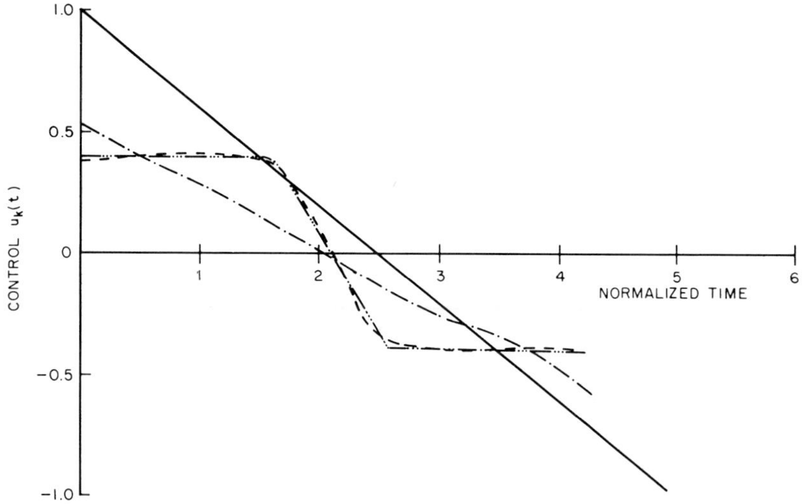

FIG. 10. Approximating controls computed by method of conjugate gradients using penalty function. —— Iteration 1, −·−· iteration 3, ---- iteration 6, —···— iteration 15.

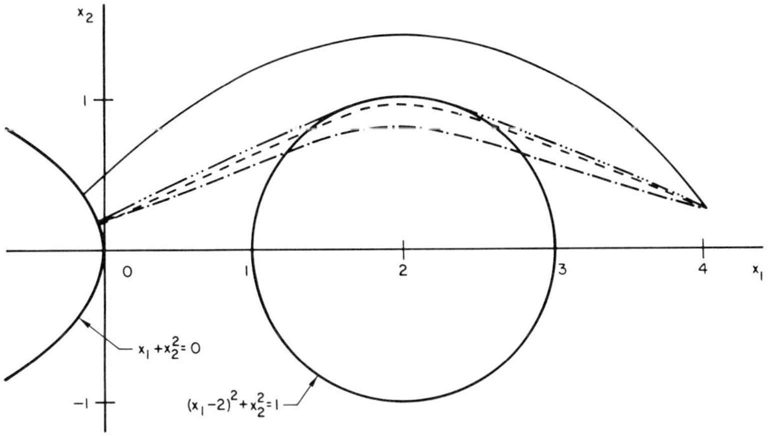

FIG. 11. Trajectories computed by method of conjugate gradients using penalty functions. —— Iteration 1, -·-· iteration 3, ---- iteration 6, —···— iteration 15.

VI. Conclusions and Remarks

The method of conjugate gradients has been shown to be a useful computational tool in solving optimal control problems with state variable constraint. The method is basically simple and relatively easy to program. Although the search directions are only locally conjugate with respect to the Hessian of the performance functional, they still provide satisfactory convergence. The results indicate that the conjugate gradient method has a higher rate of convergence in comparison with the method of steepest descent, but the difference in the rate of convergence is less pronounced for this constrained problem as compared with the cases of unconstrained problems reported by other investigators (*10, 11*). This occurs for the following reasons: (i) The set of admissible controls Q is restricted, and consequently only small step size in the search direction is permitted in Region I. That is, the convergence is along the expanding sequence of sets, the intersections of the linear spaces spanned by the search directions and the set of admissible controls instead of expanding sequence of subspaces. (ii) The rate of convergence in Region III depends heavily on the choice of the exit corner in each iteration. A considerable portion of computational time in each iteration is devoted to the determination of the optimum step size in the search (although the exact optimum is not essential) and the determination of jumps in the costate at the entering corner. In converting the constrained control problem to an equivalent unconstrained one by introducing a penalty function, the computational process involves more time in contrast to the approach which considers the constraints directly, but it requires less programming work. Its effectiveness depends heavily on the proper choice of the function π.

References

1. A. E. Bryson, Jr., W. F. Denham, and S. E. Dreyfus, Optimal programming problems with inequality constraints. I. Necessary conditions for extremal solutions. *AIAA J.* **1**, No. 11, 2544–2550 (1963).
2. W. F. Denham and A. E. Bryson, Jr., Optimal programming problems with inequality constraints. II. Solution by steepest descent. *AIAA J.* **2**, No. 1, 25–34 (1964).
3. J. L. Starr, Computation of optimal control: Solution of the multipoint boundary value problem. Ph.D. Dissertation, Dept. of Eng., Univ. of California at Los Angeles, California, (1968).
4. R. McGill, Optimal control, inequality state constraints, and the generalized Newton–Raphson algorithm. *J. SIAM Control* **3**, No. 2, 291–298 (1965).
5. M. R. Hestenes and E. Stiefel, Method of conjugate gradients for solving linear systems. *J. Res. Nat. Bur. Standards* **49**, 409–436 (1952).
6. M. R. Hestenes, The conjugate gradient method for solving linear systems. *Proc. Symp. Appl. Math.* **6**, (Numerical Analysis), 83–102 (1956).
7. R. M. Hayes, Iterative methods for solving linear problems in Hilbert space. *Nat. Bur. Standards Appl. Math. Ser.* **39**, 71–104 (1954).
8. H. A. Antosiewicz and W. C. Rheinboldt, Conjugate direction methods and the method of steepest Descent. *In* "A Survey of Numerical Analysis" (J. Todd, ed.), pp. 501–512. McGraw-Hill, New York, 1962.
9. J. W. Daniel, The conjugate gradient method for linear and nonlinear operator equations. Ph.D. Dissertation, Dept. of Math., Stanford Univ., Stanford, California, 1965.
10. L. S. Lasdon, S. K. Mitter, and A. D. Waren, The conjugate gradient method for optimal control. *IEEE Trans. Autom. Control* **AC-12**, No. 2, 133–138 (1967).
11. J. F. Sinnott and D. G. Leunberger, Solution of optimal control problems by the method of conjugate gradient. *Joint Autom. Control Conf.* pp. 566–574 (1967).
12. T. S. Fong, Optimum phase distribution for antenna aperture with specified amplitude weighting. Tech. Interdept. Correspondence, Hughes Aircraft Company, El Segundo, California, January 1969.
13. T. S. Fong, Method of conjugate gradients for optimal control problems with state variable constraint. Ph.D. Dissertation, Dept. of Eng., Univ. of California, December 1968.
14. M. Athans and P. L. Falb, "Optimal Control." McGraw-Hill, New York, 1966.
15. J. McIntyre and B. Paiewonsky, On optimal control with bounded state variables. *Advan. Control Systems* **5**, 389–419 (1966).
16. R. Courant, "Calculus of Variations and Supplementary Notes and Exercises, 1945–1946" (revised and amended by J. Moser) N.Y. Univ. Inst. Math. Sci., New York, 1956–1957.
17. D. L. Russell, Penalty functions and bounded phase coordinate control. *J. SIAM Control* **2**, No. 3, 409–422 (1965).
18. K. Okamura, Some mathematical theory of the penalty method for solving optimum control problems. *J. SIAM Control* **2**, No. 3, 317–331 (1965).

Final Value Control Systems[1]

C. E. SEAL

TRW Systems Group
Redondo Beach, California

AND

ALLEN STUBBERUD

School of Engineering, University of California
Irvine, California

I. Introduction

In many applications of control theory, it is natural and desirable to formulate a problem as a final value system. The term final value refers to the requirement that the state of the system at the terminal time exactly satisfy the desired terminal conditions. This is the case, for example, when formulating steering laws for missile systems or designing guidance policies for space rendezvous and docking missions (*1*).

It is well known that the closed-loop control policy for the final value control problem has feedback gains that become infinite as the terminal time is approached (*2, 3*). Under the assumption that the singularities are finite order poles, Holtzman and Horing (*4*) have shown that these singularities in the feedback gains force the closed-loop system to attain the

[1] This research was supported by the Air Force Office of Scientific Research Grant AFOSR 699-67.

desired terminal state even if the plant parameters have been changed by any arbitrary (but bounded) amount. This insensitivity to plant parameter variations is, of course, very desirable, but very large gains are difficult to implement. The usual procedures in practice are either to ignore the problem and allow the gains to saturate, or to switch from closed-loop to open-loop control at some time prior to the terminal time. In the first case, the system ceases to be optimal and the desired terminal conditions are not attained even if no plant disturbances are present. In the second case, the desirable properties of feedback are lost during the final portion of the control interval.

In this article, a general closed-loop final value control policy will be determined. This will then be specialized to an optimal control policy for minimum energy final value systems. In order to obtain specific results, most of this paper will deal with systems in phase-variable canonical form (PVCF). A procedure for transforming time variable linear systems into this canonical form, and necessary and sufficient conditions for the existence of this form, have been given by the authors previously (*5*). The results presented here are thus applicable to a large class of systems.

The singularity structure of the feedback gains is then developed for optimal final value control systems in PVCF. This structure is determined first for single input systems, and then for multiple input systems. It is then shown that the singularity structure for systems with general quadratic cost is identical to that for systems with minimum control energy cost.

Using the information about the singularity structure of the feedback gains of the optimal final value control functions, partially closed-loop control functions will be described that are very close in structure to the completely closed-loop functions, but do not require the implementation of infinite gains. The partially closed-loop control functions will allow the designer to set the order of the singularities in the control policy between the closed-loop maximum and zero. By use of the partially closed-loop control policy, it is thus possible to maintain as much feedback as can be physically implemented for the entire control interval.

The chapter will conclude with a discussion of performance evaluation for partially closed-loop control systems.

II. A General Final Value Control Function

Consider a linear system defined by the vector-matrix differential equation:

$$\dot{x}(t) = A(t)x(t) + B(t)u(t) \tag{1}$$

where $x(t)$ is an n-dimensional state vector, $u(t)$ is an m-dimensional control vector, and $A(t)$ and $B(t)$ are time variable matrices of the proper order. It is desired to transfer the system from (x_0, t_0) to (x_f, T) by the choice of $u(t)$.

Since there are n conditions that must be satisfied at the final time, $u(t)$ is chosen to be of the form

$$u(t) = U(t)\alpha \tag{2}$$

where α is an n-dimensional constant vector that must be determined and $U(t)$ is an $m \times n$ matrix of functions that the designer chooses. Some possible specific choices for $U(t)$ will be discussed later.

The solution for Eq. (1) can then be written as

$$x(t) = \phi(t, t_0)x_0 + \int_{t_0}^{t} \phi(t, \tau)B(\tau)U(\tau)\, d\tau\alpha \tag{3}$$

where $\phi(t, \tau)$ is the transition matrix for Eq. (1), i.e.,

$$\partial\phi(t, \tau)/\partial t = A(t)\phi(t, \tau), \qquad \phi(\tau, \tau) = I \tag{4}$$

The constant vector α is determined by the condition that at time T, $x(t)$ is given by

$$x_f = \phi(T, t_0)x_0 + \int_{t_0}^{T} \phi(T, \tau)B(\tau)U(\tau)\, d\tau\alpha \tag{5}$$

Thus

$$\alpha = W^{-1}(t_0)[x_f - \phi(T, t_0)x_0] \tag{6}$$

where $W(t_0)$ is defined by

$$W(t_0) = \int_{t_0}^{T} \phi(T, \tau)B(\tau)U(\tau)\, d\tau \tag{7}$$

and $W^{-1}(t_0)$ is assumed to exist.

The desired control function is then given by

$$u(t) = U(t)W^{-1}(t_0)[x_f - \phi(T, t_0)x_0] \tag{8}$$

This is, of course, an open-loop control. If we take the initial time to be the current time and the initial state to be the current state we obtain the closed-loop control function

$$u_{c1}(t, x(t)) = U(t)W^{-1}(t)[x_f - \phi(T, t)x(t)] \tag{9}$$

Substituting Eq. (8) into Eq. (1) yields the following equation for the system acting under open-loop control:

$$\dot{x}(t) = A(t)x(t) + B(t)U(t)W^{-1}(t_0)[x_f - \phi(T, t_0)x_0] \tag{10}$$

Substituting Eq. (9) into Eq. (1) gives

$$\dot{x}(t) = [A(t) - B(t)U(t)W^{-1}(t)\phi(T, t)]x(t) + B(t)U(t)W^{-1}(t)x_f \quad (11)$$

for the system with closed-loop control.

It is apparent that the two systems represented by Eqs. (10) and (11) have the same solution vector $x(t)$. Thus a fundamental solution matrix for the closed loop system of Eq. (11) can be represented in terms of the transition matrix of the open-loop system $\phi(t, \tau)$ by the equation

$$\psi(t) = \phi(t, T) \int_t^T \phi(T, \tau)B(\tau)U(\tau)\, d\tau = \phi(t, T)W(t) \quad (12)$$

Since $\psi(t)$ is a fundamental matrix for Eq. (11) it satisfies the equation

$$\dot{\psi}(t) = [A(t) - B(t)U(t)W^{-1}(t)\phi(T, t)]\psi(t) \quad (13)$$

The value of this result is highest in those cases where the original system is time invariant. In this case $\phi(t, \tau)$ can be generated relatively easily and then $\psi(t)$ can be determined from Eq. (12).

EXAMPLE 1. Consider a pitch steering law for a missile (1). The equation governing the radius r (from the Earth's center) which defines the missile's position is

$$\ddot{r} = \alpha_1 + \alpha_2 t \quad (14)$$

By defining

$$\begin{aligned} x_1 &= r, \\ x_2 &= \dot{r} = \dot{x}_1 \end{aligned} \quad (15)$$

Eq. (14) can be re-written in vector matrix form as

$$\begin{bmatrix} \dot{x}_1 \\ \dot{x}_2 \end{bmatrix} = \begin{bmatrix} 0 & 1 \\ 0 & 0 \end{bmatrix} \begin{bmatrix} x_1 \\ x_2 \end{bmatrix} + \begin{bmatrix} 0 & 0 \\ 1 & t \end{bmatrix} \begin{bmatrix} \alpha_1 \\ \alpha_2 \end{bmatrix} \quad (16)$$

Comparing Eq. (16) with Eqs. (1) and (2), the matrices $\alpha(t)$, $B(t)$, and $U(t)$ and the vector α can be identified as

$$A(t) = \begin{bmatrix} 0 & 1 \\ 0 & 0 \end{bmatrix}, \quad B(t) = \begin{bmatrix} 0 \\ 1 \end{bmatrix}$$
$$U(t) = [1 \quad t], \quad \alpha = \begin{bmatrix} \alpha_1 \\ \alpha_2 \end{bmatrix} \quad (17)$$

Since $A(t)$ is a constant matrix, the transition matrix can be easily generated as

$$\phi(t, \tau) = \begin{bmatrix} 1 & t - \tau \\ 0 & 1 \end{bmatrix} \quad (18)$$

The matrix $W(t)$ is obtained from Eq. (7) as

$$W(t)=\int_t^T\begin{bmatrix}1 & T-\tau\\ 0 & 1\end{bmatrix}\begin{bmatrix}0\\ 1\end{bmatrix}[1\ \tau]\,d\tau$$
$$=\begin{bmatrix}\frac{1}{2}(T-t)^2 & \frac{1}{6}(T-t)^2(T+2t)\\ (T-t) & \frac{1}{2}(T^2-t^2)\end{bmatrix} \tag{19}$$

Substituting from Eqs. (17), (18), and (19) into Eqs. (11), the vector-matrix form for the closed-loop control for the pitch steering law is

$$\begin{bmatrix}\dot{x}_1\\ \dot{x}_2\end{bmatrix}=\begin{bmatrix}0 & 1\\ \dfrac{-6}{(T-t)^2} & \dfrac{-4}{T-t}\end{bmatrix}\begin{bmatrix}x_1\\ x_1\end{bmatrix}+\begin{bmatrix}0 & 0\\ \dfrac{6}{(T-t)^2} & \dfrac{-2}{T-t}\end{bmatrix}\begin{bmatrix}x_{f1}\\ x_{f2}\end{bmatrix} \tag{20}$$

where

$$x_f=\begin{bmatrix}x_{f1}\\ x_{f2}\end{bmatrix}$$

Finally, the fundamental matrix for Eq. (20) is obtained from Eq. (12) as

$$\psi(t)=\phi(t,T)W(t)=\begin{bmatrix}-\frac{1}{2}(T-t)^2 & -\frac{1}{6}(T-t)^2(2T+t)\\ (T-t) & \frac{1}{2}(T^2-t^2)\end{bmatrix} \tag{21}$$

III. Single Input Minimum Energy Controllers

If $U(t)$ is chosen to be

$$U(t)=R^{-1}B^T(t)\phi^T(T,t) \tag{22}$$

then from Eq. (8)

$$u(t)=R^{-1}B^T(t)\phi^T(T,t)W^{-1}(t_0)[x_f-\phi(T,t_0)x_0] \tag{23}$$

It is well known (*6*) that this control is optimal in the sense that it transfers the system from (x_0, t_0) to (x_f, T) in such a way that

$$J=\frac{1}{2}\int_{t_0}^T u^T(t)R(t)u(t)\,dt$$

is minimum where it is assumed that R is positive definite on $[t_0, T]$.

If the original system has only one input and is uniformly controllable, then it can be assumed without loss of generality that it is in phase-variable canonical form (PVCF) [see, e.g., Silverman (7)]. That is, the A and B matrices have the form

$$A(t)=\begin{bmatrix} 0 & 1 & 0 & \cdots & 0 & 0 \\ 0 & 0 & 1 & \cdots & 0 & 0 \\ \vdots & \vdots & \vdots & & \vdots & \vdots \\ 0 & 0 & 0 & \cdots & 0 & 1 \\ a_0(t) & a_1(t) & a_2(t) & \cdots & a_{n-2}(t) & a_{n-1}(t) \end{bmatrix} \qquad B=\begin{bmatrix} 0 \\ 0 \\ \vdots \\ 0 \\ 1 \end{bmatrix} \tag{24}$$

We now investigate the structure of the feedback control for a single input system in phase-variable canonical form with $U(t)=R^{-1}B^T\phi^T(T,t)$. The control function is thus

$$u_{c1}(t,x(t))=R^{-1}B^T\phi^T(T,t)W^{-1}(t)[x_f-\phi(T,t)x(t)] \tag{25}$$

To simplify the devlopment it will be assumed that R is the identity matrix.

Inspection of Eq. (7) shows that $W(T)=0$. Therefore the feedback control gain becomes infinite as $t\to T$.

Of interest is the behavior of

$$W^{-1}(t)=\left[\int_t^T \phi(T,\tau)BB^T\phi^T(T,\tau)\,d\tau\right]^{-1} \tag{26}$$

as $t\to T$.

As $(T-\tau)$ becomes arbitrarily small, under the assumption that $A(t)$ is analytic in a neighborhood of T, we can approximate $\phi(T,\tau)$ by its finite power series expansion about T:

$$\phi(T,\tau)\approx\sum_{k=0}^{n-1}\left.\frac{d^k\phi(T,\tau)}{d\tau^k}\right|_{\tau=T}\frac{(T-\tau)^k(-1)^k}{k!} \tag{27}$$

Using Eqs. (4) and (27) and the assumed form for A and B, and omitting all but the lowest order terms in $(T-\tau)$ for each element in the vector, we have

$$\phi(T,\tau)B\approx\begin{bmatrix} \dfrac{(T-\tau)^{n-1}}{(n-1)!} \\ \dfrac{(T-\tau)^{n-2}}{(n-2)!} \\ \vdots \\ \dfrac{(T-\tau)^2}{2} \\ (T-\tau) \\ 1 \end{bmatrix} \tag{28}$$

Letting $W(t) = \{W_{ij}(t)\}$ and performing the indicated algebra and integration, it is seen that

$$W_{ij}(t) \approx \frac{(T-\tau)^{2n+1-(i+j)}}{(2n+1-[i+j])(n-i)!(n-j)!)} \tag{29}$$

It follows immediately that the determinant of $W(t)$ is given by

$$|W(t)| \approx |S|(T-t)^{n^2} \tag{30}$$

where $S = \{S_{ij}\}$ and

$$S_{ij} = \frac{1}{(n-i)!(n-j)!(2n+1-[i+j])} \tag{31}$$

The ijth minor of $W(t)$ is given by

$$C_{ij}(t) \approx |D_{ij}|(T-t)^{n^2-2n-1+(i+j)}, \tag{32}$$

where $|D_{ij}|$ is the ijth minor of S.

Setting $W^{-1}(t) = M(t) = \{M_{ij}(t)\}$ it is seen that

$$M_{ij}(t) \approx \frac{(-1)^{i+j}|D_{ij}|}{|S|}(T-t)^{-(2n+1-[i+j])} \tag{33}$$

Setting $B^T\phi^T(T, t)M(t) = \{\zeta_j\}$ and using Eqs. (24), (28), and (33) yields

$$\zeta_j \approx \left[\sum_{i=1}^{n} \frac{(-1)^{i+j}|D_{ij}|}{|S|(n-1)!}\right](T-t)^{-(n+1-j)} \tag{34}$$

Finally, noting that

$$\phi^T(T, t)\left[\int_t^T \phi(T, \tau)BB^T\phi^T(T, \tau)\, d\tau\right]^{-1}\phi(T, t)$$

$$= -\left[\int_T^t \phi(t, \tau)BB^T\phi^T(t, \tau)\, d\tau\right]^{-1} \tag{35}$$

results in the following expression for $u_{c1}(t, x(t))$ as $t \to T$:

$$u_{c1}(t, x(t)) \approx \sum_{j=1}^{n}\left[\frac{\left[\sum_{i=1}^{n} \frac{(-1)^{i+j}|D_{ij}|}{|S|(n-i)!}\right]x_{fj} - \frac{|D_{nj}|}{|S|}x_j(t)}{(T-t)^{n+1-j}}\right] \tag{36}$$

It is apparent that as $t \to T$, $u_{c1}(t, x(t))$ has the form

$$u_{c1}(t, x(t)) \to \sum_{j=1}^{n}[l_j x_{fj} - x_j(t)]\frac{k_j}{(T-t)^{n+1-j}} \tag{37}$$

The form of the closed-loop optimal control is thus seen to be

$$u_{c1}(t, x(t)) = \sum_{j=1}^{n} [L_j^T(t)x_f - x_j(t)]K_j(t) \tag{38}$$

where $L_j^T(t)x_f$ has no singularities and $K_j(t)$ has a singularity of order $(n+1-j)$ at $t=T$.

If the original vector-matrix system equation is written as an nth-order differential equation in terms of one dependent variable and its derivatives, it is seen that the order of the singularity in the optimal feedback control is inversely proportional to the order of the derivative of the variable being fed back. For example, in a dynamic system, the position loop has a singularity of order 2 and the velocity loop a singularity of order 1.

EXAMPLE 2. It can be shown that the choice of $U(t) = [1, t]$ made in Example 1 makes the control $u(t) = U(t)\alpha$ optimal in the sense of Section III. We will now apply the preceding dicussion to Example 1.

Using Eqs. (18) and (21) from Example 1, it is seen that

$$x(t) = \psi(t, t_0)x_0 + M(t)x_f \tag{39}$$

where

$$\psi(t, t_0) = \begin{bmatrix} \dfrac{3(T-t)^2}{(T-t_0)^2} - \dfrac{2(T-t)^3}{(T-t_0)^3} & \dfrac{(T-t)^2}{(T-t_0)} - \dfrac{(T-t)^3}{(T-t_0)^2} \\ \dfrac{-6(T-t)}{(T-t_0)^2} + \dfrac{6(T-t)^2}{(T-t_0)^3} & \dfrac{-2(T-t)}{(T-t_0)} + \dfrac{3(T-t)^2}{(T-t_0)^2} \end{bmatrix} \tag{40}$$

$$M(t) = \begin{bmatrix} 1 - \dfrac{3(T-t)^2}{(T-t_0)^2} + \dfrac{2(T-t)^2}{(T-t_0)^3} & -(T-t) + \dfrac{2(T-t)^2}{(T\ \ t_0)} - \dfrac{(T-t)^3}{(T-t_0)^2} \\ \dfrac{6(T-t)}{(T-t_0)^2} - \dfrac{6(T-t)^2}{(T-t_0)^3} & 1 - \dfrac{4(T-t)}{(T-t_0)} + \dfrac{3(T-t)^2}{(T-t_0)^2} \end{bmatrix} \tag{41}$$

Thus

$$x_1(t) = x_{f1} - x_{f2}(T-t) + C_1(T-t)^2 + C_2(T-t)^3 \tag{42}$$

$$x_2(t) = x_{f2} - 2C_1(T-t) - 3C_2(T-t)^2, \tag{43}$$

where C_1 and C_2 are the appropriate constants; and

$$u_{c1}(t, x(t)) = \frac{6(x_{f1} - x_1(t))}{(T-t)^2} + \frac{4(-\frac{1}{2}x_{f2} - x_2(t))}{(T-t)} \tag{44}$$

As $t \to T$ there is a first-order singularity in the velocity loop and a second-order singularity in the position loop, as predicted.

By inspection of $u_{c1}(t, x(t))$ it is seen that for this example

$$L_1^T = [1, 0], \qquad L_2^T = [0, -\tfrac{1}{2}]$$
$$K_1 = \frac{6}{(T-t)^2}, \qquad K_2 = \frac{4}{(T-t)} \tag{45}$$

EXAMPLE 3. Now consider the system

$$\dot{x} = \begin{bmatrix} 0 & 1 \\ -1 & 0 \end{bmatrix} x + \begin{bmatrix} 0 \\ 1 \end{bmatrix} u, \tag{46}$$

with $x(t_0) = x_0$, $x(T) = 0$.

For this system

$$\phi(t) = \begin{bmatrix} \cos t & \sin t \\ -\sin t & \cos t \end{bmatrix}, \tag{47}$$

$$W(t) = \begin{bmatrix} \dfrac{T-t}{2} - \dfrac{\sin 2(T-t)}{4} & \tfrac{1}{2}\sin^2(T-t) \\ \tfrac{1}{2}\sin^2(T-t) & \dfrac{T-t}{2} + \dfrac{\sin 2(T-t)}{4} \end{bmatrix} \tag{48}$$

and

$$W^{-1}(t) = \begin{bmatrix} \dfrac{2(T-t) + \sin 2(T-t)}{(T-t)^2 - \sin^2(T-t)} & \dfrac{-2\sin^2(T-t)}{(T-t)^2 - \sin^2(T-t)} \\ \dfrac{-2\sin^2(T-t)}{(T-t)^2 - \sin^2(T-t)} & \dfrac{2(T-t) - \sin 2(T-t)}{(T-t)^2 - \sin^2(T-t)} \end{bmatrix} \tag{49}$$

From Section III

$$u(t) = -\left[\frac{2K\sin(\tau - K) - \cos(\tau + K) + \cos(\tau - K)}{K^2 - \sin^2 K}\right]$$
$$- \left[\frac{2K\cos(\tau - K) - \sin(\tau + K) + \sin(\tau - K)}{K^2 - \sin^2 K}\right] \tag{50}$$

where $K = T - t_0$ and $\tau = T - t$. Also

$$u_{c1}(t, x(t)) = \left[\frac{-2\sin^2 \tau}{\tau^2 - \sin^2 \tau}\right] x_1(t) - \left[\frac{2\tau - \sin^2 \tau}{\tau^2 - \sin^2 \tau}\right] x_2(t) \tag{51}$$

Notice that

$$\lim_{\tau\to 0} \frac{2 \sin^2 \tau}{\tau^2 - \sin^2 \tau} \to \frac{6}{\tau^2}$$

and

$$\lim_{\tau\to 0} \frac{2\tau - \sin^2 \tau}{\tau^2 - \sin^2 \tau} \to \frac{4}{\tau} \tag{52}$$

From Eq. (12) the fundamental matrix of the closed-loop system is

$$\psi(t) = \begin{bmatrix} \dfrac{\tau \cos \tau - \sin \tau}{2} & \dfrac{-\tau \sin \tau}{2} \\ \dfrac{\tau \sin \tau}{2} & \dfrac{\tau \cos \tau + \sin \tau}{2} \end{bmatrix} \tag{53}$$

where $\tau = T - t$.

The elements of $\psi(t, t_0)$ can be calculated in a straightforward manner and finally $x(t) = \psi(t, t_0)x_0$.

IV. Multiple Input Minimum Energy Controllers

Under suitable conditions of controllability, a multiple input linear system can be transformed into a multiple input phase variable canonical form (*5*). This is a canonical form consisting of coupled single input subsystems, with each subsystem in the previously described single input phase variable canonical form. In the sequel, both single input systems in the previously described canonical form and multiple input systems in the similar form will be referred to as being in PVCF.

In particular, the multiple input phase-variable canonical form for the system of Eq. (1) is defined as follows.

The state vector is partitioned as:

$$x = \begin{bmatrix} x_1 \\ \vdots \\ x_s \end{bmatrix} \tag{54}$$

where x_i is an n_i vector ($\sum_{i=1}^{s} n_i = N$), and the control vector is partitioned as

$$u = \begin{bmatrix} u_1 \\ \vdots \\ u_s \end{bmatrix} \tag{55}$$

where u_i is a scalar. The matrices are partitioned as follows:

$$B = \begin{bmatrix} b_1 & 0 & \cdots & 0 \\ 0 & b_2 & \cdots & 0 \\ \vdots & \vdots & & \vdots \\ 0 & 0 & \cdots & b_s \end{bmatrix} \quad \text{where } b_i = \begin{bmatrix} 0 \\ 0 \\ 0 \\ \vdots \\ 1 \end{bmatrix} \tag{56}$$

is an n_i vector

$$A = \begin{bmatrix} A_1 & b_1 C_{12}^T & \cdots & b_1 C_{1s}^T \\ b_2 C_{21}^T & A_2 & \cdots & b_2 C_{2s}^T \\ \vdots & \vdots & & \vdots \\ b_s C_{s1}^T & b_s C_{s2}^T & \cdots & A_s \end{bmatrix} \tag{57}$$

where C_{ij} is an n_j vector and

$$A_i = \begin{bmatrix} 0 & 1 & 0 & \cdots & 0 \\ 0 & 0 & 1 & \cdots & 0 \\ \vdots & \vdots & \vdots & & \vdots \\ a_0{}^i & a_1{}^i & a_2{}^i & \cdots & a_{n_i-1}^i \end{bmatrix} \tag{58}$$

is an $n_i \times n_i$ matrix. In the sequel, the elements of the C_{ij} vectors will be called the cross-coupling terms, and the n_i vector will be called the ith substate of the system.

The structure of the singularities in the gains of the closed-loop control function for a minimum control energy, multiple input final value control system in PVCF will now be developed.

The minimum energy control is given in Eq. (25) and we wish to determine the behavior of

$$W^{-1}(t) = \left[\int_t^T \phi(T, \tau) B B^T \phi^T(T, \tau)\, d\tau \right]^{-1} \tag{59}$$

as $t \to T$.

It is assumed that $A(t)$ is analytic in a neighborhood of T so that the power series for $\phi(T, t)$ about T exists. Then as $(T - \tau)$ becomes arbitrarily small, $\phi(T, \tau)$ can be approximated by the first N terms of its power series expansion about T. Thus

$$\phi(T, \tau) B \cong \sum_{k=0}^{N-1} \frac{P_k(T)(-1)^k}{k!} (T - \tau)^k \tag{60}$$

where

$$P_k(T) = -A(T) P_{k-1}(T) + (d/dT) P_{k-1}(T), \; P_0(T) = B \tag{61}$$

Now define the n_i vector $(P_k)_{ij}$ by

$$P_k(T) = \begin{bmatrix} (P_k)_{11} & \cdots & (P_k)_{1s} \\ \vdots & & \vdots \\ (P_k)_{s1} & \cdots & (P_k)_{ss} \end{bmatrix} \tag{62}$$

Using Eq. (61) and the fact that A and B are in PVCF, it is seen by inspection that

$$(P_k)_{ii} = \begin{bmatrix} 0 \\ 0 \\ \vdots \\ 0 \\ (-1)^k \\ x \\ x \\ \vdots \\ x \end{bmatrix} \begin{matrix} \\ \\ \\ \\ \leftarrow (N-k)\text{th element} \\ \\ \\ \\ \\ \end{matrix} \tag{63}$$

and

$$\begin{matrix} (P_k)_{ij} \\ i \neq j \end{matrix} \begin{bmatrix} 0 \\ 0 \\ \vdots \\ 0 \\ (-1)^k d_{ij} \\ x \\ x \\ \vdots \\ x \end{bmatrix} \begin{matrix} \\ \\ \\ \\ \leftarrow (N+1-k)\text{th element} \\ \\ \\ \\ \\ \end{matrix} \tag{64}$$

where d_{ij} is the n_jth (i.e., last) element of the C_{ij} vector, and the x's denote elements that are functions of the system parameters.

Keeping only the lowest order term in $(T-\tau)$ for each element of $\phi(T, \tau)B$, it is seen that

$$\phi(T, \tau)B = \begin{bmatrix} G_{11} & \cdots & G_{1s} \\ \vdots & & \vdots \\ G_{s1} & \cdots & G_{ss} \end{bmatrix} \tag{65}$$

where G_{ij} is an n_i vector and

$$G_{ii} \approx \begin{bmatrix} \dfrac{(T-\tau)^{n_i - 1}}{(n_i - 1)!} \\ \dfrac{(T-\tau)^{n_i - 2}}{(n_i - 2)!} \\ \vdots \\ (T-\tau) \\ 1 \end{bmatrix} \tag{66}$$

and

$$G_{ij} \approx d_{ij} \begin{bmatrix} \frac{(T-\tau)^{n_i}}{n_i!} \\ \frac{(T-\tau)^{n_i-1}}{(n_i-1)!} \\ \vdots \\ (T-\tau) \end{bmatrix} \quad i \neq j \tag{67}$$

Now define

$$W(t) = \int_t^T \phi(T, \tau)BB^T\phi^T(T, \tau)\, d\tau = \begin{bmatrix} W_{11} & \dots & W_{1s} \\ \vdots & & \vdots \\ W_{s1} & \dots & W_{ss} \end{bmatrix} \tag{68}$$

where W_{ij} is an $n_i \times n_j$ matrix and $W_{ij} = W_{ji}^T$. Retaining only the lowest order term in $(T-t)$ for each element of W and letting $[W_{ij}]_{kl}$ be the klth element of W_{ij} yields

$$\begin{aligned} [W_{ii}]_{kl} &\approx \frac{(T-t)^{2n_i+1-k-l}}{(2n_i+1-k-l)(n_i-k)!\,(n_i-l)!} \\ &= [V_{ii}]_{kl}(T-t)^{2n_i+1-k-l} \qquad k, l = 1, \dots, n_i \end{aligned} \tag{69}$$

and

$$\begin{aligned} [W_{ij}]_{kl} \underset{i \neq j}{} &\approx \left[\frac{d_{ij}}{(n_i+1-k)!\,(n_j-l)!} + \frac{d_{ji}}{(n_i-k)!(n_j+1-l)!}\right] \\ &\times \left[\frac{(T-t)^{n_i+n_j+2-k-l}}{(n_i+n_j+2-k-l)}\right] \\ &= [V_{ij}]_{kl}(T-t)^{n_i+n_j+2-k-l} \\ k &= 1, \dots, n_i, \qquad l = 1, \dots, n_j \end{aligned} \tag{70}$$

Then if follows immediately that

$$|W(t)| \approx \begin{vmatrix} V_{11} & V_{12}(T-t) & \dots & V_{1s}(T-t) \\ V_{21}(T-t) & V_{22} & \dots & V_{2s}(T-t) \\ \vdots & \vdots & & \vdots \\ V_{s1}(T-t) & V_{s2}(T-t) & \dots & V_{ss} \end{vmatrix} (T-t)^{\Sigma_{r=1}^{s} n_r^2} \tag{71}$$

where V_{11} is the matrix with elements $[V_{11}]_{kl}$, etc. Since only the lowest order term in $(T-t)$ is being retained, application of Lemma 1 of the Appendix shows that

$$|W(t)| = \prod_{i=1}^{s} |V_{ii}|\, (T-t)^{\Sigma_{r=1}^{s} n_r^2} \tag{72}$$

Notice that Lemma 1 also implies that to the lowest order term in $(T-t)$, the W_{ii} matrices can be inverted individually. Thus if $[Q_{ii}]_{kl}$ is defined to be the minor associated with $[W_{ii}]_{kl}$, then to the lowest order term in $(T-t)$,

$$[Q_{ii}]_{kl} \approx [M_{ii}]_{kl}\,(T-t)^{\sum_{r=1}^{s} n_r^2 - 2n_i - 1 + k + t} \tag{73}$$

where $[M_{ii}]_{kl}$ is a constant that is independent of the parameters of the original system.

Now by use of Lemma 2 of the Appendix it is seen that to the lowest order term possible in $(T-t)$, the minor associated with $[W_{ij}]_{kl}$, $i \neq j$, is given by

$$[Q_{ij}]_{kl} \approx [M_{ij}]_{kl}(T-t)^{\sum_{r=1}^{s} n_r^2 - n_i - n_j + 1 + l} \tag{74}$$

where $[M_{ij}]_{kl}$, $i \neq j$, is a constant that depends on the cross-coupling terms of the original system.

By defining the matrix D by

$$W^{-1}(t) = \begin{bmatrix} D_{11} & \cdots & D_{1s} \\ \vdots & & \vdots \\ D_{s1} & \cdots & D_{ss} \end{bmatrix} = D \tag{75}$$

where D_{ij} is an $n_i \times n_j$ matrix and $D_{ij} = D_{ji}$, and combining Eqs. (72–74) it is clear that

$$[D_{ii}]_{kl} \approx [S_{ii}]_{kl}(T-t)^{-(2n_i + 1 - k + l)} \tag{76}$$

and

$$[D_{ij}]_{kl} \approx [S_{ij}]_{kl}(T-t)^{-(n_i + n_j - k - l)}, \qquad i \neq j \tag{77}$$

Notice that $[S_{ii}]_{kl}$ is independent of the parameters of the original system, and that $[S_{ij}]_{kl}$, $i \neq j$, is dependent upon the cross-coupling terms of the original system. This implies that $[D_{ii}]_{kl}$ always has a singularity of order $(2n_i + 1 - k - l)$, but that $[D_{ij}]_{kl}$, $i \neq j$, has *at worst* a singularity of order $(n_i + n_j - k - l)$. In a particular system, certain conditions of the cross-coupling terms could cause $[S_{ij}]_{kl}$ to be zero. In that case, higher order terms should have been kept during the original expansion of $\phi(T, t)B$. The result would be that $[D_{ij}]_{ki}$, $i \neq j$, would have a singularity of order lower than $(n_i + n_j - k - l)$. (Notice that the reduction in order could be enough so that the singularity would disappear completely.)

If ξ is defined by

$$\xi = B^T \phi^T(T, t) W^{-1}(t) = \begin{bmatrix} \xi_{11} & \cdots & \xi_{1s} \\ \vdots & & \vdots \\ \xi_{s1} & \cdots & \xi_{ss} \end{bmatrix} \tag{78}$$

where ξ_{ij} is a $1 \times n_j$ matrix (or row vector), then inspection of Eqs. (69–70) and (74–75) shows that to the lowest order term in $(T-t)$

$$[\xi_{ii}]_k \approx [\mu_{ii}]_k (T-t)^{-(n_i+1-k)}, \tag{79}$$

and

$$[\xi_{ij}]_k \approx [\mu_{ij}]_k (T-t)^{-(n_i-k)} \qquad i \neq j \tag{80}$$

where $[\xi_{ij}]_k$ is the kth element of ξ_{ij}. $[\mu_{ii}]_k$ is not a function of the system parameters, but $[\mu_{ij}]_k$, $i \neq j$, is a function of the cross-coupling terms of the system. Thus the singularity associated with $[\xi_{ij}]_k$, $i \neq j$, is a worst case singularity, in the sense discussed above.

Now if $(x_i(t))_j$ denotes the jth element of the ith vector in the partition of $x(t)$ presented in Eq. (54), and $(u_{c1})_i$ denotes the ith element of the closed-loop control function of Eq. (25), it is seen from Eqs. (76–80) that as $t \to T$ (considering the worst case for the cross-coupling terms)

$$\begin{aligned}(u_{c1})_i \to \sum_{j=1}^{n_i} [l_{ij}^i (x_{fi})_j - (x_i(t))_j] \frac{k_{ij}^i}{(T-t)^{n_i+1-j}} \\ + \sum_{\substack{r=1\\ r\neq i}}^{s} \sum_{j=1}^{n_r} [l_{rj}^i (x_{fr})_j - (x_r(t))_j] \frac{k_{rj}^i}{(T-t)^{n_r-j}}\end{aligned} \tag{81}$$

where l_{ij}^i and k_{ij}^i are constants that do not depend upon the system parameters and l_{rj}^i and k_{rj}^i, $r \neq j$, are constants that depend on the cross-coupling terms of the system.

Thus, in general, an expression for the ith component of the optimal closed-loop control function can be written in the form

$$\begin{aligned}(u_{c1}\, t, x(t))_i = \sum_{j=1}^{n_i} [L_{ij}^T(t) x_f - (x_i(t))_j] K_{ij}^i(t) \\ + \sum_{\substack{r=1\\ r\neq 1}}^{s} \sum_{j=1}^{n_r} [L_{rj}^T(t) x_f - (x_r(t))_j] K_{rj}^i(t)\end{aligned} \tag{82}$$

where $L_{ij}^T(t)x_f$ has no singularities and $K_{ij}^i(t)$ has a singularity of order $(n_i + 1 - j)$ at $t = T$; $L_{rj}^i(t)x_f$, $r \neq i$, has no singularities and $K_{rj}^i(t)$, $r \neq i$, has a singularity at $t = T$ whose highest possible order is $(n_r - j)$.

The original vector matrix system of Eqs. (54–58) can be written as a system of s equations in terms of s scalars $y_1, \ldots, y_s$ and their derivatives, where y_i corresponds to $(x_i)_1$, $\dot{y}_i$ corresponds to $(x_i)_2$, and so on. Therefore Eq. (82) shows that each PVCF subsystem of the multiple input system has the same singularity structure as the single input system of Section III, and that the cross coupling to subsystem j from subsystem i has singularities that are at worst proportional to the derivative of the substate being fed back. That is, the y_i term has a maximum singularity of order $(n_i - 1)$, and $\dot{y}_i$ term a maximum singularity of order $(n_i - 2)$, and so on.

The following result has thus been established. The feedback gains of the minimum control energy, final value, closed-loop control function for an s input, Nth-order system in multiple input phase-variable canonical form have singularities at the terminal time. The structure of the singularities is as follows: (1) each individual PVCF subsystem of the system has a singularity structure that is independent of the remainder of the system and of the form of the single input system of Section III; (2) the cross-coupling feedback gains between two of the PVCF blocks may have singularities at the terminal time. These singularities are at worst proportional to the derivative of the substate being fed back, with the feedback of the zero derivative term from subsystem i to subsystem $j (i \neq j)$ having a maximum singularity of order $(n_i - 1)$. The actual order of a cross-coupling singularity (if any) is dependent upon the cross-coupling parameters of the original system.

EXAMPLE 4. Consider the system described by

$$\dot{x} = \begin{bmatrix} 0 & 1 \\ -1 & 0 \end{bmatrix} x + \begin{bmatrix} 1 & 0 \\ 0 & 1 \end{bmatrix}_u \tag{83}$$

$$J = \tfrac{1}{2} \int_{t_0}^{T} u^T(t) u(t)\, dt \tag{84}$$

$$(x_0, t_0) \to (x_f, T) \tag{85}$$

The transition matrix is given by

$$\phi(T-t) = \begin{bmatrix} \cos(T-t) & \sin(T-t) \\ -\sin(T-t) & \cos(T-t) \end{bmatrix} \tag{86}$$

so use of Eq. (25) yields

$$u_{c1}(t, x(t)) = \begin{bmatrix} \dfrac{1}{T-t} & 0 \\ 0 & \dfrac{1}{T-t} \end{bmatrix} \left[\begin{bmatrix} \cos(T-t) & -\sin(T-t) \\ \sin(T-t) & \cos(T-t) \end{bmatrix} x_f - x(t) \right] \tag{87}$$

or

$$(u_{c1}(t, x(t)))_1 = \Big[[\cos(T-t) \quad -\sin(T-t)] x_f - x_1(t) \Big] \frac{1}{T-t} \tag{88}$$

$$(u_{c1}(t, x(t)))_2 = \Big[[\sin(T-t) \quad \cos(T-t)] x_f - x_2(t) \Big] \frac{1}{T-t} \tag{89}$$

For this example it is obvious that $n_1 = n_2 = 1$ and that the closed-loop control function has the form predicted. Notice that even though the cross coupling in the original system is nonzero, the feedback gain cross coupling between the two first-order subsystems is zero.

V. Minimum Quadratic Multiple Input Systems

Consider the time varying system

$$\dot{x}(t) = A(t)x(t) + B(t)u(t) \tag{90}$$

where $x(t)$ is an N-dimensional state vector, u(t) is an s-dimensional control vector, and $A(t)$ and $B(t)$ are matrices of the proper order.

It is desired that u be chosen to transfer the system from (x_0, t_0) to (x_f, T) in such a way that

$$J = \frac{1}{2}\int_{t_0}^{T} [x^T(t)Q(t)x(t) + u^T(t)R(t)u(t)]\, dt \tag{91}$$

is minimized. The matrix $Q(t)$ is assumed to be nonnegative definite on $[t_0, T]$, and the matrix $R(t)$ is assumed to be positive definite on $[t_0, T]$.

It is well known that necessary conditions for the solution of this problem are given by

$$u = R^{-1}B^T p \tag{92}$$

$$\dot{x} = Ax + BR^{-1}B^T p \tag{93}$$

and

$$\dot{P} = Qx - A^T p \tag{94}$$

where p is the adjoint vector for the system of Eq. (90).

If $\phi(t, t_0)$ is the transition matrix for Eq. (90) then it is easily seen that

$$u(t) = R^{-1}B^T\phi^T(T, t)W^{-1}(t_0) \times \left[x_f - \phi(T, t_0)x_0 + \int_{t_0}^{T} [W(t_0) - W(\tau)]\phi^T(\tau, T)Qx(\tau)\, d\tau\right] - B^T \int_{t}^{T} \phi^T(\tau, t)Qx(\tau)\, d\tau \tag{95}$$

where

$$W(t_0) = \int_{t_0}^{T} \phi(T, \tau)BR^{-1}B^T\phi^T(T, \tau)\, d\tau \tag{96}$$

Now collect terms in Eq. (95), and set the initial time and state equal to the current time and state. The result is the closed-loop control function

$$u_{c1}(t, x(t)) = R^{-1}B^T\phi^T(T, t)W^{-1}(t) \times \left[x_f - \phi(T, t)x(t) - \int_t^T W(\tau)\phi^T(\tau, T)Qx(\tau)\, d\tau\right] \tag{97}$$

From Eq. (96) it is clear that $W(\tau)\to 0$ as $\tau \to T$. Therefore, as $t\to T$ it is seen that

$$u_{cl}(t, x(t)) \to R^{-1}B^T\phi^T(T, t)W^{-1}(t)[x_f - \phi(T, t)x(t)] \tag{98}$$

Comparing Eq. (98) with Eq. (25) thus establishes that the singularities in the feedback gains of the closed-loop control function for a minimum quadratic, multiple input, final value control system have the same structure as the gains for the corresponding minimum control energy, final value control function for the same system.

EXAMPLE 5. Let

$$\dot{x} = -ax + bu \tag{99}$$

$$J = \frac{1}{2}\int_{t_0}^{T} [rx^2 + u^2]\, dt \tag{100}$$

$$(x_0, t_0) \to (x_f, T) \qquad x \text{ and } u \text{ scalar} \tag{101}$$

Then it can be shown that the optimal closed-loop final value control function is given by

$$u_{c1}(t, x(t)) = \left[\frac{2\lambda x_f}{(\lambda + a)e^{\lambda(T-t)} + (\lambda - a)e^{-\lambda(T-t)}} - x(t)\right] \times \left[\frac{(\lambda + a)e^{\lambda(T-t)} + (\lambda - a)e^{-\lambda(T-t)}}{b[e^{\lambda(T-t)} - e^{-\lambda(T-t)}]}\right] \tag{102}$$

where $\lambda = (a^2 + rb^2)^{1/2}$

Therefore, as $t \to T$,

$$u_{c1} \to \frac{[x_f - x(t)]}{b(T - t)} \tag{103}$$

By setting $r = 0$ in Eq. (102) it is seen that the minimum quadratic problem has the same singularity structure as the minimum control energy problem.

EXAMPLE 6. Given the problem described by

$$\dot{x} = \begin{bmatrix} 0 & 1 \\ 0 & 0 \end{bmatrix} x + \begin{bmatrix} 0 \\ 1 \end{bmatrix} u \tag{104}$$

$$J = \frac{1}{2} \int_{t_0}^{T} [x^T x + u^2] \, dt \tag{105}$$

$$(x_0, t_0) \to (x_f, T) \tag{106}$$

it can be shown that

$$u_{c1}(t, x(t)) = \left[\frac{18 - (T-t)^4}{3(T-t)^2 \left(1 - \frac{(T-t)^2}{3}\right)} \quad \frac{4}{(T-t)\left(1 - \frac{(T-t)^2}{3}\right)} \right]$$

$$\times \left[\begin{bmatrix} 1 & -(T-t) - \frac{(T-t)^3}{6} \\ \frac{(T-t)^3}{6} & 1 + \frac{(T-t)^2}{2} \end{bmatrix} x_f - x(t) \right] \tag{107}$$

or

$$u_{c1}(t, x(t)) = \left[\left[1 \quad -(T-t) - \frac{(T-t)^3}{6} \right] x_f - x_1(t) \right]$$

$$\times \left[\frac{18 - T(T-t)^4}{3(T-t)^2 (1 - \frac{(T-t)^2)}{3}} \right]$$

$$+ \left[\left[\frac{(T-t)^3}{6} \quad 1 + \frac{(T-t)^2}{2} \right] x_f - x_2(t) \right]$$

$$\times \left[\frac{4}{(T-t)\left(1 - \frac{(T-t)^2}{3}\right)} \right] \tag{108}$$

Thus as $t \to T$

$$u_{c1}(t, x(t)) \to [x_{f1} - x_1(t)] \frac{6}{(T-t)^2} + [-\tfrac{1}{2} x_{f2} - x_2(t)] \frac{4}{T-t} \tag{109}$$

Comparison of this result with Example 2 shows that the singularity structure is the same for the minimum quadratic and the minimum control energy problems.

VI. Partially Closed-Loop Control Functions

The information about the singularity structure of the feedback gains of optimal final value control systems will now be used to develop partially closed-loop control functions for such systems.

A. The Scalar Input Case

In Section III it was shown that the minimum quadratic, final value, closed-loop control function for a single input system in phase-variable canonical form (PVCF) can be written in the form of Eq. (38).

The singularities in the gains $K_j(t)$ make it impossible to implement Eq. (38) over the entire interval $[t_0, T]$. As the terminal time is approached, the gain $K_1(t)$ will be the first one to cause difficulties in implementation, as it has the highest order singularity (Nth order).

In an effort to generate an optimal control function that does not contain $K_1(t)$, consider the following expression:

$$u_{p1}(t, x(t)) = [f_1(t) - \alpha_{11}(t)x_1(t)]K_2(t) + \sum_{j=2}^{N} [L_j^T(t)x_f - x_j(t)]K_j(t) \tag{110}$$

where $f_1(t)$ is to be determined and $\alpha_{11}(t)$ is an arbitrary bounded function of time. For u_{p1} to be an optimal control function, it must be equal to u and u_{c1} when all three are considered as functions of time alone. That is

$$u_{p1}(t) = u_{c1}(t) = u(t) \tag{111}$$

Solving Eq. (110) for $f_1(t)$ yields

$$f_1(t) = \frac{u_{p1}(t), x(t)) - \sum_{j=2}^{N} [L_j^T(t)x_f - x_j(t)]K_j(t)}{K_2(t)} + \alpha_{11}(t)x_1(t) \tag{112}$$

The right-hand side of this equation is evaluated by considering $x_j(t)$ as a function of time, and not of the current state, which was the interpretation in Eq. (110).

By virtue of Eq. (111), $f_1(t)$ can also be evaluated by using either

$$f_1(t) = \frac{u(t) - \sum_{j=2}^{N} [L_j^T(t)x_f - x_j(t)]K_j(t)}{K_2(t)} + \alpha_{11}(t)x_1(t) \tag{113}$$

or

$$f_1(t) = [L_1^T(t)x_f - x_1(t)] \frac{K_1(t)}{K_2(t)} + \alpha_{11}(t)x_1(t) \tag{114}$$

If the following facts are observed—(1) $u(t)$ has no singularities, (2) $x_j(t)$ has no singularities, (3) $L_j^T(t)x_f$ has no singularities, and (4) $K_j(t)/K_i(t)$ has no singularities for $j > i$, then it is seen that Eq. (113) implies that $f_1(t)$ has no singularities.

Therefore it is possible to find an $f_1(t)$ such that u_{p1} of Eq. (110) is an optimal control function whose maximum gain singularity is of order $(N-1)$. Since $x(t)$ and $u(t)$ in Eq. (113) are functions of the initial conditions on the system, $f_1(t)$ is also a function of the initial conditions. Therefore, u_{p1} of Eq. (110) is a function of both the current state and the initial conditions on the system, i.e., u_{p1} is a partially closed-loop optimal control function.

Since u_{p1} still has singularities in its feedback gains, it cannot be implemented over the entire remaining portion of the interval $[t_0, T]$. The gain $K_2(t)$ will be the next to cause implementation difficulties as it now has the highest order singularity [$(N-1)$st order]. Repeating the arguments made above will show that a function $f_2(t)$ can be found such that

$$u_{p2}(t, x(t)) = [f_2(t) - \alpha_{21}(t)x_1(t) - \alpha_{22}(t)x_2(t)]K_3(t) + \sum_{j=3}^{N} [L_j^T(t)x_f - x_j(t)]K_j(t) \tag{115}$$

is a partially closed-loop control function whose maximum gain singularity is of order $(N-2)$.

In general, then, at the ith stage of the reduction process,

$$u_{pi}(t, x(t)) = [f_i(t) - \sum_{j=1}^{i} \alpha_{ij}(t)x_j(t)]K_{i+1}(t) + \sum_{j=i+1}^{N} [L_j^T(t)x_f - x_j(t)]K_j(t) \tag{116}$$

is a partially closed-loop, final value, optimal control function whose maximum gain singularity is of order $(N-i)$. The $\alpha_{ij}(t)$ are arbitrary bounded functions of time and $f_i(t)$ can be evaluated by use of either

$$f_i(t) = \frac{u(t) - \sum_{j=i+1}^{N} [L_j^T(t)x_f - x_j(t)]K_j(t)}{K_{i+1}(t)} + \sum_{j=1}^{i} \alpha_{ij}(t)x_j(t) \tag{117}$$

or

$$f_i(t) = \sum_{j=1}^{i} [L_j^T(t)x_f - x_j(t)] \frac{K_j(t)}{K_{i+1}(t)} + \sum_{j=1}^{i} \alpha_{ij}(t)x_j(t) \tag{118}$$

To evaluate $f_N(t)$, define $K_{N+1} = 1$.

Since the last optimal control function generated by this reduction procedure has the form

$$u_{pN}(t, x(t)) = f_N(t) - \sum_{j=1}^{N} \alpha_{Nj}(t)x_j(t) \tag{119}$$

and has no singularities, it is seen that partial feedback can be maintained over the entire interval $[t_0, T]$.

The following result has now been established. For single input, minimum quadratic, final value control systems in PVCF, it is possible to generate partially closed-loop control functions that are optimal, and that allow the designer to set the maximum order of the gain singularity in the feedback loops between N and zero.

If the original system is time invariant and the cost function is minimum quadratic (as opposed to minimum energy) then the $\alpha_{ij}(t)$ defined above can be chosen in such a way that Eq. (119) corresponds to a result presented by Rekasius (*8*).

In practice, the closed-loop control function u_{c1} would be used until it became impossible to implement the gain with the highest order singularity. At that time, say t_1, the closed-loop control function would be retired and the partially closed-loop control function u_{p1} would be used. When it became impossible to implement u_{p1}, say at time t_2, the change would be made to u_{p2}, and so on. The resulting optimal control policy could thus be implemented over the entire control interval $[t_0, T]$ without requiring infinite gains.

It is worth noting explicitly that the initial time and state used to evaluate the function $f_j(t)$ associated with u_{pj} can be taken as the time and state at any point on the interval $[t_0, t_j]$ and not just $(t_0, x(t_0))$. In fact, it will usually be desirable to evaluate $f_j(t)$ in terms of the time and state $(t_j, x(t_j))$. For in this case, if the system is subjected to disturbances over $[t_0, t_j]$ but is disturbance free over $[t_j, T]$, then the trajectory over $[t_j, T]$ is optimal.

EXAMPLE 7. For the scalar case described by

$$\dot{x} = -ax + bu \tag{120}$$

$$J = \int_{t_0}^{T} u^2 \, dt \tag{121}$$

$$(x_0, t_0) \to (x_f, T) \qquad x \text{ and } u \text{ scalar}, \tag{122}$$

the closed-loop control function is given by

$$u_{c1}(t, x(t)) = \frac{2a}{b}\left[\frac{x_{f1} - e^{-a(T-t)}x(t)}{e^{a(T-t)} - e^{-a(T-t)}}\right] \tag{123}$$

It can be shown that the optimal trajectory $x(t)$ is given by

$$x(t) = \frac{[e^{a(t-t_0)} - e^{-a(t-t_0)}]x_f + [e^{a(T-t)} - e^{-a(T-t)}]x_0}{[e^{a(T-t_0)} - e^{-a(T-t_0)}]} \tag{124}$$

The partially closed-loop control function u_{p1} is thus

$$u_{p1}(t, x(t)) = f_1(t) - \alpha_{11}(t)x(t) \tag{125}$$

where $\alpha_{11}(t)$ is arbitrary and, by use of Eqs. (117) or (118)

$$f_1(t) = \frac{[(2a + b\alpha_{11})e^{a(t-t_0)} - b\alpha_{11}e^{-a(t-t_0)}]x_f}{b[e^{a(T-t_0)} - e^{-a(T-t_0)}]} + \frac{[b\alpha_{11}e^{a(T-t)} - (2a + b\alpha_{11})e^{-a(T-t)}]x_0}{b[e^{a(T-t_0)} - e^{-a(T-t_0)}]} \tag{126}$$

Clearly, $f_1(t)$ has no singularities.

EXAMPLE 8. For the system given in Example 2, the first partially closed-loop control function is

$$u_{p1}(t, x(t)) = [f_1(t) - \alpha_{11}x_1(t)]\frac{4}{(T-t)} + [-\tfrac{1}{2}x_{f2} - x_2(t)]\frac{4}{(T-t)} \tag{127}$$

where use of Eq. (118) shows that

$$f_1(t) - (\alpha_{11}x_{f1} + \tfrac{3}{2}x_{f2}) - (\alpha_{11}x_{f2} + \tfrac{3}{2}C_1)(T-t) + (\alpha_{11}C_1 - \tfrac{3}{2}C_2)(T-t)^2 + \alpha_{11}C_2(T-t)^3 \tag{128}$$

It is obvious that $f_1(t)$ has no singularities and that the only gain singularity in u_{p1} is of order one.

The second partially closed-loop control function is given by

$$u_{p2}(t, x(t)) = f_2(t) - \alpha_{21}x_1(t) - \alpha_{22}x_2(t) \tag{129}$$

where

$$f_2(t) = (2C_1 + \alpha_{21}x_{f1} + \alpha_{22}x_{f2}) + (6C_2 - \alpha_{21}x_{f2} - 2\alpha_{22}C_1)(T-t) + (\alpha_{21}C_1 - 3\alpha_{22}C_2)(T-t)^2 + \alpha_{21}C_2(T-t)^3 \tag{130}$$

Clearly $f_2(t)$ and u_{p2} have no singularities.

B. The Multiple Input Case

It was established in Sections IV and V that the ith component of the minimum quadratic final value closed-loop control function for a multiple input system in PVCF is given by Eq. (82).

For a specific system the actual order of the singularity for each $K_{rj}^{i}(t)$ in Eq. (82) can be determined. The expression for each element of u_{c1} can then be written so that the terms in the sum appear in the order of decreasing singularities. That is, Eq. (82) can be rewritten in the form

$$(u_{c1}(t, x(t)))_i = \sum_{l=1}^{N} C_{il}(t, x(t))V_{il}(t) \tag{131}$$

where $C_{il}(t, x(t))$ has no singularities and is a linear function of $L_{r\,j}^{T}(t)x_f - (x_r(t))$ for $r = 1, \ldots, s$ and $j = 1, \ldots, n_r$ and $V_{il}(t)$ has singularities at the terminal time T, with V_{i1} having the highest order singularity (say of order M), V_{i2} the next highest order singularity, and so on.

The arguments used for the single input case may then be repeated with the obvious expansion in notation to show the following result [for details of this development, see (*9*)].

For multiple input, minimum quadratic, final value control systems in PVCF, it is possible to generate partially closed-loop control functions that are optimal and that allow the designer to set the maximum order of the gain singularity in the feedback loops between the closed-loop maximum and zero. Note that since some of the cross-coupling terms between PVCF blocks may be zero, a given order of singularity may not appear in each component of u_{c1}.

Example 9. Given the system described by

$$\dot{x} = \begin{bmatrix} 0 & 1 \\ -1 & 0 \end{bmatrix} x + \begin{bmatrix} 1 & 0 \\ 0 & 1 \end{bmatrix} u \tag{132}$$

$$J = \frac{1}{2}\int_{t_0}^{T} u^T u \, dt \tag{133}$$

$$(x_0, t_0) \rightarrow (0, T) \tag{134}$$

the closed-loop control function is

$$(u_{c1}(t, x(t)))_1 = \frac{-x_1(t)}{(T-t)} \tag{135}$$

$$(u_{c1}(t, x(t)))_2 = \frac{-x_2(t)}{(T-t)} \tag{136}$$

It can be shown that the optimal trajectory $x(t)$ is given by

$$x(t) = \frac{T - t}{T - t_0} \begin{bmatrix} \cos(t - t_0) & \sin(t - t_0) \\ -\sin(t - t_0) & \cos(t - t_0) \end{bmatrix} x_0 \tag{137}$$

The partially closed-loop control function u_{p1} is therefore seen to be

$$(u_{p1}(t, x(t)))_1 = f_1{}^1(t) - \alpha_{11}^1 x_1(t) \tag{138}$$

$$(u_{p1}(t, x(t)))_2 = f_1{}^2(t) - \alpha_{11}^2 x_2(t) \tag{139}$$

where

$$f_1{}^1(t) = \frac{[\alpha_{11}^1(T - t) - 1]x_{01} \cos(t - t_0)}{[T - t_0]} + \frac{[\alpha_{11}^1(T - t) - 1]x_{02} \sin(t - t_0)}{[T - t_0]} \tag{140}$$

$$f_1{}^2(t) = \frac{[\alpha_{11}^2(T - t) - 1][-x_{01} \sin(t - t_0) + x_{02} \cos(t - t_0)]}{[T - t_0]} \tag{141}$$

C. Performance of Partially Closed-Loop Control Functions

For the class of problems being considered here, performance is judged by the ability of the system to achieve the desired terminal state when the plant parameters have varied by an unknown amount. Of particular interest is a comparison between the performance of the partially closed-loop control functions described above, and the performance of open-loop control functions.

Consider an Nth order, single input system described by

$$\dot{x} = Ax + Bu \tag{142}$$

where u is the open-loop final value optimal control function for the system.

Now assume that A changes to $A + D$ and let z be the state of the new system under the open-loop control function u for the original system, and let y be the state of the new system under the partially closed-loop control function u_{pN} for the original system. Then

$$\dot{z} = (A + D)z + Bu \tag{143}$$

and

$$\dot{y} = (A + D)y + Bu_{pN} \tag{144}$$

From Eq. (119)

$$u_{p_N} = f_N(t) - \alpha^T y \tag{145}$$

where

$$\alpha^T = [\alpha_{N1}, \alpha_{N2}, \ldots, \alpha_{NN}]$$

and from Eq. (117)

$$f_N(t) = u(t) + \alpha^T x(t) \tag{146}$$

Thus Eq. (144) becomes

$$\dot{y} = (A + D - B\alpha^T)y + B^T x(t) + Bu(t) \tag{147}$$

Now define new variables v and w by

$$v = y - x \tag{148}$$

and

$$w = z - x \tag{149}$$

By Eqs. (142), (143), and (147),

$$\dot{v} = (A + D - B\alpha^T)v - Dx \tag{150}$$

$$\dot{w} = (A + D)w - Dx \tag{151}$$

Since it is assumed that the changes in the system parameters do not influence the choice of initial conditions on the system, the initial conditions on the systems of Eqs. (150) and (151) are

$$v(t_0) = w(t_0) = 0 \tag{152}$$

From the development above, it is clear that $v(T)$ and $w(T)$ are the terminal error vectors for the disturbed system under partially closed-loop and open-loop control, respectively.

Before further general discussion, consider the following two examples.

EXAMPLE 10. Given the time invariant system

$$\dot{x} = -ax + u \tag{153}$$

$$(x_0, t_0) \to (0, T) \tag{154}$$

where x and u are scalars, the optimal (minimum control energy) trajectory is given by

$$x(t) = \left[\frac{e^{a(T-t)} - e^{-a(T-t)}}{e^{a(T-t_0)} - e^{-a(T-t_0)}}\right] x_0 \tag{155}$$

From Eqs. (150) and (151)

$$v(T) = -\int_{t_0}^{T} e^{-(a-D+\alpha)(T-t)} Dx(t)\, dt \tag{156}$$

where α is a constant, and

$$w(T) = -\int_{t_0}^{T} e^{-(a-D)(T-t)} Dx(t)\, dt \tag{157}$$

Thus

$$v(T) - w(T) = \int_{t_0}^{T} [1 - e^{-\alpha(T-t)}] e^{-(a-D)(T-t)} Dx(t)\, dt \tag{158}$$

From Eq. (155) it is seen that $x(t)$ has a constant sign over $[t_0, T]$ and since D is a constant and e^u is a positive, it is clear from Eqs. (156)–(158) that if α is positive, then

$$|v(T)| < |w(T)|$$

and if α is negative

$$|v(T)| > |w(T)|$$

Therefore, for the scalar, time invariant case, negative partial feedback control is superior to open-loop control for any finite parameter variation.

EXAMPLE 11. Consider the following second-order, single input system

$$\dot{x} = \begin{bmatrix} 0 & 1 \\ -1 & 0 \end{bmatrix} x + \begin{bmatrix} 0 \\ 1 \end{bmatrix} u \tag{159}$$

$$J = \frac{1}{2} \int_{0}^{2\pi} u^2\, dt \tag{160}$$

$$(x_0, 0) \to (x_f, 2\pi) \tag{161}$$

where

$$x_0 = x_f = \begin{bmatrix} 0 \\ C \end{bmatrix} \tag{162}$$

The optimal trajectory is given by

$$x(t) = \begin{bmatrix} \sin t \\ \cos t \end{bmatrix} C \tag{163}$$

If the plant parameters change in such a way that

$$D = \begin{bmatrix} 0 & 0 \\ -3 & 0 \end{bmatrix} \tag{164}$$

and the α vector is chosen to be

$$\alpha = \begin{bmatrix} 9/4 \\ 0 \end{bmatrix} \tag{165}$$

then straightforward computation using Eqs. (150 and 151) shows that

$$v(T) = \begin{bmatrix} 0 \\ -8C/7 \end{bmatrix} \tag{166}$$

and

$$w(T) = \begin{bmatrix} 0 \\ 0 \end{bmatrix} \tag{167}$$

For this example, it is seen that the variation in plant parameters can be such that a particular value of negative feedback results in a worse terminal error than would result from open-loop control.

The two examples above demonstrate that negative feedback is always superior to open-loop control for the scalar case, but that for a higher order system, even negative feedback may not be superior to open-loop control for all combinations of plant parameter variations and choices of feedback gains.

When performing an error analysis, the fact that feedback is not always superior makes it necessary to consider a comparison of the form

$$\|w(T)\| - \|v(T)\| \tag{168}$$

rather than one of the form

$$\|w(T) - v(T)\| \tag{169}$$

Since the actual error vectors $v(T)$ and $w(T)$ are given by

$$v(T) = -\int_{t_0}^{T} \Psi(T, t)\, Dx(t)\, dt \tag{170}$$

and

$$w(T) = -\int_{t_0}^{T} \Theta(T, t)\, Dx(t)\, dt \tag{171}$$

where Ψ is the transition matrix for Eq. (150), and Θ is the transition matrix for Eq. (151), it is also seen that the variables α do not appear explicitly in the error vectors and that the variables D appear both explicitly and implicitly.

These considerations make it unfeasible to perform a general analytical comparison between partially closed-loop control functions and open-loop control functions. Of course, for specific systems, where ranges of parameter variations are known, a comparison could be made.

Appendix: Useful Lemmas on Determinants

The following two lemmas are presented here without proof. Proofs are available in (*10*).

LEMMA 1. The determinant of the matrix A, where

$$A = \begin{bmatrix} A_1 & 0 & \cdots & 0 \\ 0 & A_2 & \cdots & 0 \\ \vdots & \vdots & & \vdots \\ 0 & 0 & \cdots & A_s \end{bmatrix}$$

with A_i an $n_i \times n_i$ matrix, is given by

$$|A| = \prod_{i=1}^{s} |A_i|$$

LEMMA 2. Consider a matrix $Q(t)$ described by

$$Q(t) = \begin{bmatrix} A_1 & D_{12}t & \cdots & D_{1s}t \\ C_{21}t & A_2 & \cdots & D_{2s}t \\ \vdots & \vdots & & \vdots \\ C_{s1}t & C_{s2}t & \cdots & A_s \end{bmatrix}$$

where A_1 is a constant $(n_1 - 1) \times n_1$; A_2 is a constant $n_2 \times (n_2 - 1)$ matrix; A_i, $i \neq 1, 2$, is a constant $n_i \times n_i$ matrix; and C_{ij} and D_{ij} are constant matrices of the appropriate orders.
Then

$$|Q(t)| = K_1 t + K_2 t^2 + \ldots$$

where $K_1, K_2, \ldots$ are constants and, in general, K_1 is not zero. In addition, it is only necessary to evaluate

$$\begin{bmatrix} A_1 & & 0 & \cdots & 0 \\ C_{21}t & A_2 & 0 & \cdots & 0 \\ 0 & 0 & A_3 & \cdots & 0 \\ \vdots & \vdots & \vdots & & \vdots \\ 0 & 0 & 0 & \cdots & A_s \end{bmatrix}$$

to determine K_1.

References

1. A. R. STUBBERUD, On final value control. Aerospace Corp. Rep., TR-0158 (3307-02)-2, September (1967).
2. W. A. PORTER, On singularities that arise in a class of optimal feedback systems. *IEEE Trans. Autom. Control* **11**, 617–619 (1966).

3. E. R. Rang, A comment on closed loop optimal guidance systems. *IEEE Trans. Autom. Control* **11**, 616–617 (1966).
4. J. M. Holtzman and S. Horing, The sensitivity of terminal conditions of optimal control systems to parameter variations. *IEEE Trans. Autom. Control* **10**, 420–426, (1965).
5. C. E. Seal and A. R. Stubberud, Canonical forms for multiple input time variable systems. *IEEE Trans. Autom. Control* **14**, 704–707 (1969).
6. R. E. Kalman, Y. C. Ho, and K. S. Narendra, Controllability of linear dynamical systems. *Cont. Diff. Eqs.* **1**, 189–213 (1963).
7. L. M. Silverman, Transformation of time variable systems to canonical (phase-variable) form. *IEEE Trans. Autom. Control* **11**, 300–303 (1966).
8. Z. V. Rekasius, An alternate approach to the fixed terminal point regulator problem. *IEEE Trans. Autom. Control* **9**, 290–292 (1964).
9. C. E. Seal and A. R. Stubberud, The singularity structure of optimal final-value control systems. *Int. J. Control* **12**, 1029–1039 (1970).
10. C. E. Seal, The structure of optimal final value control systems. Ph.D. Dissertation, Univ. of California, Los Angeles, California (1968).

Singular Problems in Linear Estimation and Control[1]

KURT SIMON

TRW Systems, Inc.
Redondo Beach, California

AND

ALLEN STUBBERUD

School of Engineering, University of California
Irvine, California

I. Introduction

Considerable research has been devoted in the past few years to various problems in the estimation of the state of linear dynamic systems using measurements corrupted by noise which is Markov, or correlated in time (colored noise), or more generally, by noise with noninvertible covariance. This is evidenced by the large number of papers (*1–10*) dealing with colored

[1] This research was supported by the Air Force Office of Scientific Research, Grant No. AF-AFOSR-699-67.

noise filtering and smoothing in the Reference list. These problems are members of a broader class of linear optimization problems, i.e., problems in both estimation and deterministic control, in which certain critical system matrices or transformations are singular, thus posing difficulties in solution via usual techniques. In the colored noise filtering (or smoothing) problem, the inverse of the measurement noise covariance which is otherwise part of the optimal gain calculations, does not exist. An analogous difficulty occurs in the linear quadratic optimal regulator problem when the quadratic form of the control in the cost functional is not positive definite but only nonnegative definite. In this event the Euler equations cannot be solved directly for the optimal control, again due to the requirement for the nonexistent inverse of the particular matrix.

In this paper, these problems and their solutions are discussed. In Section II, the colored noise filter is rederived by a generalization of the method used by Kalman–Bucy in their original paper (*11*) on continuous-time white noise filtering. The same technique is then applied to a greatly generalized problem of filtering in which both colored and white noises are present. The duality of linear filtering and linear quadratic optimal regulation noted by Kalman and Bucy (*11–13*) suggests that the techniques used for solution of the colored noise filter might be applied to the singular control problem. Thus, in Section IV, the duality of linear estimation and control is examined in the light of the concept of duality in mathematical programming, allowing the control/estimation dual to be extended to problems such as those mentioned above. The study requires a calculus of variations approach to estimation, which is justified in Section III. The solution to the nonnegative definite control problem is then obtained by duality. For the benefit of those who are still skeptics, the same solution is derived by calculus of variations in Section IV. Additional singular problems are discussed briefly in Section V.

II. Colored Noise Filtering

A. Kalman–Bucy Approach to Colored Noise Filtering

In 1961, Kalman and Bucy derived the minimal-variance unbiased filter equations for linear systems disturbed by white noise (*11*). The state and measurement equations they assumed were of the form

$$\dot{x}(t) = F(t)x(t) + r(t), \qquad x(t_0) = x_0 \tag{1}$$

$$z(t) = H(t)x(t) + L(t)v(t) \tag{2}$$

where $r(t)$ and $v(t)$ were zero-mean independent white noises with covariances $R(t)\delta(t-\tau)$ and $V(t)\delta(t-\tau)$, respectively. They then assumed the optimal estimate was of the form

$$\hat{x}(t)=\int_{t_0}^{t} W(t,\tau)z(\tau)\,d\tau \tag{3}$$

and, from this and the orthogonality principle, derived the well-known Kalman–Bucy filter. Their method of solution notably required that $L(t)V(t)L^T(t)$ be nonsingular and that $W(t,\tau)$ be continuous at $\tau=t$. However, problems then arose in which $v(t)$ was not white, but Markov, i.e., describable by an equation such as

$$\dot{v}(t)=A(t)v(t)+u(t), \qquad v(t_0)=v_0 \tag{4}$$

where $u(t)$ is zero-mean white noise with covariance $U(t)\delta(t-\tau)$. This problem has been solved by several methods, notably Bucy (*2*), Bryson–Johansen (*1*), and Stear–Stubberud (*9, 10*). However, each of these works pre-assumes either the solution or a linear operation on the observations, and then proves that these are correct. Alternatively, the form of the solution to the colored noise filter can be *derived* by using the same approach as that used by Kalman and Bucy by removing unnecessary restrictions on the form of the estimate. This is the subject of this subsection.

The form of the optimal estimate assumed by Kalman and Bucy was

$$\hat{x}(t)=\int_{t_0}^{t} W(t,\tau)z(\tau)\,d\tau \tag{5}$$

where $W(t,\tau)$ is the impulse response of the transformation. This was justified on the basis of the fact that the optimal estimate of a Gaussian signal in additive Gaussian noise is known to be a linear function of the measurements $z(\tau)$, $t_0\leqslant\tau\leqslant t$. Equation (5) is a representation of the general form of a linear functional, provided either that $W(t,\tau)$ contain generalized functions such as the impulse function and its "derivatives," including at $t=\tau$, or that all elements of $z(t)$ contain white noise and are therefore not differentiable. However, the approach utilized by Kalman and Bucy requires that $W(t,\tau)$ be continuous at $t=\tau$, and for colored noise filtering, at least some of the measurements do not contain white noise and are differentiable. Thus, a more appropriate form for the general linear functional is (*14*)

$$\hat{x}(t)=\int_{t_0}^{t} W(t,\tau)z(\tau)\,d\tau+\sum_k K_k(t)z_2^{(k)}(t) \tag{6}$$

where $W(t,\tau)$ is continuous at $t=\tau$. The summation is carried beyond $k=0$ for those components or linear combinations of components of z whose derivatives

$$\dot{z}(t)=[\dot{H}(t)+H(t)F(t)]x(t)+H(t)r(t)$$

are noise free. If the covariance of $H(t)r(t)$ is nonsingular, then all components of $\dot{z}(t)$ contain independent components of white noise, and the following derivation is simplified. Assuming nonsingularity of $[H(t)R(t) \times H^T(t) + L(t)U(t)L^T(t)]$, it suffices to use the form of the estimate

$$\hat{x}(t) = \int_{t_0}^{t} W(t, \tau)z(\tau)\, d\tau + K(t)z(t) \tag{7}$$

Using Leibnitz' formula to differentiate with respect to time,

$$\dot{\hat{x}}(t) = K(t)\dot{z}(t) + [\dot{K}(t) + W(t, t)]z(t) + \int_{t_0}^{t} \left[\frac{\partial}{\partial t} W(t, \tau)\right] z(\tau)\, d\tau \tag{8}$$

The term $(\partial/\partial t)W(t, \tau)$ can be evaluated by differentiating the Wiener–Hopf equation

$$R_{xz}(t, \sigma) = \int_{t_0}^{t} W(t, \tau)R_{zz}(\tau, \sigma)\, d\tau + K(t)R_{zz}(t, \sigma) \tag{9}$$

where

$$R_{xz}(t, \sigma) \equiv E[x(t)z^T(\sigma)]; \qquad R_{zz}(t, \sigma) = E[z(t)z^T(\sigma)] \tag{10}$$

with respect to time as follows:

$$\frac{\partial}{\partial t} R_{xz}(t, \sigma) \equiv E[\dot{x}(t)z^T(\sigma)] = F(t)R_{xz}(t, \sigma) \qquad t > \sigma \geqslant t_0 \tag{11}$$

Similarly,

$$\frac{\partial}{\partial t} R_{zz}(t, \sigma) = E\{[(\dot{H} + HF)x + (\dot{L} + LA)v + Hr + Lu]z^T(\sigma)\} \tag{12}$$

An assumption is required at this point that $L(t)$ be nonsingular. Then,

$$\frac{\partial}{\partial t} R_{zz}(t, \sigma) = M(t)R_{xz}(t, \sigma) + D(t)R_{zz}(t, \sigma), \qquad t > \sigma \geqslant t_0 \tag{13}$$

where

$$D(t) \equiv (\dot{L} + LA)L^{-1} \tag{14}$$

$$M(t) \equiv \dot{H} + HF - DH \tag{15}$$

Also,

$$\frac{\partial}{\partial t} \int_{t_0}^{t} W(t, \tau)R_{zz}(\tau, \sigma)\, d\tau = W(t, t)R_{zz}(t, \sigma) + \int_{t_0}^{t} \left[\frac{\partial}{\partial t} W(t, \tau)\right] R_{zz}(\tau, \sigma)\, d\tau \tag{16}$$

Thus, the differentiated Wiener–Hopf equation can be written

$$\int_{t_0}^{t} \left[\frac{\partial}{\partial t} W(t, \tau) - F(t)W(t, \tau) + K(t)M(t)W(t, \tau)\right] R_{zz}(\tau, \sigma)\, d\tau$$
$$= -[W(t, t) + \dot{K}(t) + K(t)D(t) - F(t)K(t) + K(t)M(t)K(t)]R_{zz}(t, \sigma) \tag{17}$$

For this equation to hold, it suffices that

$$\frac{\partial}{\partial t} W(t, \tau) = [F(t) - K(t)M(t)]W(t, \tau) \tag{18}$$

$$\dot{K}(t) + W(t, t) - F(t)K(t) + K(t)M(t)K(t) = -K(t)D(t) \tag{19}$$

Substituting into the equation for $\hat{x}$ yields

$$\dot{\hat{x}}(t) = F(t)\hat{x}(t) + K(t)[\dot{z}(t) - D(t)z(t) - M(t)\hat{x}(t)] \tag{20}$$

For the white noise case considered by Kalman and Bucy, it is possible to show necessity of the comparable integrand. However, the colored noise filter is not unique. A higher order filter can be obtained by considering v to be a part of the state and deriving the filter for the case where the observations have no measurement noise. This is discussed in more detail for discrete-time systems in (*15*).

It remains to calculate the gain $K(t)$. The estimation error

$$\varepsilon(t) \equiv x(t) - \hat{x}(t) \tag{21}$$

satisfies the differential equation

$$\dot{\varepsilon}(t) = [F(t) - K(t)M(t)]\varepsilon(t) + [I - K(t)H(t)]r(t) - K(t)L(t)u(t) \tag{22}$$

The error covariance, $J(t) \equiv E[\varepsilon(t)\varepsilon^T(t)]$, has the derivative

$$\dot{J}(t) = E[\varepsilon(t)\dot{\varepsilon}^T(t)] + E[\dot{\varepsilon}(t)\varepsilon^T(t)] \tag{23}$$

Defining $\phi_\varepsilon(t, \tau)$ as the transition matrix for the error equation,

$$\varepsilon(t) = \phi_\varepsilon(t, t_0)\varepsilon(t_0) + \int_{t_0}^{t} \phi_\varepsilon(t, \tau)\{[I - K(\tau)H(\tau)]r(\tau) - K(\tau)L(\tau)u(\tau)\}\, d\tau \tag{24}$$

Thus,

$$E[\varepsilon(t)\dot{\varepsilon}^T(t)] = J(t)(F - KM)^T + \int_{t_0}^{t} \phi_\varepsilon(t, \tau)\{(I - KH)R(\tau)\, \delta(t - \tau)(I - KH)^T$$
$$+ KLU(\tau)\, \delta(t - \tau)L^T K^T\}\, d\tau \tag{25}$$

or

$$E[\varepsilon(t)\dot{\varepsilon}^T(t)] = J(F - KM)^T + \tfrac{1}{2}(I - KH)R(I - KH)^T + \tfrac{1}{2}KLUL^T K^T \tag{26}$$

Thus,

$$\dot{J}(t) = FJ + JF^T + R - K(MJ + HR) - (JM^T + RH^T)K^T + K(HRH^T + LUL^T)K^T \tag{27}$$

Alternatively, J can be calculated using Eq. (24) to be

$$J(t) = \phi_\varepsilon(t, t_0)J_0\phi_\varepsilon(t, t_0) + \int_{t_0}^{t} \phi_\varepsilon(t, \tau)[(I - KH)R(I - KH)^T + KLUL^TK^T] \phi_\varepsilon^T(t, \tau)\, d\tau \tag{28}$$

where the argument τ has been dropped for brevity in the integrand, and then differentiated using Leibnitz rule to again obtain Eq. (27). The minimizing $K(t)$ will be the K which minimizes $\dot{J}(t)$, and can be computed by completing the square to obtain

$$K^0(t) = (JM^T + RH^T)(HRH^T + LUL^T)^{-1} \tag{29}$$

The initial conditions on $J(t)$ and $\hat{x}(t)$ are the covariance and mean of the initial state x_0, respectively.

B. A Generalized Colored Noise Filter

The problem discussed above is in actuality not as general as that considered by Bryson and Johansen (*1*), who utilized a model such as Eqs. (1) and (2) with $v(t)$ being white noise whose covariance $V(t)\delta(t-\tau)$ does not have maximum rank. This is equivalent to considering the filtering problem where the measurements are corrupted by some white noises and some colored noises. The work of all the above-mentioned authors can be generalized to the following problem.

$$\begin{bmatrix} \dot{x}(t) \\ \dot{y}(t) \end{bmatrix} = \begin{bmatrix} F_{11}(t) & F_{12}(t) \\ F_{21}(t) & F_{22}(t) \end{bmatrix} \begin{bmatrix} x(t) \\ y(t) \end{bmatrix} + \begin{bmatrix} r_1(t) \\ r_2(t) \end{bmatrix} \quad \begin{matrix} x \in E^n \\ y \in E^m \end{matrix} \tag{30}$$

$$\begin{bmatrix} z_1(t) \\ z_2(t) \end{bmatrix} = \begin{bmatrix} H_{11}(t) & H_{12}(t) \\ H_{21}(t) & H_{22}(t) \end{bmatrix} \begin{bmatrix} x(t) \\ y(t) \end{bmatrix} + \begin{bmatrix} I \\ 0 \end{bmatrix} v(t) \quad \begin{matrix} z_1, v \in E^p \\ z_2 \in E^m \end{matrix} \tag{31}$$

where $x(t_0)$, $y(t_0)$ are random variables with means $\bar{x}_0$, $\bar{y}_0$ and covariances J_0, $\sum_0$, respectively, and where $r_1(t)$, $r_2(t)$, and $v(t)$ are zero-mean white noise processes with second-order statistics

$$\begin{aligned} E[r_i(t)r_j^T(\tau)] &= R_{ij}(t)\delta(t-\tau) \\ E[v(t)r_i^T(\tau)] &= S_i(t)\delta(t-\tau) \qquad i, j = 1, 2 \\ E[v(t)v^T(\tau)] &= V_1(t)\delta(t-\tau) \end{aligned} \tag{32}$$

It is assumed that $H_{22}(t)$ is nonsingular, as is

$$\left[\begin{array}{c|c} V_1(t) & S_0(t) \\ \hline S_0^T(t) & V_0(t) \end{array}\right] \tag{33}$$

where

$$V_0(t) \equiv H_{21}R_{11}H_{21}^T + H_{22}R_{22}H_{22}^T + H_{22}R_{12}^T H_{21} + H_{21}R_{12}H_{22}^T \tag{34}$$

$$S_0(t) \equiv S_1 H_{21}^T + S_2 H_{22}^T \tag{35}$$

THEOREM. *Given the stochastic filtering problem, Eqs.* (30)–(35), *the minimal-order optimal estimate satisfies the equations*

$$\dot{\hat{x}} = F_0 \hat{x} + (F_{12} - K_1 H_{12})H_{22}^{-1} z_2 + K_1(z_1 - H_0)\hat{x} + K_2(\dot{z}_2 - D_2 z_2 - M_2 \hat{x})$$

$$\hat{y} = H_{22}^{-1}[z_2 - H_{21}\hat{x}] \tag{36}$$

where

$$[K_1 \mid K_2] = [(JH_0^T + S_1^T) \mid (JM_2^T + S_3^T)] \left[\begin{array}{c|c} V_1 & S_0 \\ \hline S_0^T & V_0 \end{array}\right]^{-1} \tag{37}$$

and

$$D_2 \equiv (\dot{H}_{22} + H_{21}F_{12} + H_{22}F_{22})H_{22}^{-1} \tag{38}$$

$$M_2 \equiv \dot{H}_{21} + H_{21}F_{11} + H_{22}F_{21} - D_2 H_{21} \tag{39}$$

$$H_0 \equiv H_{11} - H_{12}H_{22}^{-1}H_{21} \tag{40}$$

$$F_0 \equiv F_{11} - F_{12}H_{22}^{-1}H_{21} \tag{41}$$

$$S_0 \equiv S_1 H_{21}^T + S_2 H_{22}^T \tag{42}$$

$$S_3 \equiv H_{21}R_{11} + H_{22}R_{12}^T \tag{43}$$

$$V_0 \equiv H_{21}R_{11}H_{21}^T + H_{22}R_{22}H_{22}^T + H_{21}R_{12}H_{22}^T + H_{22}R_{12}^T H_{21} \tag{44}$$

The error covariance satisfies

$$\dot{J} = F_0 J + JF_0^T + R_{11} - [K_1 \mid K_2] \left[\begin{array}{c|c} V_1 & S_0 \\ \hline S_0^T & V_0 \end{array}\right] \left[\begin{array}{c} K_1^T \\ \hline K_2^T \end{array}\right] \tag{45}$$

The initial conditions $\hat{x}(t_0)$ *and* $J(t_0)$ *are*

$$\hat{x}(t_0) = [(H_{22}^{-1}H_{21})^T \Sigma_0^{-1}(H_{22}^{-1}H_{21}) + J_0^{-1}]^{-1}$$
$$\times [(H_{22}^{-1}H_{21})^T \Sigma_0^{-1} H_{22}^{-1}(z_2(t_0) - H_{22}(t_0)\bar{y}_0) + J_0^{-1}\bar{x}_0]$$

$$J(t_0) = [(H_{22}^{-1}H_{21})^T \Sigma_0^{-1}(H_{22}^{-1}H_{21}) + J_0^{-1}]^{-1} \tag{46}$$

Before proving the Theorem, a remark is appropriate regarding the connection of this problem with those previously solved. If $m = 0$, Eqs. (30) and (31) reduce to those used by Kalman–Bucy. Further, in this case $F_0 = F_{11}$, $H_0 = H_{11}$, and Eqs. (36), (37), and (45) become

$$\begin{aligned} \dot{\hat{x}} &= F_{11}\hat{x} + K_1(z_1 - H_{11}\hat{x}); \qquad \hat{x}(t_0) = \bar{x}_0 \\ K_1 &= (JH_{11}^T + S_1{}^T)V_1^{-1} \\ \dot{J} &= F_{11}J + JF_{11}^T + R_{11} - K_1V_1K_1{}^T; \qquad J(t_0) = J_0 \end{aligned} \tag{47}$$

which is the result they obtained. If $p = 0$, $m > 0$, $R_{12} = 0$, and $F_{12} = F_{21}^T = 0$, then Eqs. (30) and (31) become those used by Bucy and Stear–Stubberud. Further, in this case, $F_0 = F_{11}$,

$$\begin{aligned} V_0 &= H_{21}R_{11}H_{21}^T + H_{22}R_{22}H_{22}^T \\ D_2 &= (\dot{H}_{22} + H_{22}F_{22})H_{22}^{-1} \\ M_2 &= \dot{H}_{21} + H_{21}F_{11} - D_2H_{21} \end{aligned} \tag{48}$$

and the filter equations become

$$\begin{aligned} \dot{\hat{x}} &= F_{11}\hat{x} + K_2(\dot{z}_2 - D_2z_2 - M_2\hat{x}) \\ K_2 &= (JM_2{}^T + R_{11}H_{21})V_0^{-1} \\ \dot{J} &= F_{11}J + JF_{11}^T + R_{11} - K_2V_0K_2 \end{aligned} \tag{49}$$

which are the results obtained by these authors. Finally, if $m = 0$ and $S_1 = 0$, then Eqs. (30) and (31) are equivalent to those treated by Bryson–Johansen, namely,

$$\dot{x} = F_{11}x + r_1 \tag{50}$$

$$\begin{bmatrix} z_1 \\ \hline z_2 \end{bmatrix} = \begin{bmatrix} H_{11} \\ \hline H_{21} \end{bmatrix} + \begin{bmatrix} I \\ \hline 0 \end{bmatrix} v \tag{51}$$

Further, in this case, $F_0 = F_{11}$, $H_0 = H_{11}$, $V_0 = H_{21}R_{11}H_{21}^T$, and the filter equations become

$$\begin{aligned} M_2 &= \dot{H}_{21} + H_{21}F_{11} \\ \dot{\hat{x}} &= F_{11}\hat{x} + K_1(Z_1 - H_{11}\hat{x}) + K_2(\dot{z}_2 - M_2\hat{x}) \\ K_1 &= JH_{11}^TV_1^{-1} \\ K_2 &= (JM_2{}^T + R_{11}H_{21}^T)(H_{21}R_{11}H_{21}^T)^{-1} \\ \dot{J} &= F_{11}J + JF_{11}^T + R_{11} - K_1V_1K_1{}^T - K_2H_{21}R_{11}H_{21}^TK_2{}^T \end{aligned} \tag{52}$$

which are equivalent to the results of Bryson–Johansen when V_0^{-1} exists.

It is noted that Eqs. (30) and (31) are of the form of Eqs. (50) and (51) if the state of Eq. (50) is subdivided into two substates $x \in E^n$, $y \in E^m$, as in Eq. (30). Then, Eqs. (52) define a filter of order $(m+n)$. However, the measurement $z_2 \in E^m$ is an exact measurement of m linearly independent combinations of elements of the state (if not, then one or more elements of z_2 is redundant), thus implying the filter need only determine the remaining n combinations of state vector elements. Similar arguments are presented in Brammer (*15*) for the discrete-time case. The Theorem stated above provides an nth order filter in place of the $(n+m)$th order filter obtained from Eqs. (50), thus suggesting the minimum-order designation.

Proof of Theorem. The proof of the theorem closely parallels the derivation of the simplified filter above. The estimate is assumed to be

$$\hat{x}(t) = \int_{t_0}^{t} [W_1(t, \tau) \vdots W_2(t, \tau)] \begin{bmatrix} z_1 \ (\tau) \\ \hline z_2 \ (\tau) \end{bmatrix} d\tau + K_2(t) z_2(t) \tag{53}$$

For notational simplicity, time arguments in the following will be dropped when no confusion will result. Define

$$\begin{aligned} C_j(t, s) &\equiv E[x(t) z_j^T(s)] \\ A_{ij}(t, s) &\equiv E[z_i(t) z_j^T(s)] \end{aligned} \qquad i, j = 1, 2 \tag{54}$$

Then the Wiener–Hopf equation becomes

$$[C_1 \vdots C_2] = K_2[A_{21} \vdots A_{22}] + \int_{t_0}^{t} [W_1 \vdots W_2] A \, d\tau \tag{55}$$

where

$$A(\tau, s) \equiv \begin{bmatrix} A_{11}(\tau, s) \vdots A_{12}(\tau, s) \\ \hline A_{21}(\tau, s) \vdots A_{22}(\tau, s) \end{bmatrix} \tag{56}$$

Differentiating $\hat{x}(t)$ with respect to time yields

$$\begin{aligned} \dot{\hat{x}}(t) = {} & K_2 \dot{z}_2 + [\dot{K}_2 + W_2(t, t)] z_2 + W_1(t, t) z_1 \\ & + \int_{t_0}^{t} \frac{\partial}{\partial t} [W_1(t, \tau) \vdots W_2(t, \tau)] \begin{bmatrix} z_1 \\ \hline z_2 \end{bmatrix} d\tau \end{aligned} \tag{57}$$

To determine $(\partial/\partial t) W_i(t, \tau)$, differentiate the Wiener–Hopf equation with respect to time as follows:

1. $\dfrac{\partial}{\partial t} [C_1(t, s) \vdots C_2(t, s)]:$

Noting from Eq. (31) that

$$y = H_{22}^{-1}(z_2 - H_{21}x) \tag{58}$$

the equation for $x(t)$ can be written as

$$\dot{x} = F_0 x + F_{12} H_{22}^{-1} z_2 + r_1 \tag{59}$$

where the notation of Eqs. (38)–(44) is used. Consequently,

$$\frac{\partial}{\partial t}[C_1(t, s) \mid C_2(t, s)] = F_0[C_1 \mid C_2] + F_{12} H_{22}^{-1}[A_{21} \mid A_{22}] \tag{60}$$

or

$$= (F_0 K_2 + F_{12} H_{22}^{-1})[A_{21} \mid A_{22}] + F_0 \int_{t_0}^{t} [W_1 \mid W_2] A \, d\tau \tag{61}$$

2. $$\frac{\partial}{\partial t}\{K_2(t)[A_{21}(t, s) \mid A_{22}(t, s)]\}:$$

First, note that

$$\dot{z}_2 = \dot{H}_{21}x + H_{21}\dot{x} + \dot{H}_{22} y + H_{22} \dot{y} \tag{62}$$

$$= (\dot{H}_{21} + H_{21}F_{11} + H_{22} F_{21})x + (H_{21}F_{12} + \dot{H}_{22} + H_{22} F_{22}) \times H_{22}^{-1}(z_2 - H_{21}x) + H_{21}r_1 + H_{22} r_2 \tag{63}$$

or

$$\dot{z}_2 = M_2 x + D_2 z_2 + H_{21}r_1 + H_{22} r_2 \tag{64}$$

Thus,

$$\frac{\partial}{\partial t}[A_{21}(t, s) \mid A_{22}(t, s)] = M_2[C_1 \mid C_2] + D_2[A_{21} \mid A_{22}] \tag{65}$$

$$= (M_2 K_2 + D_2)[A_{21} \mid A_{22}] + M_2 \int_{t_0}^{t} [W_1 \mid W_2] A \, d\tau \tag{66}$$

and

$$\frac{\partial}{\partial t}\{K_2[A_{21} \mid A_{22}]\} = (\dot{K}_2 + K_2 M_2 K_2 + K_2 D_2)[A_{21} \mid A_{22}] + K_2 M_2 \int_{t_0}^{t} [W_1 \mid W_2] A d\tau \tag{67}$$

3. $$[A_{11} \mid A_{12}]$$

Note that

$$[A_{11} \vdots A_{12}] = H_{11}[C_1 \vdots C_2] + H_{12}H_{22}^{-1}[A_{21} \vdots A_{22}]$$
$$- H_{12}H_{22}^{-1}H_{21}[C_1 \vdots C_2] \tag{68}$$
$$= H_0[C_1 \vdots C_2] + H_{12}H_{22}^{-1}[A_{21} \vdots A_{22}] \tag{69}$$

or

$$[A_{11} \vdots A_{12}] = (H_0 K_2 + H_{12}H_{22}^{-1})[A_{21} \vdots A_{22}] + H_0 \int_{t_0}^{t} [W_1 \vdots W_2]A\,dt \tag{70}$$

The differentiated Wiener–Hopf equation can now be written as

$$(F_0 K_2 + F_{12}H_{22}^{-1} - \dot{K}_2 - K_2 M_2 K_2 - K_2 D_2 - W_1 H_{12} H_{22}^{-1} - W_2 -$$
$$W_1 H_0 K_2)[A_{21} \vdots A_{22}]$$
$$= \int_{t_0}^{t} \{(K_2 M_2 + W_1 H_0 - F_0)[W_1 \vdots W_2] + \frac{\partial}{\partial t}[W_1(t, \tau) \vdots W_2(t, \tau)]\}$$
$$A(\tau, s)\,d\tau \tag{71}$$

For this equality to hold, it suffices that the coefficient of $[A_{21} \vdots A_{22}]$ on the left and the integrand on the right be zero. In this event,

$$\dot{\hat{x}} = F_0 \hat{x} + (F_{12} - K_1 H_{12})H_{22}^{-1} z_2 + [K_1 \vdots K_2]\left[\frac{(z_1 - H_0 \hat{x})}{(\dot{z}_2 - D_2 z_2 - M_2 \hat{x})}\right] \tag{72}$$

where

$$K_1(t) \equiv W_1(t, t) \tag{73}$$

Alternatively, this could be written as

$$\dot{\hat{x}} = F_{11}\hat{x} + F_{12}\hat{y} + K_1(z_1 - H_{11}\hat{x} - H_{12}\hat{y}) + K_2(\dot{z}_2 - D_2 z_2 - M_2 \hat{x}) \tag{74}$$

where

$$\hat{y} \equiv H_{22}^{-1}(z_2 - H_{21}\hat{x}) \tag{75}$$

It remains to calculate $K_1(t)$ and $K_2(t)$. Define the estimation error and its covariance by

$$\varepsilon(t) \equiv x(t) - \hat{x}(t) \tag{76}$$

$$J(t) \equiv E[\varepsilon(t)e^T(t)] \tag{77}$$

Then

$$z_1 - H_{11}\hat{x} - H_{12}\hat{y} = H_0 \varepsilon + v \tag{78}$$

and

$$\dot{z}_2 - D_2 z_2 - M_2 \hat{x} = M_2 \varepsilon + H_{21} r_1 + H_{22} r_2 \tag{79}$$

Thus,

$$\dot{\varepsilon} = F_0\,\varepsilon - K_1 H_0\,\varepsilon - K_1 v - K_2 M_2\,\varepsilon - K_2(H_{21} r_1 + H_{22} r_2) + r_1 \tag{80}$$

and

$$\begin{aligned}\dot{J} &= E[\dot{\varepsilon}\varepsilon^T] + E[\varepsilon\dot{\varepsilon}^T] \\ &= F_0 J + J F_0^T + R_{11} - K_1 H_0 J - J H_0^T K_1^T + K_1 V_1 K_1^T \\ &\quad - K_2 M_2 J - J M_2^T K_2^T \\ &\quad + K_2 V_0 K_2^T - K_1 S_1 - S_1^T K_1^T + K_1 S_0 K_2^T + K_2 S_0^T K_1^T \\ &\quad - K_2(H_{21} R_{11} + H_{22} R_{12}^T) - (R_{11} H_{21}^T + R_{12} H_{22}^T) K_2^T \end{aligned} \tag{81}$$

Finally, minimizing $\dot{J}(t)$ by completing the square in $[K_1 \mid K_2]$, yields

$$[K_1 \mid K_2] = [(J H_0^T + S_1^T) \mid (J M_2^T + S_3^T)] \begin{bmatrix} V_1 & S_0 \\ S_0^T & V_0 \end{bmatrix}^{-1} \tag{82}$$

and

$$\dot{J} = F_0 J + J F_0^T + R_{11} - [K_1 \mid K_2] \begin{bmatrix} V_1 & S_0 \\ S_0^T & V_0 \end{bmatrix} \begin{bmatrix} K_1^T \\ K_2^T \end{bmatrix} \tag{83}$$

The initial conditions $\hat{x}(t_0)$ and $J(t_0)$, are computed from the statistics of $x(t_0)$ and $y(t_0)$ by standard weighted least-square analysis. Since

$$\begin{bmatrix} z_2(t_0) - H_{22}(t_0)\bar{y}_0 \\ \bar{x}_0 \end{bmatrix} = \begin{bmatrix} H_{21}(t_0) \\ I \end{bmatrix} x(t_0) + \begin{bmatrix} H_{22}(t_0)\varepsilon_{y0} \\ \varepsilon_{x0} \end{bmatrix} \tag{84}$$

then

$$\begin{aligned}\hat{x}(t_0) = &\left\{ [H_{21}^T \mid I] \begin{bmatrix} (H_{22}\Sigma_0 H_{22}^T)^{-1} & 0 \\ 0 & J_0^{-1} \end{bmatrix} \begin{bmatrix} H_{21} \\ I \end{bmatrix} \right\}^{-1} [H_{21}^T \mid I] \\ &\times \begin{bmatrix} (H_{22}^T \Sigma_0 H_{22})^{-1} & 0 \\ 0 & J_0^{-1} \end{bmatrix} \begin{bmatrix} (z_2 - H_{22}\bar{y}_0) \\ \bar{x}_0 \end{bmatrix} \end{aligned} \tag{85}$$

and

$$J(t_0) = [H_{22}^{-1} H_{21})^T \Sigma_0 (H_{22}^{-1} H_{21}) + J_0^{-1}]^{-1}$$

which corresponds to Eq. (46) if the first equation is rewritten.

C. Discrete-Time Results

One of the prime contributing factors to the success of present day estimation and control techniques is the ready availability of high-speed large-memory digital computers for solving the equations of the solutions to the respective problems. Since digital computers are sequential machines, and thus are capable of mere approximation to integration, the question arises as to the utility of continuous-time formulations as used in the previous two subsections. If the state and measurement equations were written in discrete-time form, such as

$$x(t_{k+1}) = \phi(t_{k+1}, t_k)x(t_k) + r(t_k) \tag{86}$$

$$z(t_k) = H(t_k)x(t_k) + v(t_k) \tag{87}$$

the filter equations would also be generated in discrete-time form and could thus be programmed directly and exactly with no need for integration routines. The difficulty arises, however, in that equations for physical dynamic processes are much more easily derived in differential equation form than in difference equation form, and further, if the derived equation were

$$\dot{x}(t) = F(t)x(t) + \rho(t) \tag{88}$$

the discrete-time Eq. (86) would then be defined by

$$\frac{d}{dt}[\phi(t, t_k)] = F(t)\phi(t, t_k); \qquad \phi(t_k, t_k) = I \tag{89}$$

$$r(t_k) = \int_{t_k}^{t_{k+1}} \phi(t_{k+1}, \tau)\rho(\tau)\, d\tau \tag{90}$$

again requiring numerical integration for time-varying systems. Thus, it might seem that the choice of formulation for the state equation is relatively independent of numerical integration requirements. In the case of the measurement equation (87), the choice is usually dictated by the measurement sampling rate in comparison to the frequencies of interest in the state equation. In the following the results of the previous subsection are presented in discrete-time formulation.

Very little attention has been paid in the literature to the problem of filtering measurements in discrete-time which are corrupted by sequentially correlated (Markov, colored noise) sequences. This is probably due to the fact that the inherent difficulty is not as apparent as the vanishing of the matrix which is inverted in the continuous-time formulation of the Kalman gain. However, the same problem exists, as can be seen by considering the estimation problem defined by the following state and measurement equations:

$$x_{k+1} = \phi_{k+1,k}\, x_k + r_k \tag{91}$$

$$z_k = H_k x_k \tag{92}$$

where r_k is a white noise sequence with zero mean and covariance R_k.

The standard Kalman filter equations (*13*) would be in this case:

$$\hat{x}_{k+1} = \phi_{k+1,k}\hat{x}_k + K_{k+1}(z_{k+1} - H_{k+1}\phi_{k+1,k}\hat{x}_k) \tag{93}$$

$$K_{k+1} = J_{k+1/k}H_{k+1}^T(H_{k+1}J_{k+1/k}H_{k+1}^T)^{-1} \tag{94}$$

$$J_{k+1/k} = \phi_{k+1,k}J_k\phi_{k+1,k}^T + R_k \tag{95}$$

$$J_{k+1} = (I - K_{k+1}H_{k+1})J_{k+1/k} \tag{96}$$

If the dimension of z_k is greater than the dimension of x_k, then the required inverse in Eq. (94) will not exist, since the rank of $H_{k+1}J_{k+1/k}H_{k+1}^T$ will be no greater than the rank of H_{k+1}, which is less than the dimension of $H_{k+1}J_{k+1/k}H_{k+1}^T$. If the dimension of z_k is less than or equal to the dimension of x_k, then after a finite number of time steps the matrix J_{k+1} will become singular since some elements of x_k will be perfectly determined. If R_k does not have sufficient rank, then $H_{k+1}J_{k+1/k}H_{k+1}^T$ is again not invertible. In this event, a discrete-time version of the referenced continuous-time colored noise estimation studies may be employed. This is accomplished by considering differences in subsequent observations. To illustrate, consider the following linear estimation problem which has been generalized from the colored noise problem to include any linear Gaussian problem with measurement noise whose covariance is singular. The state and measurement equations are assumed transformed to the form

$$\begin{bmatrix} x_{k+1}^1 \\ x_{k+1}^2 \end{bmatrix} = \begin{bmatrix} \phi_{11}^k & \phi_{12}^k \\ \phi_{21}^k & \phi_{22}^k \end{bmatrix} \begin{bmatrix} x_k^1 \\ x_k^2 \end{bmatrix} + \begin{bmatrix} r_k^1 \\ r_k^2 \end{bmatrix} \tag{97}$$

$$\begin{bmatrix} z_k^1 \\ z_k^2 \end{bmatrix} = \begin{bmatrix} H_{11}^k & H_{12}^k \\ H_{21}^k & H_{22}^k \end{bmatrix} \begin{bmatrix} x_k^1 \\ x_k^2 \end{bmatrix} + \begin{bmatrix} v_k \\ 0 \end{bmatrix} \tag{98}$$

where H_{22}^k is nonsingular and where the noises have zero mean and covariance

$$E\left\{\begin{bmatrix} r_k^1 \\ r_k^2 \\ v_k \end{bmatrix} [r_j^{1T} \mid r_j^{2T} \mid v_j^T]\right\} = \begin{bmatrix} R_k^{11} & R_k^{12} & S_k^1 \\ R_k^{12T} & R_k^{22} & S_k^2 \\ S_k^{1T} & S_k^{2T} & v_k \end{bmatrix} \delta_{jk} \tag{99}$$

In this event, the filter equations can be shown by analogy with those presented previously to be

$$\begin{aligned}\hat{x}_{k+1}^1 = \phi_0^k\hat{x}_k^1 + \phi_{12}^k(H_{22}^k)^{-1}z_k^2 + K_k^1[z_k^1 - H_0^kx_k^1 - H_{12}^k(H_{22}^k)^{-1}z_k^2] \\ + K_k^2(z_{k+1}^2 - D_kz_k^2 - M_kx_k^1)\end{aligned} \tag{100}$$

$$\hat{x}_k^2 = (H_{22}^k)^{-1}(z_k^2 - H_{21}^k\hat{x}_k^1) \tag{101}$$

$$[K_k^1 \mid K_k^2] = -[(\phi_0^k J_k H_0^{kT} + S_k^1) \mid (\phi_0^k J_k M_k^T + S_0^k)] \times \left[\begin{array}{c|c} (H_0^k J_k H_0^{kT} + V_k) & (H_0^k J_k M_k^T + S_3^k) \\ \hline (H_0^k J_k M_k^T + S_3^k)^T & (M_k J_k M_k^T + V_0^k) \end{array}\right] \tag{102}$$

$$J_{k+1} = \phi_0^k J_k \phi_0^{kT} + R_k^{11} - [K_k^1 \mid K_k^2] \left[\begin{array}{c|c} (H_0^k J_k H_0^{kT} + V_k) & (H_0^k J_k M_k^T + S_3^k) \\ \hline (H_0^k J_k M_k^T + S_3^{kT}) & (M_k J_k M_k^T + V_0) \end{array}\right] \times \left[\begin{array}{c} K_k^{1T} \\ \hline K_k^{2T} \end{array}\right] \tag{103}$$

where $\hat{x}_k^1$, $\hat{x}_k^2$ are the optimal estimates and J_k is the covariance of the error in $\hat{x}_k^1$. The previously undefined matrices in Eq. (100) are given by

$$\phi_0^k = \phi_{11}^k - \phi_{12}^k (H_{22}^k)^{-1} H_{21}^k \tag{104}$$

$$H_0^k = H_{11}^k - H_{12}^k (H_{22}^k)^{-1} H_{21}^k \tag{105}$$

$$D_k = (H_{21}^{k+1} \phi_{12}^k + H_{22}^{k+1} \phi_{22}^k)(H_{22}^k)^{-1} \tag{106}$$

$$M_k = H_{21}^k \phi_{11}^k + H_{22}^k \phi_{21}^k - D_k H_{21}^k \tag{107}$$

$$V_0^k = H_{21}^{k+1} R_k^{11} (H_{21}^{k+1})^T + H_{21}^{k+1} R_k^{12} (H_{22}^{k+1} R_k^{12T} (H_{21}^{k+1})^T) + H_{22}^{k+1} R_k^{22} (H_{22}^{k+1})^T \tag{108}$$

$$S_0^k = R_k^{12} (H_{22}^{k+1})^T + R_k^{11} (H_{21}^{k+1})^T \tag{109}$$

$$S_3^k = S_k^{1T} (H_{21}^{k+1})^T + S_k^{2T} (H_{22}^{k+1})^T \tag{110}$$

III. A Calculus of Variations Formulation of Linear Estimation

In Section IV, the duality of the linear estimation problem and the linear quadratic regulator problem will be developed and extended to a point sufficient to allow utilization of colored noise estimation results to solve singular control problems. First, it will be helpful to examine in this section a calculus of variations formulation of the continuous time linear minimum-variance estimation problem. Such a formulation has been used by Bryson *et al.* (*4*, *5*) for least squares or maximum likelihood estimation, which is equivalent to minimum variance estimation for symmetric, unimodal conditional densities such as encountered in linear Gaussian estimation. However, the authors have been unable to find a rigorous derivation of the formulation, other than through a formal limiting process on discrete-time results. The desired formulation is given by the state equation of the subject system

$$\dot{x} = F(t)x + r(t) \tag{111}$$

and a cost functional to be minimized

$$\rho = \int_{t_0}^{t} (\|\hat{r}\|^2_{R^{-1}(t)} + \|z - H\hat{x}\|^2_{V^{-1}(t)})\, dt + \hat{x}(t_0) J_0^{-1} \hat{x}(t_0) \tag{112}$$

where $\hat{x}$ is the smoothed estimate of the state x based on measurements $z(t)$ over $[t_0, T]$ which are corrupted by white noise with covariance $V(t)\delta(t-\tau)$. The state is assumed driven by white noise $r(t)$ with covariance $R(t)\delta(t-\tau)$, and is initialy distributed about mean 0 with covariance J_0. The difficulty in obtaining a rigorous derivation of this formulation is that $\int_{0t}^{T} \|\dot{x} - Fx\|^2_{R^{-1}}\, dt$ does not exist, but is a formalism in itself. However, the formalism can be forestalled as long as possible by the following approach.

Assume a system described by the stochastic state and measurement equations

$$dx(t) = f(x(t), t)\, dt + dr(t) \tag{113}$$

$$dy(t) = h(x(t), t)\, dt + dv(t) \tag{114}$$

where $r(t)$ and $v(t)$ are zero-mean Brownian motion processes with covariances

$$E[(r(t) - r(t_0))(r(s) - r(t_0))^T] = \int_{t_0}^{\min[t, s]} R(\tau)\, d\tau \tag{115}$$

$$E[(v(t) - v(t_0))(v(s) - v(t_0))^T] = \int_{t_0}^{\min(t, s)} V(\tau)\, d\tau \tag{116}$$

where $R(t)$ and $V(t)$ are nonnegative and positive definite symmetric matrices, respectively, and $x(t_0)$ is normally distributed with mean zero and covariance J_0. Bucy (*12*) shows that the conditional density of $x(t)$ based on

$$Y(t) \equiv \{y(\tau), t_0 \leqslant \tau \leqslant t\} \tag{117}$$

can be written in terms of the density of $x(t)$, $p_{x(t)}(\mu_t)$, as follows:

$$p_{x(t)}(\mu_t | Y(t)) = \frac{E[x(t) | x(t) = \mu_t, Y(t)]\, p_{x(t)}(\mu_t)}{E[x(t) | Y(t)]} \tag{118}$$

where

$$x(t) \equiv \exp\left\{\int_{t_0}^{t} h^T(x(\tau), \tau) V^{-1}(\tau)\, dy(\tau) - \frac{1}{2}\int_{t_0}^{t} h^T(x(\tau), \tau) Y^{-1}(\tau) h(x(\tau), \tau)\, d\tau\right\} \tag{119}$$

the former integral being interpreted as an Ito integral.

If the conditional density is symmetric and unimodal, e.g., Gaussian, then the conditional mean will be that μ_t which yields $\max_{\mu_t} p_{x(t)}(\mu_t | Y(t))$. Since the denominator of Eq. (118) is not a function of μ_t, it suffices to maximize the numerator.

Mortenson (*16–18*) shows that the density of $x(t)$, $p_{x(t)}(\mu_t)$, may be written in terms of a Wiener integral:

$$p_{x(t)}(\mu_t | x(t_0) = x_0) = \int_A \phi(t)(\mu_t)\, d_{u_w}\mu(\cdot)$$

$$A = \{x(\cdot) : x(\cdot) \in C[t_0, t],\ x(t_0) = x_0,\ x(t) = \mu_t\} \tag{120}$$

and

$$\phi(t, \mu_t) \equiv \exp\left\{\int_{t_0}^{t} f^T(\mu(\tau), \tau) R^{-1}(\tau)\, d\mu(\tau) - \frac{1}{2}\int_{t_0}^{t} f^T(\mu(\tau), \tau) \times R^{-1}(\tau) f(\mu(\tau), \tau)\, d\tau\right\} \tag{121}$$

the former integral again being an Ito integral, and $\mu(t)$ being understood to satisfy $\mu(t) = \mu_t$. Then

$$p_{x(t)}(\mu_t) = \int_{-\infty}^{\infty} p_{x(t)}(\mu_t | x(t_0) = x_0) p_0(x_0)\, dx_0 \tag{122}$$

where $p_0(x_0)$ is the *a priori* density of the initial state. Thus, the numerator of Eq. (118) may be written as an integral whose integrand is of the form

$$\begin{aligned}\Phi(t) = \exp\Bigg\{&\int_{t_0}^{t} f^T(\mu(\tau), \tau) R^{-1}(\tau)\, d\mu(\tau) \\ &+ \int_{t_0}^{t} h^T(\mu(\tau), \tau) V^{-1}(\tau)\, dy(t) \\ &- \frac{1}{2}\int_{t_0}^{t} [f^T(\mu(\tau), \tau) R^{-1}(\tau) f(\mu(\tau), \tau) \\ &+ h^T(\mu(\tau), \tau) V^{-1}(\tau) h(\mu(\tau), \tau)]\, d\tau\Bigg\} \\ &\times \text{const} \exp\{-x_0{}^T J_0^{-1} x_0\}\end{aligned} \tag{123}$$

The former two integrals are Ito stochastic integrals and must be interpreted as such for the general nonlinear case.

If $G(w(t))$ is a twice differentiable nonlinear function of the Wiener process $w(t)$, then a theorem of Ito states (*19*)

THEOREM (ITO). *If $x(t)$ is defined by Eq.* (113) *and*

$$y(t) = g(x(t), t) \tag{124}$$

then

$$dy(t) = \frac{\partial g}{\partial t}\, dt + \frac{\partial g}{\partial x}\, dx + \frac{1}{2} tr\left\{\left[\frac{\partial^2 g}{\partial x_i\, \partial x_j}\right]\left[R_{jk}\right]\right\} \tag{125}$$

Formally dividing by dt yields

$$\frac{dy(t)}{dt}=\frac{\partial g}{\partial t}+\frac{\partial g}{\partial x}\frac{dx}{dt}+\frac{1}{2}tr\left\{\left[\frac{\partial^2 g}{\partial x_i\,\partial x_j}\right]\left[R_{jk}\right]\right\} \tag{126}$$

If $\partial^2 g/\partial x\,\partial x=0$, *or preferably, if* g *is linear in* x

$$g(x(t),t)=G(t)x(t) \tag{127}$$

then Eq. (126) *agrees with the usual calculus chain rule, indicating that the formalism inherent in*

$$\int d\mu(t)=\int \dot{\mu}(t)\,dt \tag{128}$$

will not give erroneous results. Thus, for the linear Gaussian case, Eq. (123) *can be written*

$$\Phi(t)=\text{const } x \exp\{-\tfrac{1}{2}x_0{}^T J_0^{-1}x_0+\int_{t_0}^{t}(\mu^T(\tau)[F^TR^{-1}\dot{\mu}(\tau)+H^TV^{-1}z(\tau)]$$
$$-\tfrac{1}{2}\mu^T(\tau)[F^TR^{-1}F+H^TV^{-1}H]\mu(\tau))\,d\tau\} \tag{129}$$

IV. Duality of Estimation and Control

A. Introduction

Much has been written about the duality of linear stochastic filtering and the deterministic linear regulator problems since Kalman and Bucy noted the similarity of the solutions to these problems in their earlier papers on filtering (*11–13*). The duality is usually described as a similarity of the Kalman filter gain and the regulator feedback gain and a similarity of the associated Riccati equations. The differences between the results of the two problems are characterized by a reversal of solution time and a transposition of system matrices. The work on duality may be summarized as the observation that the Kalman gain and Riccati equation of the filter for the system

$$\dot{x}(t)=-F^T(t)x(t)+r(t); \qquad E[r(t)r^T(\tau)]=R(t)\delta(t-\tau) \tag{130}$$

$$z(t)=H^T(t)x(t)+v(t); \qquad E[v(t)v^T(\tau)]=V(t)\delta(t-\tau) \tag{131}$$

$$x(t_0)=x_0, \qquad E[x_0x_0{}^T]=J_0 \tag{132}$$

are the same as that for the linear regulator for the system

$$\dot{x}(t)=F(t)x(t)+H(t)u(t), \qquad x(t_0)=x_0 \tag{133}$$

$$\text{Cost}=\int_{t_0}^{T}[x^T(\tau)R(\tau)x(\tau)+u^T(\tau)V(\tau)u(\tau)]\,d\tau+x^T(T)J_Tx(T) \tag{134}$$

with the exception that initial conditions are given for the Riccati equation for the filter solution, while final conditions are given for the regulator solution.

This duality has allowed the extension of results in control theory to results in estimation theory and vice versa. However, the mathematical foundation for this duality has not been examined in any detail. It is the purpose of the section to relate the duality of estimation and control to the concept of duality in mathematical programming, and to formulate theorems which will allow extension of the results of Section II to deterministic control problems.

B. Duality in Mathematical Programming

The linear programming problem can be defined as the problem of minimizing the linear form $y^T x$ over all $x \in E^n$ such that $Ax \geqslant b$, $x \geqslant 0$, and $b \in E^m$. The dual problem is then defined [see Hadley (*20*)] as the problem of maximizing $b^T\lambda$ over all $\lambda \in E^m$ such that $A^T\lambda \leqslant y$ and $\lambda \geqslant 0$. The duality theorem then states that existence of a solution to either problem implies existence of a solution to the other, and furthermore, $\min y^T x = \max b^T\lambda$. The significance of this result is that a linear programming problem with a large number of constraints but few variables can be more efficiently solved by solving the dual problem as pointed out by Hadley.

These results were extended to quadratic programming by W. S. Dorn and others, and further extended to nonlinear programming by P. Wolfe (*21*), who utilized the Equivalence theorem of Kuhn and Tucker (*22*). This latter theorem states that under certain constraint conditions, the solutions to the primal and dual programming problems occur at a saddle point of the Lagrangian function. M. A. Hanson (*23*) then showed that the Kuhn–Tucker theorem has a direct analogy in variational calculus, and consequently a dual problem can be constructed. This work was further generalized and extended by J. D. Pearson (*24, 25*), and it is the intent of this subsection to show how the duality of estimation and control can be derived from this framework.

The primal problem germane to this discussion can be formulated as a special case of Pearson's work as follows: Find $u(t) \in E^m$ which will minimize $\nu(u(t))$, where

$$\nu(u(t)) = g_1(x(T)) + \int_{t_0}^{T} l(x, u, t)\, dt; \qquad T, t_0 \text{ fixed} \tag{135}$$

and $x \in E^n$ satisfies

$$\dot{x}(t) = f(x, u, t); \qquad x(t_0) = x_0 \tag{136}$$

It is assumed that g_1, l, and f are doubly continuous functions of $x(t)$ and $u(t)$ and that g_1, l are nonnegative definite functions of x, u. Since inequality constraints in the primal, or control, problem will generate inequality constraints in the dual, or estimation, problem, and since estimation with constraints is not of concern in this paper, the state/control variable inequality constraints included by Pearson are not included here. This formulation applies to the fixed-time regulator, final-value control, and estimation problems through appropriate choice of the singularities and zeros of g_1. This is demonstrated later for the linear quadratic case. The prime desired characteristics of the dual problem are that it be a maximization problem whose extremal curves and optimal cost functional coincide with those of the primal problem and that existence of the solution to one of the problems implies existence of the solution to the other. The appropriate dual problem to Eqs. (135) and (136) can thus be derived as follows.

The Lagrangian of the primal problem is defined as

$$L(x, \dot{x}, u, \lambda, t) = l(x, u, t) + \lambda^T(\dot{x} - f(x, u, t)) \tag{137}$$

It is well known (*26*) that the extremal $\tilde{K}$ of the primal problem defined by $\tilde{x}(t)$, $\tilde{u}(t)$, necessarily satisfies the Euler–Lagrange equations

$$L_x(x, \dot{x}, u, \lambda, t) = (d/dt)L\dot{x}(x, \dot{x}, u, \lambda, t) \tag{138}$$

$$(d/dt)L_u(x, \dot{x}, u, \lambda, t) = 0 \tag{139}$$

or

$$l_x(x, u, t) - \lambda^T f_x(x, u, t) = \dot{\lambda}^T \tag{140}$$

$$l_u(x, u, t) - \lambda^T f_u(x, u, t) = \text{const.} \tag{141}$$

Transversality conditions for the fixed-time problem then guarantee that

$$\lambda(T) = -g_x{}^T(x(T)) \tag{142}$$

$$l_u(x, u, t) = \lambda^T f_u(x, u, t) \tag{143}$$

on the extremal $\tilde{K}$. The assumption is made at this point that Eq. (143) can be solved for the optimal $u = \tilde{u}(x, \lambda, t)$.

Now, consider the following problem. Find $x(t) = \hat{x}(t)$ giving $\max\limits_{x(t)} \omega(x(t))$, where

$$\omega(x(t)) \equiv g_0{}^*(\lambda(t_0), x(t_0)) + g_1{}^*(\lambda(T), x(T)) + \int_{t_0}^{T} l^*(\lambda, x, t)\, dt \tag{144}$$

$$g_0{}^*(\lambda(t_0), x(t_0)) \equiv -\lambda^T(t_0)x(t_0) \tag{145}$$

$$g_1{}^*(\lambda(T), x(T)) \equiv g_1(x(T)) + \lambda^T(T)x(T) \tag{146}$$

$$l^*(\lambda, x, t) \equiv l(x, \tilde{u}(x, \lambda, t), t) - (d/dt)[\lambda^T(t)x(t)] \tag{147}$$

subject to the differential equation constraints of Eq. (140) which can be written as

$$\dot{\lambda} = f^*(\lambda, x, t) \tag{148}$$

$$f^*(\lambda, x, t) \equiv l_x^T(x, u(x, \lambda, t), t) - f_x^T(x, \tilde{u}(x, \lambda, t), t)\lambda \tag{149}$$

If the extremals of this problem provide the desired maximization, then Eqs. (144)–(146) and (148) define the dual problem. The dual Lagrangian, using $-q(t)$ as the Lagrange multipliers, is thus

$$L^*(\lambda, \dot{\lambda}, x, q, t) = l^*(\lambda, x, t) - q^T(\dot{\lambda} - f^*(\lambda, x, t)) \tag{150}$$

The corresponding Euler–Lagrange equations are

$$L_\lambda^*(\lambda, \dot{\lambda}, x, q, t) = (d/dt)L_{\dot{\lambda}}^*(\lambda, \dot{\lambda}, x, q, t) \tag{151}$$

$$L_x^*(\lambda, \dot{\lambda}, x, q, t) = 0 \tag{152}$$

or

$$-l_\lambda^*(\lambda, x, t) - q^T f_\lambda^*(\lambda, x, t) = \dot{q}^T \tag{153}$$

$$-l_x^*(\lambda, x, t) = q^T f_x^*(\lambda, x, t) \tag{154}$$

From Eqs. (147) and (148), l^* can be written as

$$l^*(\lambda, x, t) = l(x, \tilde{u}, t) - \lambda^T f(x, u, t) - x^T f^*(\lambda, x, t) \tag{155}$$

Thus, Eq. (153) becomes

$$\dot{q}^T = f^T(x, \tilde{u}, t) - (q - x)^T f_\lambda^*(\lambda, x, t) + [l_u(x, \tilde{u}, t) - \lambda^T f_u(x, \tilde{u}, t)]\tilde{u}_\lambda(x, \lambda, t) \tag{156}$$

Using Eqs. (136) and (143),

$$(d/dt)(q - x)^T = -(q - x)^T f_\lambda^*(\lambda, x, t) \tag{157}$$

The transversality conditions for this problem guarantee that

$$q(T) = g_{1\lambda}^*(\lambda(T), x(T)) \tag{158}$$

or

$$q(T) = x(T) \tag{159}$$

implying that the optimal $x = \hat{x}(q, t)$ satisfies

$$x(t) = q(t) \tag{160}$$

or the state of the primal problem is the multiplier for the dual, and vice versa. Equation (154) is thus also satisfied since

$$(l_x - \lambda^T f_x - f^{*T}) + (q - x)^T f_x^* = 0 \tag{161}$$

It is apparent that the extremals of the primal problem of Eqs. (135) and (136) and those of the problem of Eqs. (144)–(147) coincide. Moreover, by the definitions of ν and ω

$$\nu(\tilde{u}(t)) = \omega(\hat{x}(t)) \tag{162}$$

Thus, Eqs. (144)–(147) is the desired dual problem. It is noted that the natural conditions of one problem are the constraints of the other. Further, it is easily shown that the primal problem can be derived as the dual of the problem of Eqs. (144)–(147). Finally, it is seen that the nonintegral portions of the cost functionals, i.e., g_1, g^*, do not affect the differential equations of the extremals of the problems except through their initial and final conditions.

C. Duality of Linear Estimation and Control

It is shown in Section III that the minimum-variance, unbiased estimate for the linear smoothing problem with Gaussian statistics given by Eqs. (1) and (2) will be that $\hat{x}(t\,|\,T)$ which minimizes

$$\text{Cost} = \int_{t_0}^{T} \{\tfrac{1}{2}\|\hat{r}(t\,|\,T)\|^2_{R^{-1}(t)} + \tfrac{1}{2}\|z(t) - H(t)\hat{x}(t\,|\,T)\|^2_{V^{-1}(t)}\}\,dt + \tfrac{1}{2}\|\hat{x}_0\|^2_{J_0^{-1}} \tag{163}$$

where

$$\dot{\hat{x}}(t\,|\,T) = F(t)\hat{x}(t\,|\,T) + \hat{r}(t\,|\,T), \qquad \hat{x}(t_0\,|\,T) = \hat{x}_0 \tag{164}$$

The relationship of this problem to the deterministic linear optimal control problem will now be discussed in the light of the previous subsection.

The linear, quadratic problem of variational calculus will be defined to be the optimization problem of the form of Eqs. (135) and (136) where the third- and higher order partial derivatives of the loss functional components with respect to x and u are zero, and where the differential equation constraints are linear in x and u. This problem is of prime interest since it arises from approaching nonlinear optimization in an approximation to solution by first linearizing, such as with neighboring optimal controllers and with Gaussian noise filtering.

Assume the following linear quadratic generalized control problem as the primal problem. Find $u = \tilde{u}(t)$ to minimize $\nu(u(t))$, where

$$\nu(u(t)) \equiv \tfrac{1}{2}x^T(T)P_T x(T) + \int_{t_0}^{T} \left\{ [x^T \,\vdots\, u^T] \begin{bmatrix} R & S \\ S^T & V \end{bmatrix} \begin{bmatrix} x \\ u \end{bmatrix} + [y^T \,\vdots\, z^T] \begin{bmatrix} x \\ u \end{bmatrix} \right\} dt \tag{165}$$

where y, z are known functions of time only, and $x(t)$ satisfies

$$\dot{x}(t) = F(t)x(t) + H(t)u(t), \qquad x(t_0) = x_0 \qquad (n\text{-dim}) \tag{166}$$

It is well known (26, 27) that

$$\tilde{u}(x, \lambda, t) = V^{-1}(t)[H^T\lambda(t) - z(t) - S^T(t)x(t)] \qquad (m\text{-dim}) \tag{167}$$

where $\lambda(t)$ is determined from the Euler equations to satisfy

$$\dot{\lambda}(t) = -F^T(t)\lambda(t) + R(t)x(t) + S(t)u(t) + y(t) \qquad (n\text{-dim}) \tag{168}$$

with final condition

$$\lambda(T) = -P_T x(T) \tag{169}$$

It is assumed that $V^{-1}(t)$ exists for all t, although it will be shown later that this is unnecessary in certain cases.

Using the results of the previous section with a judicious application of algebra yields the following as the dual problem to the above. Find $x(t)$ to maximize $\omega(x(t))$, where

$$\omega(x(t)) \equiv -\int_{t_0}^{T} \tfrac{1}{2}[(r-y)^T \mid (H^T\lambda - z)^T] \begin{bmatrix} R & S \\ S^T & V \end{bmatrix}^{-1} \begin{bmatrix} (r-y) \\ (H^T\lambda - z) \end{bmatrix} dt$$

$$-x_0{}^T\lambda(t_0) - \tfrac{1}{2}x^T(T)P_T x(T) \tag{170}$$

where $\lambda(t)$ satisfies

$$\dot{\lambda}(t) = -F^T(t)\lambda(t) + r(t) \tag{171}$$

and where

$$r(t) = (R - SV^{-1}S^T)x + SV^{-1}(H^T\lambda - z) + y \tag{172}$$

Equation (171) is obtained either from Eq. (168) of the primal problem or from the Euler equations using $x(t)$ as the adjoint multipliers for the dual problem which satisfy Eq. (166).

Comparing Eqs. (170)–(172) with Eqs. (163) and (164), the dual problem is seen to correspond to the linear estimation problem in which the state and measurement equations are

$$\dot{\lambda}(t) = -F^T\lambda(t) + r(t) \tag{173}$$

$$z(t) = H^T(t)\lambda(t) + v(t) \tag{174}$$

where

$$\begin{aligned} E[r(t)] &= y(t) \\ E[r(t)r^T(\tau)] &= R(t)\,\delta(t-\tau) \\ E[v(t)] &= 0 \\ E[v(t)v^T(\tau)] &= V(t)\,\delta(t-\tau) \\ E[r(t)v^T(\tau)] &= S(t)\,\delta(t-\tau) \end{aligned} \tag{175}$$

with the exception of the boundary conditions, which are determined by g_0^* and g_1^*. The problem of Eqs. (173)–(175) with initial condition $\lambda(t_0)$ such that

$$E[\lambda(t_0)] = 0$$

$$E[\lambda(t_0)\lambda^T(t_0)] = J_0 \tag{176}$$

is a generalization of the control/estimation dual to the control problem of Eqs. (165) and (166) as well as the programming dual of the problem of Eqs. (170)–(172), boundary conditions notwithstanding. However, as noted in the previous section, the equations of the extremal curves of the dual will coincide with those of the primal, which is the prime desired result.

The difficulty with boundary conditions can be investigated further for the linear quadratic case by considering the solutions to the primal problem of Eqs. (165) and (166), and its programming dual and generalized control/estimation dual. Using the well-known [e.g. (*27*)] successive sweep method for the primal problem of Eqs. (165) and (166),

$$\mu(t) = \lambda(t) + P(t)x(t) \tag{177}$$

it can be shown by differentiation and by Eqs. (166)–(168) that

$$\dot{\mu}(t) = F^T(t)\mu(t) + y(t) - (PH + S)V^{-1}(z - H^T\mu) \tag{178}$$

$$\dot{p}(t) = -(F - HV^{-1}S^T)^T P - P(F - HV^{-1}S^T) - (R - SV^{-1}S^T) + PHV^{-1}H^T P \tag{179}$$

$$\tilde{u}(t) = -V^{-1}[(H^T P + S^T)x(t) + (z - H^T\mu)] \tag{180}$$

with boundary conditions

$$P(T) = P_T \tag{181}$$

$$\mu(T) = 0 \tag{182}$$

The solution to the programming dual of Eqs. (170)–(172) can be determined with the same transformation equation (177), to be given by Eqs. (178) and (179) and

$$r(t) = R(t)x(t) + y(t) - SV^{-1}(PH + S)^T x - SV^{-1}(z - H^T\mu) \tag{183}$$

with the same boundary conditions, Eqs. (181) and (182).

The solution to the desired dual, the smoothing problem of Eqs. (173)–(175), is also obtained from Eqs. (177)–(179) and (183), but with different boundary conditions:

$$P(t_0) = J_0 \tag{184}$$

$$\mu(t_0) = 0 \tag{185}$$

In this smoothing problem, $\mu(t)$ has the significance of being the filter solution, i.e., the best estimate of the state $\lambda(t)$ at time t based on measurements $z(\tau)$, $t_0 \leqslant \tau \leqslant t$, up to time t only. A comparison of Eqs. (184) and (185) with Eqs. (181) and (182) indicates that the boundary conditions for the estimation problem are given at the opposite end of the extremals in time from those of the programming dual.

In summary, with the transposition of boundary conditions, this control/estimation dual is the programming dual. The duality as observed by Kalman and Bucy is exemplified by comparison of Eq. (178), when $y(t)$ and $S(t)$ are both zero; with Eq. (180), when $S(t)$ and $z(t) - H^T\mu(t)$ are zero, i.e., the filter gain in Eq. (178) is the transpose of the controller gain in Eq. (180); and $P(t)$ for each problem satisfies the same Riccati equation (179), but with interposed boundary conditions.

This has been extended above to show that the dual to the regulator problem is more rightly the fixed-interval smoothing problem. Completing the square in the integrand of ν in Eq. (165), yields the control problem in which it is desired to have $R(t)x(t)$ track $y(t)$ and $V(t)u(t)$ track $z(t)$, i.e., the dual of the path which $R(t)x(t)$ is to follow is the mean of the state noise $r(t)$, and the dual of the path which $V(t)u(t)$ is to follow is the observation vector $z(t)$ in the estimation problem of Eqs. (173)–(176).

D. Dual of the Colored Noise Filter

It was assumed in the development of the duality relationships that Eq. (167) could be solved for the optimal $u = \tilde{u}(x, \lambda, t)$ in terms of the state, the adjoint multipliers, and time. This will not be the case for the linear quadratic control problem of Eqs. (165) and (166), or the linear estimation problem of Eqs. (173)–(176), whenever $V(t)$ has less than maximum rank, i.e., whenever $V^{-1}(t)$ does not exist. However, the duality can still be derived for these problems as follows.

Assume for the linear quadratic problem in the notation of Eqs. (135) and (136) that

$$\operatorname{rank}[l_{uu}(x, u, t)] \equiv p < m \equiv \dim[u] \tag{186}$$

Then the Euler–Lagrange equations remain

$$\dot{\lambda} = -f_x^T(x, u, t)\lambda + l_x(x, u, t) \tag{187}$$

$$l_u(x, u, t) - \lambda^T f_u(x, u, t) = 0 \tag{188}$$

However, Eq. (143) can now only be solved for p-independent components of u, and the remaining $(m - p)$ equations represent $(m - p)$ finite subsidiary conditions for the dual problem. In the case of the control problem of Eqs. (165) and (166) when V and S are identically zero, the Euler equations (168) and (171) become

$$\dot{\lambda} = -F^T\lambda + Rx + y \tag{189}$$

$$z = H^T\lambda \tag{190}$$

which is a formulation of a colored noise estimation problem as discussed in Section II.

Extending this further, it can be similarly shown that the dual to the control problem

$$\min \nu(\mathbf{x}_0, \mathbf{u}(t))$$

where

$$\begin{bmatrix} \dot{x}_1 \\ \dot{x}_2 \end{bmatrix} = \begin{bmatrix} -F_{11}^T & F_{21}^T \\ -F_{12}^T & F_{22}^T \end{bmatrix} \begin{bmatrix} x_1 \\ x_2 \end{bmatrix} + \begin{bmatrix} H_{11}^T & H_{21}^T \\ H_{12}^T & H_{22}^T \end{bmatrix} \begin{bmatrix} u_1 \\ u_2 \end{bmatrix}; \qquad \mathbf{x} \equiv \begin{bmatrix} x_1 \\ x_2 \end{bmatrix}; \qquad \mathbf{x}(t_0) = \mathbf{x}_0 \tag{191}$$

$$\nu = \tfrac{1}{2}\|\mathbf{x}(T)\|_{\hat{P}}^2 + \int_{t_0}^{T} \left\{ \tfrac{1}{2}[x_1^T \mid x_2^T \mid u_1^T] \begin{bmatrix} R_{11} & R_{12} & S_1 \\ R_{12}^T & R_{22} & S_2 \\ S_1^T & S_2^T & V_{11} \end{bmatrix} \begin{bmatrix} x_1 \\ x_2 \\ u_1 \end{bmatrix} + [y_1^T \mid y_2^T \mid z_1^T] \begin{bmatrix} x_1 \\ x_2 \\ u_1 \end{bmatrix} + z_2^T u_1 \right\} dt \tag{192}$$

is the generalized colored noise estimation problem of Eqs. (30)–(32) with the exception that $E[u_i] = y_i$. Thus, by duality, the extremals of the two problems will coincide, and the solution to one problem defines the solution to the other. The extremals for either problem will exist whenever u can be partitioned into

$$u^T = [u_1^T \mid u_2^T]; \qquad \dim(u_1) = p, \ \dim(u_2) = m - p \tag{193}$$

such that

$$(f_{u_2}^T \, l_{xx} f_{u_2} + l_{u_1 u_1}) > 0 \tag{194}$$

is nonsingular.

The significance of this dual control problem to the colored noise estimation problem can be appreciated by considering it to be a generalization of the following problem. Find the control u to drive the system

$$\dot{x} = F_1 x + H_1 u; \qquad x(t_0) = x_0 \tag{195}$$

in such a manner as to minimize the cost functional

$$\nu = \int_{t_0}^{T} \tfrac{1}{2}(x^T R_{11} x + \beta^T R_{22} \beta)\, dt \tag{196}$$

where β is a measure of the control u defined by the linear transformation

$$\dot{\beta} = F_2 \beta + H_2 u, \qquad \beta(t_0) = \beta_0 \tag{197}$$

and $H_2(t)$ is assumed to be invertible.

The technique of solution to be employed here is as follows: The indeterminate control u_2 of the general problem is solved for from Eq. (191) in terms of $\dot{x}_2$, x_2, x_1, and t. Then x_2 and u are solved for as optimal controls in terms of the state x_1 and u_2, determined from

$$u_2 = H_{22}^{-1T}[\dot{x}_2 + F_{21}^T x_1 + F_{22}^T x_2 - H_{12}^T u_1] \tag{198}$$

This is the dual approach to treating $\dot{z}_2 - D_2$ as an observation in the generalized colored noise filter of Eqs. (36)–(46). Thus u_2 is substituted into the state equation (191), for x_2. The state x_1 is transformed by

$$x_3 \equiv x_1 - H_{21}^T H_{22}^{-1T} x_2 \tag{199}$$

to yield the transformed state equation

$$\dot{x}_3 = -F_0^T x_3 - M^T H_{22}^{-1T} x_2 + H_0^T u_1 \tag{200}$$

where M, D, F_0, and H_0 are defined by Eqs. (38)–(41). This state transformation is necessary to eliminate $\dot{x}_2$ as a control input to the state equation and thus allow use of the Riccati transformation

$$\lambda = \mu + P x_3 \tag{201}$$

as in the previous section.

By duality with the generalized colored noise filter of Section II, the extremal curves of this control problem are defined by the same equations as those given in Eqs. (36)–(43), i.e.,

$$[K_1 \,\vdots\, K_2] = [(PH_0^T + S_1^T) \,\vdots\, (PM^T + S_3^T)] \begin{bmatrix} V_{11} & S_0 \\ S_0^T & V_0 \end{bmatrix}^{-1} \tag{202}$$

$$S_3 \equiv H_{21} R_{11} + H_{22} R_{12}^T \tag{203}$$

$$\dot{P} = F_0 P + P F_0^T + R_{11} - [K_1 \,\vdots\, K_2] \begin{bmatrix} V_{11} & S_0 \\ S_0^T & V_0 \end{bmatrix} \begin{bmatrix} K_1^T \\ K_2^T \end{bmatrix} \tag{204}$$

$$\begin{aligned} \dot{\mu} = {} & F_0 \mu + (F_{12} - K_1 H_{12}) H_{22}^{-1} z_2 + K_1(z_1 - H_0 \mu) \\ & + K_2(\dot{z}_2 - D z_2 - M\mu - H_{21} y_1 - H_{22} y_2) \end{aligned} \tag{205}$$

and V_0, S_0 are defined by Eqs. (44) and (42), respectively. The controls u_1, u_2 are given by Eq. (198) and

$$\begin{bmatrix} u_1 \\ \hdashline H_{22}^{-1T} x_2 \end{bmatrix} = -\begin{bmatrix} K_1 \\ \hdashline K_2 \end{bmatrix} x_3 - \left[\begin{array}{c:c} V_{11} & S_0 \\ \hdashline S_0^T & V_0 \end{array}\right]^{-1} \begin{bmatrix} (z_1 - H_{12} H_{22}^{-1T} z_2 - H_0 \mu) \\ \hdashline (\dot{z}_2 - D z_2 - M\mu - H_{21} y_1 - H_{22} y_2) \end{bmatrix} \tag{206}$$

The boundary conditions on Eqs. (204) and (205) are defined as in Section II by

$$P(T) = (P_{11T}^{-1} + H_{21}^T H_{22}^{-1T} P_{22T}^{-1} H_{22}^{-1} H_{21})^{-1} \tag{207}$$

$$\mu(T) = -P(T) H_{21}^T P_{11T} z(T) \tag{208}$$

In summary, the optimal control has been determined for a system in which the Euler–Lagrange equations cannot be solved directly for the control. This has been done at the expense of feedback around part of the state vector and at the additional cost of an ideal differentiator. The solution was obtained through the use of results in colored noise filtering and the properties of duality of estimation and control. Finally, it is noted that the dual of the solution [Eqs. (201)–(205)] yields a formulation of the optimal fixed-interval smoother as well as the filter for colored measurement noise.

E. Calculus of Variations Solution to the Singular Control Problem

As an alternative proof of the solution to the singular linear regulator problem to the expediency of invoking duality and colored noise filtering results, the following is offered. The problem of interest in this subsection is that of finding the optimal control $u(t)$ which will drive the system state

$$\begin{bmatrix} \dot{x}_1 \\ \hdashline \dot{x}_2 \end{bmatrix} = \left[\begin{array}{c:c} F_{11} & F_{12} \\ \hdashline F_{21} & F_{22} \end{array}\right] \begin{bmatrix} x_1 \\ \hdashline x_2 \end{bmatrix} + \left[\begin{array}{c:c} H_{11} & H_{12} \\ \hdashline H_{21} & H_{22} \end{array}\right] \begin{bmatrix} u_1 \\ \hdashline u_2 \end{bmatrix}; \quad \begin{bmatrix} x_1(t_0) \\ \hdashline x_2(t_0) \end{bmatrix} = \begin{bmatrix} x_{10} \\ \hdashline x_{20} \end{bmatrix} \tag{209}$$

from time t_0 to fixed time T in such a way as to minimize the cost functional

$$\nu(u_1, u_2) = \int_{t_0}^{T} \left\{ \tfrac{1}{2} [x_1^T \,\vdots\, x_2^T \,\vdots\, u_1^T] \left[\begin{array}{c:c:c} R_{11} & R_{12} & S_1 \\ \hdashline R_{12}^T & R_{22} & S_2 \\ \hdashline S_1^T & S_2^T & V_1 \end{array}\right] \begin{bmatrix} x_1 \\ \hdashline x_2 \\ \hdashline u_1 \end{bmatrix} + [y_1^T \,\vdots\, y_2^T \,\vdots\, z_1^T] \begin{bmatrix} x_1 \\ \hdashline x_2 \\ \hdashline u_1 \end{bmatrix} + z_2^T u_2 \right\} dt$$

$$+\tfrac{1}{2}[x_1^T(T) \mid x_2^T(T)]\left[\begin{array}{c|c} P_{11T} & 0 \\ \hline 0 & P_{22T}\end{array}\right]\left[\begin{array}{c} x_1(T) \\ \hline x_2(T)\end{array}\right] \tag{210}$$

where the system matrices (with exception of P_{ijT}) are functions of time, and y_1, y_2, z_1, and z_2 are *a priori* known vector functions of time. If the integrand of ν has the appropriate constant added to it to complete the square in x_1, x_2, and u_1, then y_1, y_2, and z_2 will be seen to be related to the paths which are desired for x_1, x_2, u_1, and u_2, respectively. The usual approach to solving the linear quadratic control problem fails in this case, since the second partial derivative of the Hamiltonian for this problem with respect to the control $[u_1^T \mid u_2^T]$ is singular, implying that the canonical Euler equations cannot be directly solved for all elements of the control. In other words, the inverse matrix required by the usually obtained feedback gain does not exist.

The problem can be solved, however, by the following artifice if H_{22}^{-1} exists and if V_{11}^{-1} and V_0^{-1} exist where

$$V_0 \equiv H_{12}^T R_{12}^T R_{11} H_{12} + H_{22}^T R_{12}^T H_{12} + H_{12}^T R_{12} H_{22} + H_{22}^T R_{22} H_{22} \tag{211}$$

Note from Eq. (209) that

$$u_2 = H_{22}^{-1}(\dot{x}_2 - F_{21}x_1 - F_{22}x_2 - H_{21}u_1) \tag{212}$$

Substituting into Eq. (209)

$$\dot{x}_1 = F_0 x_1 + H_0 u_1 + H_{12}H_{22}^{-1}\dot{x}_2 + (F_{12} - H_{12}H_{22}^{-1}F_{22})x_2 \tag{213}$$

where

$$F_0 \equiv F_{11} - H_{12}H_{22}F_{21} \tag{214}$$

$$H_0 \equiv H_{11} - H_{12}H_{22}^{-1}H_{21} \tag{215}$$

The appropriate Lagrangian for this modified problem after substituting Eq. (212) for u_2 is given by

$$F_1 = \tfrac{1}{2}[x_1^T \mid x_2^T \mid u_1^T]\left[\begin{array}{c|c|c} R_{11} & R_{12} & S_1 \\ \hline R_{12}^T & R_{22}^T & S_2 \\ \hline S_1^T & S_2^T & V_1\end{array}\right]\left[\begin{array}{c} x_1 \\ \hline x_2 \\ \hline u_1\end{array}\right] + [y_1^T y_2^T z_2^T]\left[\begin{array}{c} x_1 \\ \hline x_2 \\ \hline u_1\end{array}\right]$$
$$+ z_2^T H_{22}^{-1}(\dot{x}_2 - F_{21}x_1 - F_{22}x_2 - H_{21}u_1)$$
$$+ \lambda^T[\dot{x}_1 - F_0 x_1 - H_0 u_1 - (F_{12} - H_{12}H_{22}^{-1}F_{22})x_2 - H_{12}H_{22}^{-1}\dot{x}_2] \tag{216}$$

where λ is the vector of Lagrange multipliers.

The Euler–Lagrange equations are then

$$F_{u_1} = 0 \tag{217}$$

or

$$S_1{}^T x_1 + S_2{}^T x_2 + V_{11} u_1 + z_1 - H_{21}^T (H_{22}^{-1})^T z_2 - H_0{}^T \lambda = 0 \tag{218}$$

$$\frac{d}{dt} [F\dot{x}_1] = F_{x1} \tag{219}$$

or

$$\dot{\lambda} = -F_0{}^T \lambda + y_1 + R_{11} x_1 + R_{12} x_2 + S_1 u_1 - F_{21}^T (H_{22}^{-1})^T z_2 \tag{220}$$

$$\frac{d}{dt} [F\dot{x}_2] = F_{x2} \tag{221}$$

or

$$\frac{d}{dt} [(H_{22}^{-1})^T (z_2 - H_{121}^T \lambda)] = -(F_{12} - H_{12} H_{22}^{-1} F_{22})^T \lambda + R_{12}^T x_1 + R_{22} x_2$$
$$+ S_2 u_1 + y_2 - F_{22}^T H_{22}^{-1T} z_2 \tag{222}$$

With a judicious application of the chain rule of differentiation, algebra, and Eq. (220), Eq. (222) can be written

$$S_3 x_1 + (H_{22}^T R_{22} + H_{12}^T R_{12}) x_2 + S_0{}^T u_1 + H_{22}^T y_2 + H_{12}^T y_1 = \dot{z}_2 + D^T z_2 + M^T \lambda \tag{223}$$

where

$$S_3 \equiv H_{22}^T R_{12}^T + H_{12}^T R_{11} \tag{224}$$

$$S_0 \equiv S_2{}^T H_{22} + S_1{}^T H_{12} \tag{225}$$

$$D \equiv -H_{22}^{-1} (\dot{H}_{22} - F_{21} H_{12} - F_{22} H_{22}) \tag{226}$$

$$M \equiv -\dot{H}_{12} + F_{12} H_{22} + F_{11} H_{12} - H_{12} D \tag{227}$$

In order to apply the Riccati transformation as used by McReynolds–Bryson (*28*), x_2 can be treated as a control variable for purposes of computing the extremal curves, but Eq. (213) must be modified to eliminate the $\dot{x}_2$ driving term. This can be accomplished by the transformation

$$x_3 \equiv x_1 - H_{12} H_{22}^{-1} x_2 \tag{228}$$

With this transformation, Eqs. (213) and (220) become

$$\dot{x}_3 + F_0 x_3 + M H_{22}^{-1} x_2 + H_0 u_1; \qquad x_3(t_0) = x_{10} - H_{12} H_{22}^{-1} x_{20} \tag{229}$$

$$\dot{\lambda} = -F_0{}^T \lambda + S_1 u_1 + y_1 + R_{11} x_3 + S_3{}^T H_{22}^{-1} x_2 \tag{230}$$

and Eqs. (218) and (223) can be solved for u_1 and x_2 as

$$\begin{bmatrix} u_1 \\ H_{22}^{-1}x_2 \end{bmatrix} = \begin{bmatrix} V_1 & S_0 \\ S_0^T & V_0 \end{bmatrix}^{-1} \begin{bmatrix} H_0^T\lambda - S_1^T x_3 + H_{21}^T H_{22}^{-1} z_2 - z_1 \\ M^T\lambda - S_3 x_3 + \dot{z}_2 + D^T z_2 - H_{21}^T y_1 - H_{22}^T y_2 \end{bmatrix} \tag{231}$$

The appropriate Riccati transformation is thus

$$\lambda = \mu - Px_3 \tag{232}$$

Differentiating Eq. (232) in time yields with Eqs. (229) and (230)

$$\dot{\mu} = -F_0^T\mu + y_1 + (PH_0 + S_1)u_1 + (PM + S_3^T)H_{22}^{-1}x_2 + (\dot{P} + F_0^TP + PF_0)x_3 \tag{233}$$

Substituting for u_1, x_2 using Eq. (231) and equating the coefficient of x_3 to zero yields

$$\dot{P} = -F_0^TP - PF_0 - R_{11} + [K_1 \mid K_2]\begin{bmatrix} V_1 & S_0 \\ S_0^T & V_0 \end{bmatrix}^{-1}\begin{bmatrix} K_1^T \\ K_2^T \end{bmatrix} \tag{234}$$

$$\dot{\mu} = -F_0^T\mu + y_1 + [K_1 \mid K_2]\begin{bmatrix} V_1 & S_0 \\ S_0^T & V_0 \end{bmatrix} \times \begin{bmatrix} H_0^T\mu - z_1 + H_{21}^T(H_{22}^{-1})^T z_2 \\ M^T\mu + \dot{z}_2 + D^T z_2 - H_{12}^T y_1 - H_{22}^T y_2 \end{bmatrix} \tag{235}$$

where

$$K_1 \equiv PH_0 + S_1 \tag{236}$$

$$K_2 \equiv PM + S_3^T \tag{237}$$

The optimum u_1 and u_2 are then given by Eq. (212) and

$$\begin{bmatrix} u_1 \\ H_{22}^{-1}x_2 \end{bmatrix} = -\begin{bmatrix} V_1 & S_0 \\ S_0^T & V_0 \end{bmatrix}^{-1} \begin{bmatrix} (K_1^T x_3 + z_1 - H_0^T\mu - H_{21}^T(H_{22}^{-1})^T z_2) \\ (K_2^T x_3 + \dot{z}_2 + D^T z_2 - M^T\mu + H_{12}^T y_1 + H_{22}^T y_2) \end{bmatrix} \tag{238}$$

The boundary conditions on Eqs. (234) and (235) are obtained from the transversality conditions to be

$$P(T) = (P_{11T}^{-1} + H_{12}H_{22}^{-1}P_{22T}^{-1}(H_{22}^{-1})^T H_{12}^T)^{-1} \tag{239}$$

$$\mu(T) = -P(T)H_{12}P_{11T}z(T) \tag{240}$$

V. Singular End-Point Problems

The colored noise filter and singular regulator problem of Sections II through IV are not the only types of singular optimization problems.

Another well-known singular problem is that of the final value controller. The singularity in this problem occurs at one important instant of time—the terminal time—thus causing the feedback gains to become infinite. The singularities of the final value control problem are discussed in much greater detail in the chapter by Seal and Stubberud in this volume. However, it is reviewed briefly in the following, and then duality is once again invoked to discuss the filtering problem with no *a priori* state information.

A. Final Value Control

Briefly, the final value control problem is defined by that state equation and cost functional

$$\dot{x}(t) = F(t)x(t) + H(t)u(t) \tag{241}$$

where

$$x(t_0) = x_0$$

$$x(T) = x_f$$

and

$$J(u) = \frac{1}{2}\int_{t_0}^{T} [x^T(t)R(t)x(t) + u^T(t)V(t)u(t)]\, dt \tag{242}$$

It is assumed here that $V(t)$ is nonsingular on $t_0 \leqslant t \leqslant T$. The Euler–Lagrange equations for this problem are then

$$\begin{bmatrix} \dot{x} \\ \dot{\lambda} \end{bmatrix} = \begin{bmatrix} F & (HV^{-1}\ \ H^T) \\ R & -F^T \end{bmatrix} \begin{bmatrix} x \\ \lambda \end{bmatrix} \tag{243}$$

where λ are the Lagrange multipliers and the optimal control is

$$u = V^{-1}H^T\lambda \tag{244}$$

Since initial and final conditions are given for x but not λ, Eq. (243) defines a two-point boundary value problem which can be solved as follows.

Define the transition matrix corresponding to Eq. (243)

$$\begin{bmatrix} \dot{\phi}_x & \dot{\phi}_{x\lambda} \\ \dot{\phi}_{\lambda x} & \dot{\phi}_\lambda \end{bmatrix}_{(t,\,t_0)} = \begin{bmatrix} F & HV^{-1}H^T \\ R & -F^T \end{bmatrix}_{(t)} \begin{bmatrix} \phi_x & \phi_{x\lambda} \\ \phi_{\lambda x} & \phi_\lambda \end{bmatrix}_{(t,t_0)}$$

$$\begin{bmatrix} \phi_x & \phi_{x\lambda} \\ \phi_{\lambda x} & \phi_\lambda \end{bmatrix}_{(t,\,t)} = \begin{bmatrix} I & 0 \\ 0 & I \end{bmatrix} \tag{245}$$

Then

$$\begin{bmatrix} x(t) \\ \hline \lambda(t) \end{bmatrix} = \begin{bmatrix} \phi_x & \phi_{x\lambda} \\ \hline \phi_{\lambda x} & \phi_\lambda \end{bmatrix}_{(t,\,t_0)} \begin{bmatrix} x_0 \\ \hline \lambda(t_0) \end{bmatrix} \tag{246}$$

Solving for $\lambda(t_0)$ yields

$$\lambda(t_0) = \phi_{x\lambda}^{-1}(T, t_0)[x_f - \phi_x(T, t_0)x_0] \tag{247}$$

Solving for $u(t)$ yields the optimal open-loop control

$$u(t) = V^{-1}H^T\{\phi_{\lambda x}(t, t_0)x_0 + \phi_\lambda(t, t_0)\phi_{x\lambda}^{-1}(T, t_0)[x_f - \phi_x(T, t_0)x_0] \tag{248}$$

Letting $t = t_0$, the closed-loop control law is obtained.

$$u(t) = V^{-1}(t)H^T(t)\phi_{x\lambda}^{-1}(T, t)[x_f - \phi_x(T, t)x(t)] \tag{249}$$

Note that as t approaches T, $\phi_{x\lambda}(T, t)$ becomes singular by Eq. (245) thus the justification for terming this a "singular" problem. To avoid the unbounded gain at $t = T$, the closed-loop solution can be used until some time t_1, $t_0 < t_1 < T$, and the open-loop solution used over the interval $(t_1, T]$. Alternatively, the Lagrange multipliers can be extrapolated forward from t_1 by

$$\dot{\lambda}(t) = -F^T(t)\lambda(t) + R(t)x(t) \tag{250}$$

with I.C.

$$\lambda(t_1) = \phi_{x\lambda}^{-1}(T, t_1)[x_f - \phi_x(T, t_1)x(t_1)] \tag{251}$$

and the control determined from Eq. (244). The dual results in estimation will now be discussed in the light of the above.

B. Linear Filtering with No *a Priori* State Information

Consider the linear estimation problem defined by

$$\dot{x}(t) = F(t)x(t) + r(t), \qquad x(t_0) = x_0 \tag{252}$$

$$z(t) = H(t)x(t) + v(t) \tag{253}$$

where $r(t)$ and $v(t)$ are Gaussian white noise processes with

$$\begin{aligned} E[r(t)] &= E[x_0] = 0 \\ E[v(t)] &= 0 \\ E[r(t)r^T(\tau)] &= R(t)\,\delta(t-\tau) \\ E[v(t)v^T(\tau)] &= V(t)\,\delta(t-\tau) \\ E[r(t)v^T(\tau)] &= 0 \\ E[x_0 x_0^T] &= J_0 \end{aligned} \tag{254}$$

where $V(t)$ is assumed nonsingular, and where no *a priori* information about x_0 exists, i.e., J_0 is singular. As shown in Section III, this problem can be solved by the calculus of variations, which yields the following two-point boundary value problem.

$$\begin{bmatrix} \dot{\xi} \\ \dot{\lambda} \end{bmatrix} = \left[\begin{array}{c|c} F & R \\ \hline H^T V^{-1} H & -F^T \end{array}\right] \begin{bmatrix} \xi \\ \lambda \end{bmatrix} - \left[\begin{array}{c} 0 \\ \hline H^T V^{-1} \end{array}\right] z(t) \tag{255}$$

where

$$\xi(t) \equiv \hat{x}(t \mid T, t_0), \tag{256}$$

the minimum variance estimate of $x(t)$ based on measurements over (t_0, T), and where the transversality conditions ensure that

$$\lambda(t_0 \mid T) = \lambda(T \mid T) = 0 \tag{257}$$

Defining the usual state transition matrix for Eq. (255) yields

$$0 = \lambda(T \mid T) = \phi_{\lambda x}(T, t_0)\hat{x}(t_0 \mid T, t_0) - \int_{t_0}^{T} \phi_\lambda(T, \tau) H^T V^{-1} z(\tau)\, d\tau \tag{258}$$

Thus

$$\hat{x}(t_0 \mid T, t_0) = \phi_{x\lambda}^{-1}(T, t_0) \int_{t_0}^{T} \phi_\lambda(T, \tau) H^T V^{-1} z(^T)\, d\tau \tag{259}$$

Also

$$\hat{x}(t \mid T, t_0) = \phi_x(t, t_0)\phi_{\lambda x}^{-1}(T, t_0) \int_{t_0}^{T} \phi_\lambda(T, \tau) H^T V^{-1} z(\tau)\, d\tau - \int_{t_0}^{t} \phi_{x\lambda}(t, \tau) H^T V^{-1} z(\tau)\, d\tau \tag{260}$$

Note that for $t \in [t_0, T]$, $\hat{x}(t \mid T, t_0)$ is the smoothed estimate of $x(t)$. The filtered estimate is $\hat{x}(t \mid t, t_0)$, which is thus

$$\hat{x}(t \mid t, t_0) = \int_{t_0}^{T} [\phi_x(t, t_0)\phi_{\lambda x}^{-1}(t, t_0)\phi_\lambda(t, \tau) - \phi_{x\lambda}(t, \tau)] H^T V^{-1} z(\tau)\, d\tau \tag{261}$$

Differentiating with respect to t yields

$$\frac{\partial}{\partial t} \hat{x}(t \mid t, t_0) = J(t, t_0) H^T V^{-1} z(t) + \int_{t_0}^{T} \left\{ \left[\frac{\partial}{\partial t} J(t, t_0)\right] \phi_\lambda(t, \tau) + J(t, t_0)\left[\frac{\partial}{\partial t}\phi_\lambda(t, \tau)\right] - \frac{\partial}{\partial t}\phi_{x\lambda}(t, \tau)\right\} \times H^T(\tau) V^{-1}(\tau) z(\tau)\, d\tau \tag{262}$$

where

$$J(t, t_0) \equiv \phi_x(t, t_0)\phi_{\lambda x}^{-1}(t, t_0) \tag{263}$$

Utilizing the defining properties of the transition matrices, Eqs. (262) and (263) yield the standard Kalman–Bucy estimate and error covariance equations. Unfortunately, for this problem with no *a priori* estimate of the initial state $x(t_0)$, $J(t, t_0)$ by definition is singular at $t = t_0$. This implies that for $(\partial/\partial t)\hat{x}(t \mid t, t_0)$ to be finite at $t = t_0$, it suffices that

$$z(t_0) = H(t_0)\hat{x}(t_0 \mid t_0, t_0)$$

If the inverse of $H^T(t_0)H(t_0)$ exists, then $\hat{x}(t_0 \mid t_0, t_0)$ is specified.

Due to the singularity of $J(t, t_0)$ at $t = t_0$, a solution for small $(t - t_0)$ may be difficult to obtain. However, the duality of this problem with the final value control problem suggests an alternative solution. The observations can be directly integrated over a small time interval $[t_0, t_1]$ to obtain $\hat{x}(t_1 \mid t_1, t_0)$ and then using this as the initial condition on the filter equations at time t_1. This is equivalent to obtaining the smoothed estimate of x over $[t_0, t_1]$. To accomplish this, Eq. (261) is used directly

$$\hat{x}(t_1 \mid t_1, t_0) = \int_{t_0}^{t_1} [J(t_1, t_0)\phi_\lambda(t_1, \tau) - \phi_{x\lambda}(t_1, \tau)]H^T V^{-1} z(\tau)\, d\tau \tag{264}$$

where $J(t_1, t_0)$ is precalculated from $\phi_x(t_1, t_0)$ and $\phi_{\lambda x}(t_1, t_0)$, and $\phi_\lambda(t_1, \tau)$ and $\phi_{x\lambda}(t_1, \tau)$ are calculated as a function of τ by first precalculating $\phi_\lambda(t_1, t_0)$ and $\phi_{x\lambda}(t_1, t_0)$ and then integrating the adjoint homogeneous matrix equation from t_0 to τ. This procedure is the direct dual to the technique in a final value controller of opening the feedback loops a short time before the terminal time in a final value controller in order to avoid the singularities in the gain at the endpoint. The disadvantage of this approach in the filtering problem is that no estimate is obtained until time t_1.

References

1. A. E. Bryson and D. E. Johansen, Linear filtering for time-varying systems using measurements containing colored noise. *IEEE Trans. Autom. Control* **10**, 4–10 (1965).
2. R. S. Bucy, Optimal filtering for correlated noise. Rand Corp. Rep. RM5107-PR. Santa Monica, California, September, 1966.
3. J. S. Meditch, On optimum linear filtering in the presence of correlated measurement noise. Aerospace Corp., Rep. TDR-469 (5540-10)-1, El Segundo, California, August, 1964.
4. R. K. Mehra and A. E. Bryson, Jr., Smoothing for time-varying systems using measurements containing colored noise. Harvard Univ., Rep. NASA-CR-89757, Cambridge, Massachusetts, June 1967.
5. R. K. Mehra and A. E. Bryson, Jr., Linear smoothing using measurements containing correlated noise with an application to inertial navigation. *Joint Autom. Control Conf., Proc., Univ. of Michigan, Ann Arbor*, pp. 871–883 (1968).

6. A. P. Roberts, Optimum linear control in the presence of colored measurement noise. *Int. J. Control* **3**, 397–411 (1966).
7. A. P. Roberts, Lagging filtering and progressive interpolation. *Int. J. Control* **6**, 461–479 (1967).
8. A. P. Roberts, More on lagging filtering of colored noise. *Int. J. Control* **8**, 621–627 (1968).
9. E. B. Stear and A. R. Stubberud, Optimal filtering for Gauss-Markov noise. *Int. J. Control* **8**, 123–130 (1968).
10. A. R. Stubberud, Optimal filtering for Gauss–Markov noise. Aerospace Corp., Rep. TR-0158(3307-01)-10, El Segundo, California, December, 1967.
11. R. E. Kalman and R. S. Bucy, New results in linear filtering and prediction theory. *J. Basic Eng. Trans. ASME, Ser. D* **83**, 95–108 (1961).
12. R. S. Bucy and P. D. Joseph, "Filtering for Stochastic Processes with Applications to Guidance." Wiley (Interscience), New York, 1968.
13. R. E. Kalman, A new approach to linear filtering and prediction problems. *J. Basic Eng. Trans. ASME, Ser. D* **82**, 35–45 (1960).
14. V. Volterra, "Theory of Functionals and of Integral and Integro-Differential Equations." Dover, New York, 1959.
15. K. G. Brammer, Lower order optimal linear filtering of non-stationary random sequences. *IEEE Trans. Autom. Control* **13**, 198–199 (1968).
16. R. E. Mortenson, Continuous-time stochastic problems. Lecture Notes, Engineering Extension Course 867.10, Univ. of California, Los Angeles.
17. R. E. Mortenson, Mtahematical problems of modeling stochastic nonlinear dynamic systems. TRW Systems, Rep. 3412.1-18, Redondo Beach, California, April 16, 1968.
18. R. E. Mortenson, On the resolution of certain questions associated with nonlinear filtering. TRW Systems, Rep. 3412.2-118, Redondo Beach, California, September 5, 1968.
19. R. J. Stuart, Continuous-time nonlinear filtering. PhD. Dept. Eng., Univ. of California, Los Angeles, January, 1969.
20. G. Hadley, "Nonlinear and Dynamic Programming." Addison-Wesley, Reading, Massachussetts, 1964.
21. P. Wolfe, A duality theorem for non-linear programming. *Quart. Appl. Math. 19*, 239–244 (1961).
22. H. W. Kuhn and A. W. Tucker, Nonlinear programming. *2nd Berkeley Symp. Math. Stat. Prob., Proc., Berkeley, Calif.* pp. 481–492. Univ. of California Press, 1951.
23. M. A. Hanson, Bounds for functionally convex optimal control problems. *J. Math. Anal. Appl.* **8**, 84–89 (1964).
24. J. D. Pearson, Reciprocity and duality in control programming problems. *J. Math. Anal. Appl.* **10**, 388–408 (1965).
25. J. D. Pearson, Duality and a decomposition technique. *J. SIAM Ser. A (Control)* **4**, 164–172 (1966).
26. G. A. Bliss, "Lectures on the Calculus of Variations." Univ. of Chicago Press, Chicago, Illinois, 1946.
27. I. M. Gelfand and S. V. Fomin, "Calculus of Variations." Prentice-Hall, Englewood Cliffs, New Jersey, 1963.
28. S. R. McReynolds and A. E. Bryson, Jr., A successive sweep method for solving optimal programming problems. *Joint Autom. Control Conf., Proc., Rensselaer Polytech. Inst., Troy, New York*, pp. 551–555 (1965).

Discrete Stochastic Differential Games[1]

KENNETH B. BLEY

Hughes Aircraft Company
El Segundo, California

AND

EDWIN B. STEAR

School of Electrical Engineering
University of California
Santa Barbara, California

[1] This research was supported in part under United States Air Force Contract AFOSR Grant 699-67.

I. Introduction

A. History of Differential Games

Differential games came into existence in 1954 with the publication of several RAND Corporation reports written by Rufus Isaacs (*1–4*). This work, and a great deal more, was incorporated into his book *Differential Games* (*5*) published in 1965.

The original impetus for his investigations was the problem of pursuit and evasion of hostile aircraft. Following his original work, the field of differential games became almost entirely the province of mathematicians who made no attempt to give any physical meaning to their results (*6–8*). At the same time that American mathematicians were delving into the field, Soviet mathematicians also were exploring it [see bibliography in Simakova (*9*)].

Differential games became better known to engineers in the middle 1960s with publication of *Differential Games* and its review (*10*), and a small flurry of papers in engineering journals (*11–15*). Following these came several other papers involving stochastic differential games (*16–18*). Today the subject represents a rich field of investigation to those interested in control theory and the quantifiable aspects of conflict. The most complete bibliography presently available may be found in reference (*18*). This exceedingly short summary is by no means exhaustive of the work that has been done.

B. The Theory of Games

As the name differential games implies, it is a derivative of the mathematical theory of games first developed by von Neumann and Morgenstern (*19*). Many good books on game theory are available (*20–23*).

Games can have many forms depending on the number of players and the way in which winnings and losses are computed. The work herein involves only two players, where, essentially, the loser pays the winner a specified amount after the play of a given game. Since the algebraic sum of the winner's game (positive) and loser's gain (negative) is zero, this type of game is known as two-player zero sum game.

Games may be presented either in extensive form—a set of rules and a succession of choices for each player—or in normal form—a matrix or function which relates the amount due to the winner to the choices made by the two players. The amount, as a function of the choices, is known as the payoff of the game.

The choices may involve only a limited number of individual elements—matrix games—or they may involve an infinite number of elements—infinite or continuous games. Each player wishes to find a strategy that allows him to make his choices (choose his control) so as to optimize the payoff. In general, these strategies are functions of the payoff. These strategies may be (1) pure—given a fully specified payoff function, there is a single value of the control which should be chosen; or (2) randomized (mixed)—given a fully specified payoff function, there is a probability density function which should be chosen with the actual control found by a chance device having an output governed by the optimal probability density.

It can be shown that every matrix game, and some types of continous games, admits of a pair of strategies, pure or mixed, such that, if the minimizing player uses his optimal strategy, the payoff to the maximizing player will be no greater than a certain amount. Conversely, if the maximizing player uses his optimal strategy, he is assured of receiving at least the same amount. This amount is known as the Value of the game. The condition that expresses the inequalities of the payoff is known as the saddle point condition. Control strategies that satisfy the saddle point condition are such that both players can compute them, or, equivalently, that both players may announce their strategies and still be assured that the payoff will be no worse, from each point of view, than the Value.

An important concept in game theory is information. In games of perfect information, each player knows the exact value of the payoff and all that has occurred in the past. Such games as chess and checkers are examples of games of perfect information. It can be shown that such games have saddle points for pure strategies for both sides. Games of imperfect information have some elements that are unknown or given by a probability distribution; bridge is such a game. Games of imperfect information may or may not have pure strategies that satisfy the saddle point condition.

C. Differential Games

Differential games involve a payoff which is in some way related to a dynamical system. The two players attempt to optimize this payoff by choosing game optimal control strategies. The evolution of the state, as a function of the players' control variables, is described by differential equations (continuous time) or difference equations (discrete time); thus the name.

Because of the interaction among the state of the system, the dynamical relationship between the state and the controls, and the payoff, it is necessary that the game optimal control strategies be feedback strategies, ones that use information on the current state. Thus the central problem for the engineer is to find these feedback strategies. (Mathematicians must still deal with the many unsolved problems concerning the existence, uniqueness, and optimality of solutions.)

In general, there is no reason to assume that a given differential game has a Value or that its Value, when it exists, is obtained by using pure strategies. There are problems arising from the fact that the payoff is generally a continuous functional of the controls and, as noted in Section II, not all continuous payoffs admit of a Value, or, if they do, a Value resulting from pure strategies. Fortunately, there are cases where the structure of the payoff and the dynamical equations do result in a Value obtained by using pure strategies (*24*).

Differential games can be divided into classes: those where observations of the state are perfect, and those where they are not. The latter are referred to as stochastic games. Up to the present, they have involved linear observations of the state corrupted by additive noise. The addition of such noise means that a deterministic payoff function is no longer meaningful; instead, it is replaced with an expected value which is then optimized.

It must be noted that the descriptions of the theory of games and of differential games are included mainly for orientation purposes; they are neither rigorous nor complete. Full expositions are to be found among the references already cited.

II. Multistage Differential Games with Perfect Information

A. Introduction

Many papers published in the last 15 years have dealt with differential games involving perfect information. Almost without exception, they have dealt with problems leading to pure strategies. Some of the exceptions are noted by Berkovitz and Dresher (*25–27*); in addition, Chapter 12 in Issacs (*5*) discusses the subject.

In a sense, this is a very surprising turn of events since the whole theory of differential games is based on the theory of games—a discipline which is more concerned with randomized strategies than with pure ones. Further, until quite recently, the limited work done in the field of differential games has been performed by mathematicians (as opposed to engineers) who might have been thought to be more interested in questions of randomized strategies.

While engineers involved in doing research are quick to use some of the better known mathematical results in differential games involving pure strategies (*28*), there seems to be no such inclination with regard to the theory of sequentially compounded two-person games (*21*, *23*). Thus the available work in stochastic and recursive games has not received its due attention.

The work in this section is directed toward the complete solution of a multistage linear differential game with a quadratic payoff function. For convenience, only the scalar case is considered, but, at the cost of more work, the results go over identically when the dynamics are given in terms of matrix equations.

The solution is complete in that both deterministic and randomized control strategies, as required by the relative value of system parameters, are derived. To solve this problem, it is assumed that both players know the system parameters and are able to observe the true state of the system at all times.

B. Derivation of Pure Control Strategies when Control Magnitudes Are Unbounded

The evolution of the state of the system is determined by a linear difference equation

$$z_{i-1} = k_i z_i + a_i u_i + b_i v_i \tag{1}$$

where

$$z_i = \text{state at the } i\text{th stage,} \tag{2}$$

$$u_i = \text{minimizing player's control at the } i\text{th stage} \tag{3}$$

$$v_i = \text{maximizing player's control at the } i\text{th stage} \tag{4}$$

Both u_i and v_i can be functions of any or all of the past and present values of the state. (In game theory, the maximizing player is generally referred to as player I and the minimizing player as player II; these designations also are occasionally used here.)

The subscript indicates the stage number. Equation (1) is written in terms of time (stages)-to-go rather than the usual time measured from the initiation of the differential game. This is done because the stage number represents the number of times each player must choose a control —the actual value for u_i and v_i. Thus an N stage game, which begins in state z_N and terminates in state z_0, requires N choices of each player's control.

The object of the differential game is to optimize, in a game sense, a quadratic payoff function

$$I_N(U, V) = \sum_{i=1}^{N} c_i z_{i-1}^2 + d_i u_i^2 - e_i v_i^2 \tag{5}$$

That is, the minimizing player wishes to choose $u_N, \ldots, u_1$ so as to minimize I_N, while the maximizing player wishes to pick $v_N, \ldots, v_1$ so as to maximize it. Because there is only a single payoff functional, the problem falls within the general purview of zero sum game theory.

The value of the game is given by

$$J_N = \underset{U,\,V}{\text{val}}\, J_N(U, V) = \underset{U,\,V}{\text{val}} \sum_{i=1}^{N} c_i z_{i-1}^2 + d_i u_i^2 - e_i v_i^2 \tag{6}$$

where U and V represent the set of $2N$ controls $u_N, \ldots, u_1, v_N, \ldots, v_1$, and the "val" operator means the minimax value of I_N over the set of controls U and V.

The parameters of the system, a_i, b_i, c_i, d_i, e_i, and k_i, are all assumed to be real; a_i, b_i, d_i, e_i, and c_1 are assumed to be positive; $c_i (i \neq 1)$ is assumed to be nonnegative; and k_i can be positive, negative, or zero. These restrictions are required to produce meaningful results. If a_i or b_i is zero, the associated control can have no effect on the state at the next stage. Similarly, if d_i or e_i is zero, there is no penalty associated with the use of a control, and, if otherwise called for, infinite control magnitudes could be used. If c_1 were zero, the effect would be to terminate the game a stage early since neither player would wish to incur a penalty in the payoff by using his control when there was no attendant change due to a change in state. On the other hand, if $c_i = 0 (i \neq 1)$, the game is still well defined as to the number of stages, and the control at that stage is not, in general, zero for either player. (This is the analog to terminal control problem in optimal control.) The controls u_i and v_i are also assumed to be real with no restrictions on their sign or magnitude.

The principle of optimality of the theory of dynamic programming (29), along with simple variational principles, is used to find the desired control strategies (*30*). (Control strategies are defined to be rules that tell each player the value he should choose for his control at each stage based on the information available to him. The control is defined to be the value actually chosen.)

As is usual in dynamic programming, the single-stage game is first solved. To do this, assume that pure strategies exist for both players, strategies that permit each player to use the actual value of the state. Denoting these game optimal strategies by overbars, it follows that the value of the single-stage game J_1 is achieved when

$$u_1 = \bar{u}_1(z_1) \tag{7}$$

$$v_1 = \bar{v}_1(z_1) \tag{8}$$

The saddle point condition states that if one player uses his game optimal strategy and the other does not, then the payoff is as good or better than that which would have been achieved if both players had used their game optimal strategies. In terms of the payoff functional, Eq. (5),

$$I_1(\tilde{u}_1, \bar{v}_1) \geqslant I_1(\bar{u}_1, \bar{v}_1) = J_1 \geqslant I_1(\bar{u}_1, \tilde{v}_1) \tag{9}$$

where $\tilde{u}_1$ and $\tilde{v}_1$ are any real functions of z_1. Putting it another way,

$$I_1(\tilde{u}_1, \bar{v}_1) - I_1(\bar{u}_1, \bar{v}_1) \geqslant 0 \tag{10}$$

$$I_1(\bar{u}_1, \tilde{v}_1) - I_1(\bar{u}_1, \bar{v}_1) \leqslant 0 \tag{11}$$

If

$$\tilde{u}_1 = \bar{u}_1 + \varepsilon\delta(z_1) \tag{12}$$

where ε is a small number and $\delta(z_1)$ is any real function of z_1, then Eqs. (1), (5), (10), and (12) lead to

$$\begin{aligned} I_1(\bar{u}_1 + \varepsilon\delta_1 \bar{v}_1) - I_1(\bar{u}_1, \bar{v}_1) &= c_1(k_1 z_1 + a_1\bar{u}_1 + a_1\varepsilon\delta + b_1\bar{v}_1)^2 \\ &\quad + d_1(\bar{u}_1 + \varepsilon\delta)^2 - e_1\bar{v}_1{}^2 \\ &\quad - c_1(k_1 z_1 + a_1\bar{u}_1 + b_1\bar{v}_1)^2 \\ &\quad - d_1\bar{u}_1{}^2 + e_1\bar{v}_1{}^2 \\ &= 2[a_1c_1k_1z_1 + (a_1{}^2c_1 + d_1)\bar{u}_1 \\ &\quad + a_1b_1c_1\bar{v}_1]\varepsilon\delta + (a_1{}^2c_1 + d_1)\varepsilon^2\delta^2 \geqslant 0 \end{aligned} \tag{13}$$

where the argument of q has been dropped for brevity. Standard variational arguments lead to the following necessary conditions for inequality (13) to hold

$$a_1c_1k_1z_1 + (a_1{}^2c_1 + d_1)\bar{u}_1 + a_1b_1c_1\bar{v}_1 = 0 \tag{14}$$

$$a_1{}^2c_1 + d_1 \geqslant 0 \tag{15}$$

A similar approach leads to

$$\begin{aligned} I_1(\bar{u}_1, \bar{v}_1 + \varepsilon\Delta) - I_1(\bar{u}_1, \bar{v}_1) &= 2[b_1c_1k_1z_1 + a_1b_1c_1\bar{u}_1 - (e_1 - b_1{}^2c_1)\bar{v}_1] \\ &\quad \times \varepsilon\Delta - (e_1 - b_1{}^2c_1)\varepsilon^2\Delta^2 \leqslant 0 \end{aligned} \tag{16}$$

so that necessary conditions for inequality (16) to hold are

$$b_1c_1k_1z_1 + a_1b_1c_1\bar{u}_1 - (e_1 - b_1{}^2c_1)\bar{v}_1 = 0 \tag{17}$$

$$e_1 - b_1{}^2c_1 \geqslant 0 \tag{18}$$

The simultaneous solution of Eqs. (14) and (17) results in the game optimal control strategies for the single-stage game

$$\bar{u}_1 = -\frac{a_1 c_1 e_1 k_1}{(a_1^2 c_1 + d_1)(e_1 - b_1^2 c_1) + a_1^2 b_1^2 c_1^2} z_1 \tag{19}$$

$$\bar{v}_1 = \frac{b_1 c_1 d_1 k_1}{(a_1^2 c_1 + d_1)(e_1 - b_1^2 c_1) + a_1^2 b_1^2 c_1^2} z_1 \tag{20}$$

Substitution of (1), (19), and (20) into (6) yields

$$J_1 = \frac{c_1 d_1 e_1 k_1^2}{(a^2 c_1 + d_1)(e_1 - b_1^2 c_1) + a_1^2 b_1^2 c_1^2} z_1^2 \tag{21}$$

since $\bar{u}_1$ and $\bar{v}_1$ are precisely the pure control strategies which optimize, in a game theory sense, the payoff functional, Eq. (5).

Rewriting the denominator of Eq. (21) as

$$(a_1^2 c_1 + d_1)(e_1 - b_1^2 c_1) + a_1^2 b_1^2 c_1^2 = c_1(a_1^2 e_1 - b_1^2 d_1) + d_1 e_1 \tag{22}$$

indicates that a sufficient condition for pure strategies to exist is

$$a_1^2 e_1 - b_1^2 d_1 \geqslant 0 \tag{23}$$

When the equality in inequality (23) holds, it is easy to show, using Eqs. (19), (20), and (1), that

$$z_0 = k_1 z_1 \tag{24}$$

so that the change of state is governed by the homogenous equation in this case. This might be called a case of equal efficiency.

Having found the game optimal pure strategies for single-stage game, it is now possible to solve the two-stage game. Applying the principle of optimality yields

$$J_2 = \underset{u_2,\, v_2}{\text{val}} \{c_2 z_1^2 + d_2 u_2^2 - e_2 v_2^2 + J_1\} \tag{25}$$

Substituting Eq. (21) into Eq. (25) leads to

$$J_2 = \underset{u_2,\, v_2}{\text{val}} \{\tilde{c}_2 z_1^2 + d_2 u_2^2 - e_2 v_2^2\} \tag{26}$$

where

$$\tilde{c}_2 = c_2 + \frac{c_1 e_1 d_1 k_1^2}{(a_1^2 c_1 + d_1)(e_1 - b_1^2 c_1) + a_1^2 b_1^2 c_1^2} \tag{27}$$

The use of Eq. (27) has changed the two-stage problem into a single-stage problem so that all that has gone before applies now with the subscript 2 replacing 1 and $\tilde{c}_2$ instead of c_1. Thus

$$\bar{u}_2 = -\frac{a_2 \tilde{c}_2 e_2 k_2}{(a_2^2 \tilde{c}_2 + d_2)(e_2 - b_2^2 \tilde{c}_2) + a_2^2 b_2^2 \tilde{c}_2^2} z_2 \tag{28}$$

$$\bar{v}_2 = \frac{b_2 \tilde{c}_2 d_2 k_2}{(a_2{}^2\tilde{c}_2 + d_2)(e_2 - b_2{}^2\tilde{c}_2) + a_2{}^2 b_2{}^2 \tilde{c}_2{}^2} z_2 \tag{29}$$

$$J_2 = \frac{\tilde{c}_2 d_2 e_2 k_2{}^2}{(a_2{}^2\tilde{c}_2 + d_2)(e_2 - b_2{}^2\tilde{c}_2) + a_2{}^2 b_2{}^2 \tilde{c}_2{}^2} z_2{}^2 \tag{30}$$

with sufficient conditions being

$$a_2{}^2\tilde{c}_2 + d_2 > 0 \tag{31}$$

$$e_2 - b_2{}^2\tilde{c}_2 > 0 \tag{32}$$

[The other necessary conditions involving the first variation are inherent in Eqs. (28) and (29).]

The general solution for any number of stages is quite clear. For $i = 1, \ldots, N$

$$J_i = A_i z_i{}^2 \tag{33}$$

$$A_i = \frac{\tilde{c}_i d_i e_i k_i{}^2}{(a_i{}^2\tilde{c}_i + d_i)(e_i - b_i{}^2\tilde{c}_i) + a_i{}^2 b_i{}^2 \tilde{c}_i{}^2} \tag{34}$$

$$\tilde{c}_i = c_i + A_{i-1}; \qquad A_0 = 0 \tag{35}$$

$$\bar{u}_i = -\frac{a_i}{d_i k_i} A_i z_i = -\frac{a_i}{2d_i k_i} \frac{\partial J_i}{\partial z_i} \tag{36}$$

$$\bar{v}_i = \frac{b_i}{e_i k_i} A_i z_i = \frac{b_i}{2e_i k_i} \frac{\partial J_i}{\partial z_i} \tag{37}$$

[The fact that the game optimal controls are specifically related to the Value of the game is no coincidence; the same behavior is exhibited in optimal control problems involving linear dynamics and quadratic cost functionals (*31*).]

These results are, of course, not new. A slightly different approach was used by Ciletti (*32*). In the case of continuous, instead of discrete, dynamics, the analogous result was obtained by Ho *et al.* (*12*) using straightforward variational arguments, and functional analysis techniques were used by Porter (*33*).

C. Randomized Control Strategies

Prior to this subsection and in the following sections, only the pure strategy aspects of game theory are used to derive control strategies. In this section, a wider (but still very limited) appeal is made to other aspects. In particular, the following derivation is based on the theory of infinite convex games (*20*, *34*).

Roughly speaking, an infinite convex game is one where each player is free to choose his control from a region of an appropriately (finite) dimensioned, Euclidean space. The game is called infinite because of the infinite number of possible choices of a control within the region (as opposed to a finite number of possible choices in a matrix game). The game is called convex if the scalar payoff function is convex in the minimizing player's control variable.

It has been shown that when the payoff is both convex in the minimizing control variable and continuous in both control variables, the game has a Value. Further, if the minimizing control must take its value from a compact and convex region of the control space, then the minimizing player has a pure strategy. Finally, if the minimizing player must choose his control from an arbitrary n-dimensional region, then the optimal control strategy of the maximizing player will require randomization over, at most, $n+1$ points.

The theory of infinite convex games also describes how to find solutions (control strategies) for each player. The application of this theory to the scalar case is carried out in the following work as an illustration. The pertinent theorems, can be found in Chapter 12 of McKinsey (*20*) (theorems 12.2 and 12.5).

Both payoff, Eq. (5), and the dynamics of the system, Eq. (1), remain unchanged. In this subsection, however, it is assumed that both u_i and v_i are limited, in absolute value, to be less than or equal to one. That is, both u_i and v_i belong to sets U and V such that

$$U = \{u_i : |u_i| \leqslant 1\} \tag{38}$$

$$V = \{v_i : |v_i| \leqslant 1\} \tag{39}$$

(Previously, it was assumed that u_i and v_i could take on any value.)

As before, the principle of optimality is used to derive the control strategies for all N stages. Before, at each stage, the value was found from the (implicit) fact that

$$J_i = I_i(\bar{U}, \bar{V}) = \underset{U,\,V}{\text{val}}\, I_i(U, V) = \underset{U}{\text{min}}\ \underset{V}{\text{max}}\ I_i(U, V) = \underset{V}{\text{max}}\ \underset{U}{\text{min}}\ I_i(U, V) \tag{40}$$

Where now U and V refer to the set $U_i, U_{i-1}, \ldots, U_0, V_i, V_{i-1}, \ldots, V_0$. In general, that is, when pure strategies do not exist for both players, this is not true. It is true, however, that for the game under consideration,

$$J_i = \underset{U}{\text{min}}\ \underset{V}{\text{max}}\ I_i(U, V) \tag{41}$$

Note that the order of the min–max operations is strictly a result of the convexity of the payoff in U which implies a pure strategy for player II.

Having found J_i, $\bar{v}$ is found from the solution of

$$J_i = \max_V \; I_i(\bar{U}, V) \tag{42}$$

Equations (41) and (42) provide the tools needed to solve the problem at hand.

As usual, the single-stage game is solved first. Since

$$\partial^2 J_1/\partial u_1^{\,2} = 2(a_1^{\,2}c_1 + d_1) \tag{43}$$

$$\partial^2 J_1/\partial v_1^{\,2} = -2(e_1 - b_1^{\,2}c_1) \tag{44}$$

A pure strategy u_i for player II exists whenever

$$a_1^{\,2}c_1 + d_1 > 0 \tag{45}$$

Player I's strategy then calls for randomization over, at most, two points (randomization over a single point is the same thing as a pure strategy). Completely analogous results are obtained for a payoff that is concave in the maximizing player's control variable, i.e., when

$$e_1 - b_1^{\,2}c_1 > 0 \tag{46}$$

A pure strategy exists for player I, and player II's optimal strategy requires randomization over, at most, two points.

The rest of this chapter is concerned with the case where the payoff is strictly convex in U and where it may or may not be concave in V. (The last section dealt with a payoff which was convex in U—a pure strategy for player II—and which was concave in V—a pure strategy for player I.)

Making use of Eqs. (1) and (5), it follows that

$$\begin{aligned} I_1(u_1, v_1) &= c_1(k_1 z_1 + a_1 u_1 + b_1 v_1)^2 + d_1 u_1^{\,2} - e_1 v_1^{\,2} \qquad (47)\\ &= A + Bv_1 + Cv_1^{\,2} \\ &= C\left(v_1 + \frac{B}{2C}\right)^2 + A - \frac{B^2}{4C} \end{aligned}$$

where

$$A = c_1(k_1 z_1 + a_1 u_1)^2 + d_1 u_1^{\,2} \tag{48}$$

$$B = 2b_1 c_1(k_1 z_1 + a_1 u_1) \tag{49}$$

$$C = c_1 b_1^{\,2} - e_1 \tag{50}$$

The payoff, as a function of v_1, can take on either the shape of a straight line ($C = 0$) or a parabola ($C \neq 0$); if $C > 0$, then the parabola opens upward; if $C < 0$, it opens downward. If it opens downward, then the payoff is concave in v_1 and so a pure strategy exists for player I.

The parabola is symmetric about the line

$$v_1 = -\frac{B}{2C} = -\frac{b_1 c_1(k_1 z_1 + a_1 u_1)}{b_1^2 c_1 - e_1} \tag{51}$$

and, of course, the maximum ($C < 0$) or minimum ($C > 0$) value of $I_1(u_1, v_1)$ occurs at the same value of v_1. It is important to know where the maximum or minimum value occurs as a function of u_1 and z_1.

D. Derivation of Pure Control Strategies when Control Magnitudes Are Bounded

It is instructive to see what happens to pure strategies when the magnitudes of u_i and v_i are constrained to belong to U and V, respectively, instead of taking on any value. The major result is, naturally, to complicate the form of the solution since the control strategies are no longer linear functions of the state. The theorems on convex games already cited are used to find the solution.

It has already been noted that pure strategies exist for both players whenever inequalities (45) and (46) hold (for this section the same assumption holds). However, because of the constraints on the magnitude of u_1 and v_1, it is not possible to simply apply the techniques of Section II to this problem. Instead, the optimal strategies for the single-stage game are found by

(1) Finding $v_1(u_1)$ such that $I_1(u_1, v_1(u_1)) = \max_{v_1} I_1(u_1, v_1)$

(2) Finding $\bar{u}_1$ such that $\min_{u_1} I_1(u_1, v_1(u_1)) = J_1$

(The technique is the same whether the control strategies are pure or randomized.) Both $\bar{u}_1$ and $\bar{v}_1$, the optimal strategies, are functions of the state z_1.

From (51) it follows that v_1 is equal to minus one whenever

$$-\frac{b_1 c_1(k_1 z_1 + a_1 u_1)}{b_1^2 c_1 - e_1} \leqslant -1 \tag{52}$$

or whenever

$$u_1 \leqslant \frac{b_1^2 c_1 - e_1}{a_1 b_1 c_1} - \frac{k_1 z_1}{a_1} \tag{53}$$

Also v_1 is equal to plus one whenever

$$-\frac{b_1 c_1(k_1 z_1 + a_1 u_1)}{b_1^2 c_1 - e_1} \geqslant 1 \tag{54}$$

which occurs when

$$u_1 \geqslant -\frac{b_1{}^2c_1 - e_1}{a_1b_1c_1} - \frac{k_1z_1}{a_1} \tag{55}$$

When neither inequalities (53) nor (55) hold, v_1 is given by Eq. (51) directly. Thus $v_1(u_1)$ is given by

$$v_1(u_1) = \begin{cases} -1 & ; \quad -1 \leqslant u_1 \leqslant \dfrac{b_1{}^2c_1 - e_1}{a_1b_1c_1} - \dfrac{k_1z_1}{a_1} \\[2ex] -\dfrac{b_1c_1(k_1z_1 + a_1u_1)}{b_1{}^2c_1 - e_1} & ; \quad \dfrac{b_1{}^2c_1 - e_1}{a_1b_1c_1} - \dfrac{k_1z_1}{a_1} < u_1 < -\dfrac{b_1{}^2c_1 - e_1}{a_1b_1c_1} - \dfrac{k_1z_1}{a_1} \\[2ex] +1 & ; \quad -\dfrac{b_1{}^2c_1 - e_1}{a_1b_1c_1} - \dfrac{k_1z_1}{a_1} \leqslant u_1 \leqslant 1 \end{cases} \tag{56}$$

It may happen that some of the sets of inequalities are incompatible in (56). For instance, it could be that

$$\frac{b_1{}^2c_1 - e_1}{a_1b_1c_1} - \frac{k_1z_1}{a_1} \leqslant -1 \tag{57}$$

As an example, this could occur for k_1z_1 sufficiently large and positive. The meaning of such an incompatibility is merely that such a value for $v_1(u_1)$ is never an optimal choice, since either u_1, from the middle inequality of (56), or $+1$ would be chosen. From a (somewhat) practical point of view, replace any expression in the inequalities of (56) whose absolute magnitude is greater than one by one times the algebraic sign of the expression. Disregard any values of $v_1(u_1)$ where the right side of an expression minus the left side (where no expression is larger than one in absolute magnitude) is zero.

Defining

$$D = \begin{cases} -1 & ; \quad \dfrac{b_1{}^2c_1 - e_1}{a_1b_1c_1} - \dfrac{k_1z_1}{a_1} \leqslant -1 \\[2ex] \dfrac{b_1{}^2c_1 - e_1}{a_1b_1c_1} - \dfrac{k_1z_1}{a_1} & ; \quad -1 < \dfrac{b_1{}^2c_1 - e_1}{a_1b_1c_1} - \dfrac{k_1z_1}{a_1} < 1 \\[2ex] +1 & ; \quad 1 \leqslant \dfrac{b_1{}^2c_1 - e_1}{a_1b_1c_1} - \dfrac{k_1z_1}{a_1} \end{cases} \tag{58}$$

$$E = \begin{cases} -1 & ; \quad -\dfrac{b_1{}^2 c_1 - e_1}{a_1 b_1 c_1} - \dfrac{k_1 z_1}{a_1} \leqslant -1 \\ -\dfrac{b_1{}^2 c_1 - e_1}{a_1 b_1 c_1} - \dfrac{k_1 z_1}{a_1}; & \quad -1 < -\dfrac{b_1{}^2 c_1 - e_1}{a_1 b_1 c_1} - \dfrac{k_1 z_1}{a_1} < 1 \\ +1 & ; \quad 1 \leqslant -\dfrac{b_1{}^2 c_1 - e_1}{a_1 b_1 c_1} - \dfrac{k_1 z_1}{a_1} \end{cases} \tag{59}$$

the Value of the single-stage game is given by

$$J_1 = \min\Big\{ \min_{-1 \leqslant u_1 \leqslant D} c_1(k_1 z_1 + a_1 u_1 - b_1)^2 + d_1 u_1{}^2 - e_1;$$

$$\min_{D < u_1 < E} -\frac{c_1 e_1 (k_1 z_1 + a_1 u_1)^2}{b_1{}^2 c_1 - e_1} + d_1 u_1{}^2; \min_{E \leqslant u_1 \leqslant 1}$$

$$c_1(k_1 z_1 + a_1 u_1 + b_1)^2 + d_1 u_1{}^2 - e_1 \Big\} \tag{60}$$

Equation (60) is precisely the implementation of Eq. (41). For any value of the state z_1, it is a straightforward task to find the value of u_1 which minimizes any of the pertinent expressions in Eq. (60). The least of the three is then the Value of the game. The optimal control for v_1 is found from Eq. (56). Thus the single-stage game is completely solved.

The solution to the two-stage game is still given by Eq. (25). Unfortunately, in the general case, it is no longer possible to express the control strategies and the Value by simple expressions similar to Eqs.(28), (29), and (30). This comes as no particular surprise since it is a result of the nonlinearity of the control strategies and is not specifically related to differential games. The same behavior is exhibited when dynamic programming is used to solve optimal control problems involving constraints on the controls.

The same sort of a statement can be made concerning the solution to the N stage game. The problems encountered are those inherent in dynamic programming; no more theory is required. Accordingly, nothing more will be said about the case where the payoff is concave in the maximizing control variable.

E. Derivation of Randomized Control Strategies

This section deals with a case where the payoff function is not strictly concave, that is, it is assumed that

$$b_1{}^2 c_1 - e_1 \geqslant 0 \tag{61}$$

(This is actually equivalent to saying that the payoff is convex in the maximizing control since every quadratic expression is either a concave or a convex function.)

It follows immediately from the second line of Eq. (47) that the maximum of $I_1(u_1, v_1)$ is achieved for

$$v_1 = \text{sgn}[B] = \text{sgn}[b_1 c_1(k_1 z_1 + a_1 u_1)] \tag{62}$$

where

$$\text{sgn}[x] = \frac{x}{|x|}; \qquad x \neq 0 \tag{63}$$

and is to be defined for $x = 0$.

Consider first what happens when

$$k_1 z_1 / a_1 > 1 \tag{64}$$

When inequality (64) holds, it is impossible for any choice of u_1 to change the sign of B; it must remain positive, which, by Eq. (62), means that the Value is given by

$$J_1 = \min_{u_1} c(k_1 z_1 + a_1 u_1 + b_1)^2 + d_1 u_1{}^2 - e_1 \tag{65}$$

The optimal value for u_1 is

$$\bar{u}_1 = \max\left[-1, -\frac{a_1 c_1(k_1 z_1 + b_1)}{a_1{}^2 c_1 + d_1}\right] \tag{66}$$

When

$$\frac{k_1 z_1}{a_1} < -1 \tag{67}$$

then the same reasoning leads to the conclusion that

$$J_1 = \min_{u_1} c_1(k_1 z_1 + a_1 u_1 - b_1)^2 + d_1 u_1{}^2 - e \tag{68}$$

where

$$\bar{u}_1 = \min\left[1, -\frac{a_1 c_1(k_1 z_1 - b_1)}{a_1{}^2 c_1 + d_1}\right] \tag{69}$$

In both Eqs. (66) and (69), $\bar{u}_1$ takes on a value in the interior of U only if the weighting on the square of the control d_1, is sufficiently large. Combining the two expressions shows that $\bar{u}_1$ is an interior point of U only if

$$d_1 > a_1 c_1(|k_1 z_1| + b_1) - a_1{}^2 c_1 > 0 \tag{70}$$

Even though the minimizing control may be forced to assume an interior value of U (not reducing the state component of the cost as much as possible), the maximizing player need never worry about a similar condition. This follows from the fact that the increase in the payoff due to a change in the state is greater than the cost incurred due to the use of the maximizing control—this is the real meaning of the payoff not being strictly concave in v_1. The concrete result is that player I always uses the largest magnitude of the control available to him for these two cases.

Finally, there is the case where

$$\frac{|k_1 z_1|}{|\ a_1\ |} \leqslant 1 \tag{71}$$

which is the most interesting of all, since it can lead to randomized control strategies. In this case, $\operatorname{sgn}[k_1 z_1 + a_1 u_1]$ may be equal to plus or minus one or $\operatorname{sgn}[0]$, depending on u_1. Because $\bar{v}_1$ is well defined when $k_1 z_1 + a_1 u_1$ is not equal to zero, it is possible to write

$$\begin{aligned} J_1 = \min\Bigg\{ & \min_{-1 \leqslant u_1 < -\frac{k_1 z_1}{a_1}} c_1(k_1 z_1 + a_1 u_1 - b_1)^2 + d_1 u_1^2 - e_1; \\ & \max_{v_1}^{u_1 = -\frac{k_1 z_1}{a_1}} c_1(b_1 v_1)^2 + d_1\left(\frac{k_1 z_1}{a_1}\right)^2 - e_1 v_1^2; \\ & \min_{-\frac{k_1 z_1}{a_1} < u_1 \leqslant 1} c_1(k_1 z_1 + a_1 u_1 + b_1)^2 + d_1 u_1^2 - e_1 \Bigg\} \end{aligned} \tag{72}$$

Consider the middle term first. Since $b_1{}^2 c_1 - e_1$ is nonnegative,

$$\max_{v_1} (b_1 c_1 - e_1) v_1{}^2 + d_1\left(\frac{k_1 z_1}{a_1}\right)^2 = b_1{}^2 c_1 - e_1 + d_1\left(\frac{k_1 z_1}{a_1}\right)^2 \tag{73}$$

so that the maximum of v_1 (within V, of course) is achieved for v_1 equal to plus or minus one. Since these are precisely the values used for v_1 in the first and third terms of Eq. (72), the two half-open intervals for u_1 can be replaced by closed intervals, and the second term can be discarded so that

$$\begin{aligned} J_1 = \min\Bigg\{ & \min_{-1 \leqslant u_1 \leqslant -\frac{k_1 z_1}{a_1}} c_1(k_1 z_1 + a_1 u_1 - b_1)^2 + d_1 u_1^2 - e_1; \\ & \min_{-\frac{k_1 z_1}{a_1} \leqslant u_1 \leqslant 1} c_1(k_1 z_1 + a_1 u_1 + b_1)^2 + d_1 u_1^2 - e_1 \Bigg\} \end{aligned} \tag{74}$$

The result of Eq. (73) is effectively to define

$$|\operatorname{sgn}[0]| = 1 \tag{75}$$

although saying nothing about how an algebraic sign is to be attached.

The first term in Eq. (74) has a minimum, as a function of u_1, that need not lie between minus one and $-(k_1z_1/a_1)$. Using ordinary calculus, the minimizing u_1 is found to be

$$u_1 = -\frac{a_1c_1(k_1z_1 - b_1)}{a_1^2c_1 + d_1} \tag{76}$$

which means that the absolute minimum of the term lies within the half-open interval $[-1, -(k_1z_1/a_1))$ when

$$-1 \leqslant -\frac{a_1c_1(k_1z_1 - b_1)}{a_1^2c_1 + d_1} < -\frac{k_1z_1}{a_1} \tag{77}$$

The left-hand inequality always holds since it can be rewritten as

$$-1 - \frac{d_1}{a_1^2c_1} \leqslant -\frac{k_1z_1}{a_1} + \frac{b_1}{a_1} \tag{78}$$

where the first term on the right of (78) is always equal to or greater than minus one and the second term on the right is always positive, while the second term on the left is always negative.

Simple algebra shows that the right-hand inequality holds whenever k_1z_1 is positive and

$$d_1 < -\frac{a_1b_1c_1}{(k_1z_1/a_1)} \leqslant 0 \tag{79}$$

Since d_1 is assumed to be positive, inequality (79) can never hold if $k_1z_1 > 0$ and, for this case, the absolute minimum occurs for a value of u_1 greater than $-(k_1z_1/a_1)$. If k_1z_1 is negative and

$$d_1 > -\frac{a_1b_1c_1}{(k_1z_1/a_1)} \tag{80}$$

then the absolute minimum occurs for a value of u_1 less than or equal to $-(k_1z_1/a_1)$.

Investigation of the second term of Eq. (74) shows that the absolute minimum is achieved for value of u_1 less than one and falls within the interval $(-(k_1z_1/a_1), 1]$ whenever k_1z_1 is positive and

$$d_1 > \frac{a_1b_1c_1}{(k_1z_1/a_1)} \tag{81}$$

The absolute minimum occurs for

$$u_1 = -\frac{a_1c_1(k_1z_1 + b_1)}{a_1^2c_1 + d_1} \tag{82}$$

so that (76), (82), (80), and (81) can be summed up by saying that if

$$d_1 > \frac{a_1 b_1 c_1}{|k_1 z_1 / a_1|} \tag{83}$$

then

$$\bar{u}_1 = -\frac{a_1 c_1 (k_1 z_1 + b_1 \operatorname{sgn}[k_1 z_1])}{a_1^2 c_1 + d_1} \tag{84}$$

If inequality (83) holds, then $\bar{v}_1$ is given by

$$\bar{v}_1 = \operatorname{sgn}[k_1 z_1] \tag{85}$$

The game optimal minimizing control resulting from Eq. (84) means that $k_1 z_1 + a_1 \bar{u}_1$ has the same sign as $k_1 z_1$.

The value of the game is then given by

$$J_1 = c_1 d_1 \frac{(|k_1 z_1| + b_1)^2}{a_1^2 c_1 + d_1} - e_1 \tag{86}$$

If inequality (83) does not hold, then the absolute minimum of each expression falls outside the half open intervals previously defined. The minimum is then achieved for

$$\bar{u}_1 = -(k_1 z_1 / a_1) \tag{87}$$

with a corresponding Value of

$$J_1 = b_1^2 c_1 + d_1 (k_1 z_1 / a_1)^2 - e_1 \tag{88}$$

Equation (75) has already established that $\bar{v}_1$ will take on the values plus or minus one; having this knowledge, Theorem 12.5 of McKinsey (*20*) can be used to find the optimal mixed strategy for the maximizing player. Using this theorem, it is seen that the optimal mixed strategy involves randomizing over the two points

$$\bar{v}_1^{\,1} = -1 \tag{89}$$

$$\bar{v}_1^{\,2} = +1 \tag{90}$$

with probabilities α and $(1 - \alpha)$, respectively, where α and $1 - \alpha$ are nonnegative. The optimal strategy is then given by a probability distribution

$$\bar{v}_1 = \alpha H(\bar{v}_1^{\,1}) + (1 - \alpha) H(\bar{v}_1^{\,2}) \tag{91}$$

where $H(x)$ means the step function with the jump occurring at x. An expression for α is found from the requirement that

$$\alpha \left.\frac{\partial I_1}{\partial u_1}\right|_{\bar{u}_1,\, \bar{v}_1{}^1} + (1-\alpha) \left.\frac{\partial I_1}{\partial u_1}\right|_{\bar{u}_1,\, v_1{}^2} = 0 \tag{92}$$

and

$$\left.\frac{\partial I_1}{\partial u_1}\right|_{\bar{u}_1, \bar{v}_1{}^1} \leqslant 0 \tag{93}$$

$$\left.\frac{\partial I_1}{\partial u_1}\right|_{\bar{u}_1, v_1{}^2} \geqslant 0 \tag{94}$$

Since

$$\frac{\partial I_1}{\partial u_1} = 2a_1c_1(k_1z_1 + a_1u_1 + b_1v_1) + 2\, d_1u_1 \tag{95}$$

$$\left.\frac{\partial I_1}{\partial u_1}\right|_{\bar{u}_1, v_1{}^1} = -2a_1b_1c_1 - 2\, d_1 \left(\frac{k_1z_1}{a_1}\right) \tag{96}$$

$$\left.\frac{\partial I_1}{\partial u_1}\right|_{\bar{u}_1, \bar{v}_1{}^2} = 2a_1b_1c_1 - 2\, d_1\left(\frac{k_1z_1}{a_1}\right) \tag{97}$$

It follows that the right side of Eq. (96) must be nonpositive and the right side of Eq. (97) nonnegative. But those are precisely the requirement imposed by inequality (83). Accordingly, α can be found from the solution of

$$-\alpha[a_1b_1c_1 + d_1(k_1z_1/a_1)] + (1-\alpha)[a_1b_1c_1 - d_1(k_1z_1/a_1)] = 0 \tag{98}$$

so that

$$\alpha = \frac{a_1b_1c_1 - d_1(k_1z_1/a_1)}{2a_1b_1c_1} \tag{99}$$

and the game optimal maximizing strategy, Eq. (91), is

$$\bar{v}_1 = \begin{cases} -1 & \text{with probability } \dfrac{a_1b_1c_1 - d_1(k_1z_1/a_1)}{2a_1b_1c_1} \\[2ex] 1 & \text{with probability } \dfrac{a_1b_1c_1 + d_1(k_1z_1/a_1)}{2a_1b_1c_1} \end{cases} \tag{100}$$

The game optimal control strategies and the Value for the single-stage game, as a function of the state and the various system parameters, are summarized in Table I.

TABLE I

STRATEGIES AND PAYOFF FOR SINGLE-STAGE GAME

$\left\lvert \frac{k_1 z_1}{a_1} \right\rvert > 1$	
$0 < d_1 \leqslant a_1{}^2 c_1 \left(\left\lvert \frac{k_1 z_1}{a_1} \right\rvert + \frac{b_1}{a_1} - 1 \right)$	$d_1 > a_1{}^2 c_1 \left(\left\lvert \frac{k_1 z_1}{a_1} \right\rvert + \frac{b_1}{a_1} - 1 \right) > 0$
$\bar{u}_1 = -\operatorname{sgn} \left[\frac{k_1 z_1}{a_1} \right]$	$u_1 = -\frac{a_1 c_1 (k_1 z_1 + b_1 \operatorname{sgn}[k_1 z_1])}{a_1{}^2 c_1 + d_1}$
$\bar{v}_1 = \operatorname{sgn} \left[\frac{k_1 z_1}{a_1} \right]$	$\bar{v}_1 = \operatorname{sgn} \left[\frac{k_1 z_1}{a_1} \right]$
$J_1 = a_1{}^2 c_1 \left[\left\lvert \frac{k_1 z_1}{a_1} \right\rvert - 1 + \frac{b_1}{a_1} \right]^2 + d_1 - e_1$	$J_1 = c_1 d_1 \frac{(\lvert k_1 z_1 \rvert + b_1)^2}{a_1{}^2 c_1 + d_1} - e_1$
$\left\lvert \frac{k_1 z_1}{a_1} \right\rvert \leqslant 1$	
$d_1 \leqslant \frac{a_1 b_1 c_1}{\left\lvert \frac{k_1 z_1}{a_1} \right\rvert}$	$d_1 > \frac{a_1 b_1 c_1}{\left\lvert \frac{k_1 z_1}{a_1} \right\rvert}$
$\bar{u}_1 = -\frac{k_1 z_1}{a_1}$	$\bar{u}_1 = -\frac{a_1 c_1 (k_1 z_1 + b_1 \operatorname{sgn}[k_1 z_1])}{a_1{}^2 c_1 + d_1}$
$\bar{v}_1 = \begin{cases} -1 & \text{with probability } \dfrac{a_1 b_1 c_1 - d_1 \left(\frac{k_1 z_1}{a_1} \right)}{2 a_1 b_1 c_1} \\ 1 & \text{with probability } \dfrac{a_1 b_1 c_1 + d_1 \left(\frac{k_1 z_1}{a_1} \right)}{2 a_1 b_1 c_1} \end{cases}$	$\bar{v}_1 = \operatorname{sgn} \left[\frac{k_1 z_1}{a_1} \right]$
$J_1 = b_1{}^2 c_1 + d_1 \left(\frac{k_1 z_1}{a_1} \right)^2 - e_1$	$J_1 = c_1 d_1 \frac{(\lvert k_1 z_1 \rvert + b_1)^2}{a_1{}^2 c_1 + d_1} - e_1$

Table I illustrates the nonlinear nature of the strategies as functions of both the state and the relative values of the system parameters. And, for the first time, a situation exists where a randomized strategy is optimal.

Notice that e_1 does not appear except in the Value. This is to be expected since $\lvert \bar{v}_1 \rvert$ is always equal to one. Accordingly, the penalty incurred through the use of v_1 is always the same.

As noted in the last section, the nonlinear nature of the game optimal control strategies makes it impossible to solve the multistage differential game explicitly in a few statements. The general solution is still given by functional equations of the form of Eq. (25) using the techniques outlined in this chapter.

F. Example

This section illustrates the solution to a multistage differential game having randomized strategies. To do this, it is assumed that (1) the system parameters a, b, c, d, e, and k are constant; (2) the sytem parameters a, b, c, d, and e are positive; (3) the initial state z_N is such that $|kz_N/a| < 1$; (4) the control magnitudes are such that $a \geqslant b$; and (5) the weighting on the use of u_i is small enough so that $d < ab\tilde{c}/|kz_1/a|$, where $\tilde{c}$ is to be defined.

Table I supplies the solutions to the single-stage game. Substituting J_1 into Eq. (25) and replacing "val" by "min max" yields

$$J_2 = \min_{u_2} \max_{v_2} [cz_1^2 + du_2^2 - ev_2^2 + b^2c^2 + d(kz_1/a)^2 - e]$$

$$= \min_{u_2} \max_{v_2} [(c + dk^2/a^2)z_1^2 + du_2^2 - ev_2^2 + b^2c - e] \tag{101}$$

Letting

$$\tilde{c} = c + dk^2/a^2 \tag{102}$$

and substituting Eqs. (1) and (102) into Eq. (101) leads to

$$J_2 = \min_{u_2} \max_{v_2} [\tilde{c}(kz_2 + au_2 + bv_2)^2 + du_2^2 - ev_2^2 + bc^2 - e] \tag{103}$$

which has the same form, except for a constant term, as Eq. (47). In other words, the same techniques used to solve the single-stage game will suffice to solve stage 2 of a two-stage game.

Since the constant term affects only the magnitude of the Value (and not the control strategies), it follows immediately that

$$\bar{u}_2 = -(kz_2/a) \tag{104}$$

$$\bar{v}_2 = \begin{cases} -1 & \text{with probability } \dfrac{ab\tilde{c} - d(kz_2/a)}{2ab\tilde{c}} \\ 1 & \text{with probability } \dfrac{ab\tilde{c} + d(kz_2/a)}{2ab\tilde{c}} \end{cases} \tag{105}$$

and that the Value for the two-stage game is given by

$$J_2 = 2b^2c - 2e + d(kb/a)^2 + d(kz_2/a)^2 \tag{106}$$

Repeated application of Eq. (25) leads to

$$J_N = d(kz_N/a)^2 + N(cb^2 - e) + (N-1)d(kb/a)^2 \tag{107}$$

with the game optimal control strategies being given by

$$\bar{u}_N = -(kz_N/a) \tag{108}$$

$$\bar{v}_N = \begin{cases} -1 & \text{with probability } \dfrac{ab\tilde{c} - d(kz_N/a)}{2ab\tilde{c}} \\ 1 & \text{with probability } \dfrac{ab\tilde{c} + d(kz_N/a)}{2ab\tilde{c}} \end{cases} \tag{109}$$

The Value of the game is a function only of the initial state z_N, and the number of stages, as it should be. It is not a random variable. The same is not true for the trajectory. It describes a stochastic process taking on the values plus or minus b at each stage. Thus there are 2^N possible paths for the system to follow. It should be clear now why assumption 4 is required: without it the state at stage $N-1$ would be such that the randomized control strategy would no longer be necessary. [This is the case, with d and e equal to zero, covered in Chapter III of Meschler (*35*).]

G. Concluding Comments

This section has dealt with the solution to multistage scalar games with linear dynamics and quadratic payoff functions. This was done for convenience rather than out of necessity, particularly in the case of randomized strategies. As Bohnenblust *et al.* (*34*) indicate, the solution of convex games is, in theory, identical for finite dimensional systems; practically speaking, the added notational complexity would only obscure an already diffuse solution.

Results, completely analogous to those obtained in this section, are obtained under the assumption that the payoff is strictly concave in the maximizing control variable.

III. Multistage Stochastic Differential Games

A. Introduction

This section deals with the multistage, discrete time stochastic differential game. The dynamics are described by a linear difference equation having time varying deterministic coefficients, with the possible exception of a noisy forcing function. Both players wish to choose controls so as to either maximize (player I) or minimize (player II) the expected value of a quadratic cost functional. Neither player can observe the actual state of the system; instead, each player has an observation of the state which is corrupted by additive noise.

The purpose of this section is to derive game optimal strategies so as to allow the determination of the appropriate controls at each stage. It is assumed that pure strategies exist; necessary and sufficient conditions are derived for this to be true.

B. Notation

An N-stage game is defined as one requiring that each player choose a value for his control at N instants of time. Time-to-go, rather than the usual forward flowing time, is treated as the independent variable. A subscript i indicates that the subscripted variable is at the ith stage. Thus z_N represents the state at the Nth (initial stage—N stages to go) stage, while z_0 represents the state of the system at termination.

A superscript is used to indicate the set of present and all past values of the variable under discussion. Thus z^1 is the set of the present state, z_1 (the state when there is one stage-to-go), as well as all past values $z_2, z_3, \ldots, z_N$, i.e., $z^1 = (z_1, z_2, \ldots, z_N)$. Naturally, $z^N = z_N$.

A similar convention is used to indicate integration over a set of variables. Thus $dz_1\, dz_2 \ldots dz_N$ is written dz^1. Further, when several different variables of integration are used, only a single integral sign is used; the number of integrations is indicated by the differential. Thus

$$\int \cdots \int p(z_1, x_1, \ldots, x_N | y_1, \ldots, y_N)\, dz_1\, dx_1 \cdots dx_N$$

is written as

$$\int p(z_1, x^1 | y^1)\, d(z_1, x^1)$$

When no limits of integration are specified, the integration is considered to be from minus infinity to plus infinity.

Quadratic forms are given by

$$x^T A x = \|x\|_A{}^2$$

so that a Gaussian probability density is given by

$$p(x) = \frac{1}{(2\pi)^{n/2} |\sigma|} \exp\left\{-\tfrac{1}{2} \|x - \bar{x}\|^2_{\sigma^{-2}}\right\}$$

where x is a vector with n components, $\bar{x}$ is the mean of x, and σ^2 is the $n \times n$ covariance matrix of x. For simplicity, only twice the negative of the exponent is used when computations are required. Thus the probability density given above is denoted

$$p(x) = \|x - \bar{x}\|^2_{\sigma^{-2}}$$

The Gaussian (normal) probability density is also denoted as

$$x : N(\bar{x}, \sigma^2)$$

where $\bar{x}$ and σ^2 are, respectively, the mean and covariance of the random variable x, i.e.,

$$\bar{x} = E\{x\}$$

$$\sigma^2 = E\{(x - \bar{x})(x - \bar{x})^T\}$$

where E is the expected value operator.

Various other subscripts are used to identify variables as required. Thus $\sigma^2_{\eta 2}$ indicates the covariance matrix of the random variable η at stage 2, when two stages-to-go remain.

C. Derivation of Pure Control Strategies

The evolution of the state is described by a linear vector difference equation

$$z_i = k_{i+1} z_{i+1} + a_{i+1} u_{i+1} + b_{i+1} v_{i+1} + \lambda_{i+1}, \qquad i = 0, 1, \ldots, N-1 \tag{110}$$

where z_i = n-component vector representing the state at stage i; u_i = m-component vector representing the minimizing player's control at stage i; v_i = m'-component vector representing the maximizing player's control at stage i; λ_i = n-component vector representing the realization of an independent noise sequence at stage i; and k_i, a_i, b_i = deterministic matrices of the appropriate dimensions.

Both players make observations of linear combinations of the elements of the state vector, but each observation is corrupted by an additive, independent noise sequence so that

$$x_i = G_i z_i + \eta_i \tag{111}$$

$$y_i = H_i z_i + \xi_i \tag{112}$$

where x_i = q-component vector representing the minimizing player's observation at stage i; y_i = q'-component vector representing the maximizing player's observation at stage i; η_i = q-component vector representing the realization of an independent noise sequence; ξ_i = q'-component vector representing the realization of an independent noise sequence; and H_i, G_i = deterministic matrices of the appropriate dimensions.

The Value of the multistage game J_N is given by

$$J_N = \overset{\text{val}}{u^1, v^1} E\left\{ \sum_{i=1}^{N} \|z_{i-1}\|_{c_i}^2 + \|u_i\|_{d_i}^2 - \|v_i\|_{e_i}^2 \right\}$$

$$= \overset{\min}{u^1} \; \overset{\max}{v^1} E\left\{ \sum_{i=1}^{N} \|z_{i-1}\|_{c_i}^2 + \|u_i\|_{d_i}^2 - \|v_i\|_{e_i}^2 \right\} \tag{113}$$

("Min max" could be replaced by "max min" since only pure strategies are considered.) u_i and v_i can be any vectors of real numbers; however,

$$c_1, d_i, e_i > 0, \qquad i = 1, 2, \ldots, N \tag{114}$$

where the inequality in (114) means that each criterion parameter is a real positive definitive matrix. Inequality signs are used as needed and should be read to mean positive definite (instead of greater than zero), positive semidefinite (instead of greater than or equal to zero), etc.

Only c_1 need be positive; $c_i (i \neq 1)$ need only be nonnegative. If c_i does equal zero, then the result is a terminal control problem. The remaining inequalities of (114) are required to make the game meaningful. If any parameter were to be zero, then either there would be no effect due to a control at that stage (a_i or b_i equal to zero) or there would be no cost for using control at that stage (d_i or e_i equal to zero).

For convenience, it is assumed that all the critera parameters in (114) are symmetric.

Each of the various noises is assumed to have a Gaussian (normal) probability density as follows:

$$\lambda_i : N(0, \sigma_{\lambda i}^2) \tag{115}$$

$$\eta_i : N(0, \sigma_{\eta i}^2) \tag{116}$$

$$\xi_i : N(0, \sigma_{\xi i}^2) \tag{117}$$

The initial state z_N also will be a Gaussian random variable:

$$z_N : N(m, \sigma_z{}^2) \tag{118}$$

It is assumed that both players know the information contained in (110) through (118). This does not mean that player I knows the actual value for x_i—the observation of the state at the ith stage made by player II—but that he does know the structure of the observation, as given by Eq. (111), and the probability density of the additive noise, as given by (116).

To actually solve the multistage game, the principle of optimality of the theory of dynamic programming will be used. To do this, game optimization is first carried out for the controls chosen with one stage-to-go,

u_1 and v_1. The technique used is similar, in terms of the basic structure, to that used to solve multistage stochastic optimal control problems (*36*). The Value for this one-stage game is

$$J_1 = \min_{u_1} \max_{v_1} E\left\{ \|z_0\|_{c1} + \|u_1\|_{d1}^2 - \|v_1\|_{e1}^2 \right\}$$

$$= \min_{u_1} \max_{v_1} \int \left\{ \|z_0\|_{c1}^2 + \|u_1\|_{d1}^2 - \|v_1\|_{e1}^2 \right\} \times p(z_0, u_1, v_1)\, d(z_0, u_1, v_1) \tag{119}$$

where $p(z_0, u_1, v_1)$ is the joint (Gaussian) probability density function of z_0, u_1, and v_1. Since (*37*)

$$\begin{aligned} p(z_0, u_1, v_1) &= \int p(z_0, z_1, u_1, v_1)\, dz_1 \\ &= \int p(z_0 | z_1, u_1, v_1) p(z_1, u_1, v_1)\, dz_1 \end{aligned} \tag{120}$$

Equation (119) can be written as

$$J_1 = E\left\{ \|\lambda_1\|_{c1}^2 \right\} + \min_{u_1} \max_{v_1} \int \left\{ \|k_1 z_1 + a_1 u_1 + b_1 v_1\|_{c1}^2 + \|u_1\|_{d1}^2 - \|v_1\|_{e1}^2 \right\}$$
$$\times\, p(z_1, u_1, v_1)\, d(z_1, u_1, v_1) \tag{121}$$

Noting that

$$\begin{aligned} p(z_1, u_1, v_1) &= \int p(z_1, x^1, y^1, u^1, v^1)\, d(x^1, y^1, u^2, v^2) \\ &= \int p(u_1, v_1 | z_1, x^1, y^1, u^2, v^2) p(z_1, x^1, y^1, u^2, v^2) \\ &\quad \times d(x^1, y^1, u^2, v^2) \end{aligned} \tag{122}$$

where the entire past history of each player's observations, x^1 and y^1, and controls, u^2 and v^2, has been introduced, Eq. (121) can be rewritten as

$$J_1 = E\left\{ \|\lambda_1\|_{c1}^2 \right\} + \min_{u_1} \max_{v_1} \int \left\{ \|k_1 z_1 + a_1 u_1 + b_1 v_1\|_{c1}^2 + \|u_1\|_{d1}^2 - \|v_1\|_{e1}^2 \right\}$$
$$\times\, p(u_1, v_1 | z_1, x^1, y^1, u^2, v^2)\, d(u_1, v_1)$$
$$\times\, p(z_1, x^1, y^1, u^2, v^2)\, d(z_1, x^1, y^1, u^2, v^2) \tag{123}$$

It is at this point that admissible strategies are introduced. Equation (123) indicates that the probability density for u_1 and v_1 can be, if desired, conditioned on the actual value of the state, z_1; all or part of player I's past observations y^1 and controls v^2; and all or part of player II's past history of observations and controls, x^1 and u^2, respectively. Each choice of the characterization of information available leads to a different problem with different results. Further, if desired, the allowable structure of the controls may be specified. (This will be delineated in Section III, E.)

A very reasonable set of controls may be found which uses only information reasonably available to each player. That is, player I may choose a control strategy with one stage-to-go using only his own history of observations and controls (and, of course, his knowledge of the dynamics and payoff of the game as given by (110) through (118), while player II chooses his control strategy based on his own history of observations and controls.

Assuming that nonrandomized (pure) control strategies exist for both players, and denoting them by an overbar, the game optimal control strategies are given by

$$\bar{u}_1 = \bar{u}_1(x^1, u^2) \tag{124}$$

$$\bar{v}_1 = \bar{v}_1(y^1, v^2) \tag{125}$$

Note that nothing has been said at this point about the strategies used to determine u^2 and v^2. In particular, note that no assumptions concerning their optimality have been made.

In view of Eqs. (124) and (125), let

$$p(u_1, v_1 \mid z_1, x^1, y^1, u^2, v^2) = \delta(u_1 - \bar{u}_1)\, \delta(v_1 - \bar{v}_1) \tag{126}$$

where δ represents the Dirac delta (impulse) function. Substituting Eq. (126) into Eq. (123) and integrating over u_1 and v_1 yields

$$\begin{aligned} J_1 = E\{\|\lambda_1\|^2_{c1}\} + \int \{\|k_1 z_1 + a_1 \bar{u}_1 + b_1 \bar{v}_1\|^2_{c1} + \|\bar{u}_1\|^2_{d1} - \|\bar{v}_1\|^2_{e1}\} \\ \times p(z_1, x^1, y^1, u^2, v^2)\, d(z_1, x^1, y^1, u^2, v^2) \end{aligned} \tag{127}$$

where the "min max" operation no longer need be performed since $\bar{u}_1$ and $\bar{v}_1$ are precisely those control strategies which satisfy the min max $=$ max min requirement.

Variational arguments can be used to find the actual form of the game optimal controls based on the strategies allowed by Eqs. (124) and (125). Define

$$\begin{aligned} I_1(\tilde{u}_1, \tilde{v}_1) = E\{\|\lambda_1\|^2_{c1}\} + \int \{\|k_1 z_1 + a_1 \tilde{u}_1 + b_1 \tilde{v}_1\|^2_{c1} + \|\tilde{u}_1\|^2_{d1} - \|\tilde{v}_1\|^2_{e1}\} \\ \times p(z_1, x^1, y^1, u^2, v^2)\, d(z_1, x^1, y^1, u^2, v^2) \end{aligned} \tag{128}$$

where $\tilde{u}_1$ and $\tilde{v}_1$ are any admissible strategies. It immediately follows that

$$\min_{\tilde{u}_1} \max_{\tilde{v}_1} I_1(\tilde{u}_1, \tilde{v}_1) = I_1(\bar{u}_1\ \bar{v}_1) = J_1 \tag{129}$$

Game optimal controls must satisfy the saddle point conditions which are

$$I_1(\tilde{u}_1, \bar{v}_1) \geqslant J_1 \geqslant I_1(\bar{u}_1, \tilde{v}_1) \tag{130}$$

where J_1 is given by Eq. (127).

Let

$$\tilde{u}_1 = \bar{u}_1 + \varepsilon\, \delta(x^1, u^2) \tag{131}$$

where ε is a small number and $\delta(x^1, u^2)$ is any real vector function, of the appropriate dimension, of x^1 and u^2. Using (22), the left-hand inequality of (130) can be written as

$$I_1(\bar{u}_1 + \varepsilon\delta, \bar{v}_1) - J_1 \geqslant 0 \tag{132}$$

where the arguments of δ have been omitted for brevity. Substituting (127) and (128) into Eq. (132) yields

$$\begin{aligned} I_1(\bar{u}_1 + \varepsilon\delta, \bar{v}_1) - J_1 = \int \{ &\|k_1 z_1 + a_1\bar{u}_1 + a_1\varepsilon\delta + b_1\bar{v}_1\|_{c1}^2 + \|\bar{u}_1 + \varepsilon\delta\|_{d1}^2 - \|\bar{v}_1\|_{e1}^2 \\ &- \|k_1 z_1 + a_1\bar{u}_1 + b_1\bar{v}_1\|_{c1}^2 - \|\bar{u}_1\|_{d1}^2 + \|v_1\|_{e1}^2\} \\ &\times p(z_1, x^1, y^1, u^2, v^2)\, d(z_1, x^1, y^1, u^2, v^2) \\ = \int \{ &2[a_1{}^T c_1 k_1 z_1 + (a_1{}^T c_1 a_1 + d_1)\bar{u}_1 + a_1{}^T c_1 b_1 \bar{v}_1]\varepsilon\delta \\ &+ \delta^T (a_1{}^T c_1 a_1 + d_1)\,\delta\varepsilon^2\} p(z_1, x^1, y^1, u^2, v^2) \\ &\times d(z_1, x^1, y^1, u^2, v^2) \geqslant 0 \end{aligned} \tag{133}$$

Using the chain rule of conditional probability densities and applying it to the probability density of inequality (133) yields

$$\begin{aligned} p(z_1, x^1, y^1, u^2, v^2) &= p(z_1 | x^1, y^1, u^2, v^2) p(x^1, y^1, u^2, v^2) \\ &= p(z_1 | x^1, y^1, u^2, v^2) p(y^1 | x^1, u^2, v^2) p(x^1, u^2, v^2) \\ &= p(z_1 | x^1, y^1, u^2, v^2) p(y^1 | x^1, u^2, v^2) p(v^2 | x^1, u^2) \\ &\quad \times p(x^1, u^2) \end{aligned} \tag{134}$$

The means associated with the first three conditional probability densities of Eq. (134) have the following meanings:

$p(z_1|x^1, y^1, u^2, v^2)$ = minimum mean square estimate (MMSE) of the state z_1, given all past and present observations and past controls for both players.

$p(y^1|x^1, u^2, v^2)$ = MMSE of all observations of player I, y^1, given player II's past and present observations and all of both players past controls.

$p(v^2|x^1, u^2)$ = MMSE of all past controls of player I, v^2, given only player I's past and present observations and past controls.

It is important to note again that Eq. (134) involves estimation only. No assumptions concerning the game optimality of any of the past controls of either player have been made.

Substituting Eq. (134) into inequality (133) yields, after some slight manipulation,

$$\begin{aligned} I_1(\bar{u}_1 + \varepsilon\delta, \bar{v}_1) - J_1 = \int 2[\{&a_1{}^T c_1 k_1 z_1 + (a_1{}^T c_1 a_1 + d_1)\bar{u}_1 + a_1{}^T c_1 b_{11}\bar{v}\} \\ &\times p(z_1 \mid x^1, y^1. u^2, v^2)\, dz_1 \\ &\times p(y^1 \mid x^1, u^2, v^2)\, dy^1 p(v^2 \mid x^1, u^2)\, dv^2]\varepsilon\delta(x^1, u^2) \\ &\times p(x^1, u^2)\, d(x^1, u^2) \\ &+ \{\delta^T(x^1, u^1)(a_1{}^T c_1 a_1 + d_1)\delta(x^1, y^1)\varepsilon^2\} \\ &\times p(z_1, x^1, y^1, u^2, v^2)\, d(z_1, x^1, y^1, u^2, v^2) \geqslant 0 \qquad (135) \end{aligned}$$

In view of inequality (114) and, because $\delta(x^1, u^2)$ and (x^1, u^2) are real, it is clear that the second integral of inequality (135) is positive semidefinite. Invoking the standard variational arguments of the calculus of variations, it follows that the coefficient of $\varepsilon\delta(x^1, u^2)$ in inequality (135) must be equal to zero. If it were not zero, then $\delta(x^1, u^2)$ could be chosen to have the opposite sign as its coefficient. For ε small enough, the first integral would be larger in magnitude than the second and the inequality would not hold. Thus a necessary condition that a pure strategy exist for player II is that

$$\begin{aligned} \int \{a_1{}^T c_1 k_1 z_1 + (a_1{}^T c_1 a_1 + d_1)\bar{u}_1 + a_1{}^T c_1 b_1 \bar{v}_1\} p(z_1 \mid x^1, y^1, u^2, v^2)\, dz_1 \\ \times p(y^1 \mid x^1, u^2, v^2)\, dy^1 p(v^2 \mid x^1, u^2)\, dv^2 = 0 \qquad (136) \end{aligned}$$

[It is assumed that $p(x^1, u^2)$ is nonzero for all values of its arguments.]

Looking now at the right-hand inequality of (130), it is easy to see that

$$\begin{aligned} I_1(\bar{u}_1, \bar{v}_1 + \varepsilon\Delta) - J_1 = \int 2[\{&b_1{}^T c_1 k_1 z_1 + b_1{}^T c_1 a_1 \bar{u}_1 - (e_1 - b_1{}^T c_1 b_1)\bar{v}_1\} \\ &\times p(z_1 \mid x^1, y^1, u^2, v^2)\, dz_1 \\ &\times p(x^1 \mid y^1, u^2, v^2)\, dx^1 p(u^2 \mid y^1, v^2)\, du^2]\varepsilon\Delta(y^1, v^2) \\ &\times p(y^1, v^2)\, d(y^1, v^2) \\ &- \int \{\Delta^T(y^1, v^2)(e_1 - b_1{}^T c_1 b_1)\, \Delta(y^1, v^2)\varepsilon^2\} \\ &\times p(z_1, x^1, y^1, u^2, v^2)\, d(z_1, x^1, y^1, u^2, v^2) \leqslant 0 \qquad (137) \end{aligned}$$

where $\Delta(y^1, v^2)$ is any real vector function of the appropriate dimension of y^1 and v^2. It immediately follows that the necessary condition for a pure strategy to exist for player I is that

$$\begin{aligned} \int \{b_1{}^T c_1 k_1 z_1 + b_1{}^T c_1 a_1 \bar{u}_1 - (e_1 - b_1{}^T c_1 b_1)\bar{v}_1\} p(z_1 \mid x^1, y^1, u^2, v^2)\, dz_1 \\ \times p(x^1 \mid y^1, u^2, v^2)\, dx^1 p(u^2 \mid y^1, v^2)\, du^2 = 0 \qquad (138) \end{aligned}$$

$$e_1 - b_1{}^T c_1 b_1 \geqslant 0 \qquad (139)$$

Equations (131) and (133) can be solved simultaneously for $\bar{u}_1$ and $\bar{v}_1$. To do this it is useful to introduce a set of linear transformations defined on suitable Hilbert spaces (*38*). In each of the following transformations $\alpha(\cdot)$ is an element in the domain of the transformation and $\beta(\cdot)$ is an element in its range.

$$\beta(x^1, y^1, u^2, v^2) = T_{11}\alpha(z_1) = \int \alpha(z_1)p(z_1 \mid x^1, y^1, u^2, v^2)\, dz_1 \tag{140}$$

where

$$T_{11} : L_2[-\infty, \infty; p(z_1 \mid x^1, y^1, u^2, v^2)] \to L_2[-\infty, \infty; p(y^1 \mid x^1, u^2, v^2)] \tag{141}$$

Both the domain and the range of the transformation are thus defined to be Hilbert spaces, with the appropriate conditional probability density taken as a measure on the space. By introducing such a measure, a number of functions, which would not ordinarily be L_2 when the limits of integration are plus and minus infinity, can be considered elements of a Hilbert space. In particular, the element z_1 is now L_2.

It should also be noticed that the range of T_{11} is multidimensional, since y^1 represents the N values of y_i. This does not add any conceptual difficulties although the practical problems of evaluation are increased.

The remaining transformations are

$$\beta(x^1, u^2, v^2) = T_{12}\,\alpha(y^1) = \int \alpha(y^1)p(y^1 \mid x^1, u^2, v^2)\, dy^1 \tag{142}$$

where

$$T_{12} : L_2[-\infty, \infty; p(y^1 \mid x^1, u^2, v^2)] \to L_2[-\infty, \infty; p(v^2 \mid x^1, u^2)] \tag{143}$$

$$\beta(x^1, u^2) = T_{13}\,\alpha(v^2) = \int \alpha(v^2)p(v^2 \mid x^1, u^2)\, dv^2 \tag{144}$$

where

$$T_{13} : L_2[-\infty, \infty; p(v^2 \mid x^1, u^2)] \to L_2[-\infty, \infty; p(x^1 \mid y^1, u^2, v^2)] \tag{145}$$

$$\beta(y^1, u^2, v^2) = T_{14}\,\alpha(x^1) = \int \alpha(x^1)p(x^1 \mid y^1, u^2, v^2)\, dx^1 \tag{146}$$

where

$$T_{14} : L_2[-\infty, \infty; p(x^1 \mid y^1, u^2, v^2)] \to L_2[-\infty, \infty; p(u^2 \mid y^1, v^2)] \tag{147}$$

$$\beta(y^1, v^2) = T_{15}\,\alpha(u^2) = \int \alpha(u^2)p(u^2 \mid y^1, v^2)\, du^2 \tag{148}$$

where

$$T_{15} : L_2[-\infty, \infty; p(u^2 \mid y^1, v^2)] \to L_2[-\infty, \infty; p(y^1 \mid x^1, u^2, v^2)] \tag{149}$$

and

$$\beta(x^1, y^1, u^2, v^2) = T_{16}\,\alpha(z_1) = \int \alpha(z_1)p(z_1 \mid x^1, y^1, u^2, v^2)\, dz_1 \tag{150}$$

where

$$T_{16} : L_2[-\infty, \infty; p(z_1 \mid x^1, y^1, u^2, v^2)] \to L_2[-\infty, \infty; p(x^1 \mid y^1, u^2, v^2)] \tag{151}$$

T_{16} and T_{11} differ only in the measure defined on the range space. For all practical purposes, they are identical since, for the elements of the domain of T_{11} and T_{16} encountered in this problem, an element in the range of one is also an element in the range of the other. This is, of course, not an intrinsic property of linear transformations but is a direct consequence of the simple structure of the problem under consideration.

Using the transformations defined in Eqs. (140) through (150), it is possible to write Eqs. (136) and (138) as linear operator equations as follows:

$$a_1{}^T c_1 k_1 T_{13} T_{12} T_{11} z_1 + (a_1{}^T c_1 a_1 + d_1)\bar{u}_1 + a_1{}^T c_1 b_1 T_{13} T_{12} \bar{v}_1 = 0 \tag{152}$$

$$b_1{}^T c_1 k_1 T_{15} T_{14} T_{16} z_1 + b_1{}^T c_1 a_1 T_{15} T_{14} \bar{u}_1 - (e_1 - b_1{}^T c_1 b_1)\bar{v}_1 = 0 \tag{153}$$

Solving Eqs. (162) and (153) simultaneously for $\bar{u}_1$ and $\bar{v}_1$ yields

$$\begin{aligned}\bar{u}_1 = &-\{I - (a_1{}^T c_1 a_1 + d_1)^{-1} a_1{}^T c_1 b_1 (b_1{}^T c_1 b_1 - e_1)^{-1} b_1{}^T c_1 a_1 T_{13} T_{12} T_{15} T_{14}\}^{-1} \\ &\times (a_1{}^T c_1 a_1 + d_1)^{-1} a_1{}^T c_1 T_{13} T_{12} \{T_{11} + b_1 (e_1 - b_1{}^T c_1 b_1)^{-1} b_1{}^T c_1 T_{15} T_{14} T_{16}\} k_1 z_1\end{aligned} \tag{154}$$

$$\begin{aligned}\bar{v}_1 = &\{I - (b_1{}^T c_1 b_1 - e_1)^{-1} b_1{}^T c_1 a_1 (a_1{}^T c_1 a_1 + d_1)^{-1} a_1{}^T c_1 b_1 T_{15} T_{14} T_{13} T_{12}\}^{-1} \\ &\times (e_1 - b_1{}^T c_1 b_1)^{-1} b_1{}^T c_1 T_{15} T_{14} \{T_{16} - a_1 (a_1{}^T c_1 a_1 + d_1)^{-1} a_1{}^T c_1 T_{13} T_{12} T_{11}\} k_1 z_1\end{aligned} \tag{155}$$

where I is an appropriately dimensioned unit matrix.

Since $T_{16} z_1$ is an element of the range space containing $T_{11} z_1$, Eqs. (154) and (155) can be (slightly) rewritten as

$$\begin{aligned}\bar{u}_1 = &-\{I - (a_1{}^T c_1 a_1 + d_1)^{-1} a_1{}^T c_1 b_1 (b_1{}^T c_1 b_1 - e_1)^{-1} b_1{}^T c_1 a_1 T_{13} T_{12} T_{15} T_{14}\}^{-1} \\ &\times (a_1{}^T c_1 a_1 + d_1)^{-1} a_1{}^T c_1 T_{13} T_{12} \{I + b_1 (e_1 - b_1{}^T c_1 b_1)^{-1} b_1{}^T c_1 T_{15} T_{14}\} T_{11} k_1 z_1\end{aligned} \tag{156}$$

$$\begin{aligned}\bar{v}_1 = &\{I - (b_1{}^T c_1 b_1 - e_1)^{-1} b_1{}^T c_1 a_1 (a_1{}^T c_1 a_1 + d_1)^{-1} a_1{}^T c_1 b_1 T_{15} T_{14} T_{13} T_{12}\}^{-1} \\ &\times (e_1 - b_1{}^T c_1 b_1)^{-1} b_1{}^T c_1 T_{15} T_{14} \{I - a_1 (a_1{}^T c_1 a_1 + d_1)^{-1} a_1{}^T c_1 T_{13} T_{12}\} T_{11} k_1 z_1\end{aligned} \tag{157}$$

Equations (156) and (157) represent, in functional form, the game optimal control strategies to be used by each player. But, unless a way to evaluate the inverses is found, the solutions are formal and essentially meaningless. Happily, they can be evaluated, under certain circumstances, in an infinite series. This series, a Neumann expansion (*38*), converges (the inverse exists and has meaning) whenever the norm of the second term of the inverse is less than one. In other words,

$$(I - RT)^{-1} = I + RT + (RT)^2 + (RT)^3 + \cdots \tag{158}$$

whenever the norm of RT, denoted $\|RT\|$, is less than one. For the present case, the inverses exist whenever

$$\|(a_1{}^T c_1 a_1 + d_1)^{-1} a_1{}^T c_1 b_1 (b_1{}^T c_1 b_1 - e_1)^{-1} b_1{}^T c_1 a_1 T_{13} T_{12} T_{15} T_{14}\| < 1 \quad (159)$$

$$\|(b_1{}^T c_1 b_1 - e_1)^{-1} b_1{}^T c_1 a_1 (a_1{}^T c_1 a_1 + d_1)^{-1} a_1{}^T c_1 b_1 T_{15} T_{14} T_{13} T_{12}\| < 1 \quad (160)$$

where the norm of a transformation RT is given by (*38*)

$$\|RT\| = \sup_{\alpha} \frac{\|RT\alpha\|}{\|\alpha\|} \quad (161)$$

and α is any nonzero element of the domain of the transformation RT. Naturally, the norms of α and $RT\alpha$ are computed according to the weighting function defined on the appropriate Hilbert space.

Thus sufficient conditions for the existence of game optimal controls are Eqs. (152) and (153), and inequalities (159) and (160), and

$$a_1{}^T c_1 a_1 + d_1 > 0 \quad (162)$$

$$e_1 - b_1{}^T c_1 b_1 > 0 \quad (163)$$

where the strict inequality has replaced the positive semidefiniteness of inequality (139).

When $\bar{u}_1$ and $\bar{v}_1$ exist, it is a straightforward (although extremely tedious) task to verify that the following assumption is valid: each involves only the past and present observations and past controls available to the appropriate player. The required admissible game optimal control strategies thus have been found for the last stage of an N stage game. There is still the matter of actually evaluating the various conditional probability densities; this is discussed later.

Having found the game optimal controls for the last stage, it is now possible to use the principle of optimality of the theory of dynamic programming to find the game optimal control strategies at stage 2, 3, . . . , N.

In other words, the game optimal control strategies are chosen to optimize the payoff resulting from the application of controls at stages 1 and 2. Thus controls are applied at stage 2, which have an effect on the payoff and serve to change the state. Whatever the state resulting (and whatever the actual observations occurring at stage 1), game optimal control strategies $\bar{u}_1$ and $\bar{v}_1$ will be used. Symbolically, this is written

$$J_2 = \min_{u_2} \max_{v_2} \Big[\int \{\|z_1\|^2_{c2} + \|u_2\|^2_{d2} - \|v_2\|^2_{e1}\} \times p(z_1, u_2, v_2)\, d(z_1, u_2, v_2) + J_1\Big] \quad (164)$$

Analogous to Eq. (120)

$$p(z_1, u_2, v_2) = \int p(z_1 \mid z_2, u_2, v_2) p(z_2, u_2, v_2)\, dz_2 \quad (165)$$

Substituting Eq. (165) into Eq. (164) and integrating over z_1 yields

$$J_2 = E\{\|\lambda_2\|_{c2}^2\} + \underset{u_2}{\min}\ \underset{v_2}{\max}\ [\textstyle\int\{\|k_2 z_2 + a_2 u_2 + b_2 v_2\|_{c2}^2 + \|u_2\|_{d2}^2 - \|v_2\|_{e2}^2\} \times p(z_2, u_2, v_2)\, d(z_2, u_2, v_2) + J_1] \tag{166}$$

Consider J_1, as given by Eq. (127), where $\bar{u}_1$ and $\bar{v}_1$ are given by Eqs. (156) and (157). It also holds that

$$p(z_1, x^1, y^1, u^2, v^2) = \int p(z_1, z_2, x^1, y^1, u^2, v^2)\, dz_2 \tag{167}$$

and

$$p(z_1, z_2, x^1, y^1, u^2, v^2) = p(z_1, x_1, y_1 \mid z_2, x^2, y^2, u^2, v^2) \times p(z_2, x^2, y^2, u^2, v^2) \tag{168}$$

where

$$p(z_1, x_1, y_1 \mid z_2, z^2, y^2, u^2, v^2) = p(x_1, y_1 \mid z_1, z_2, x^2, y^2, u^2, v^2) \times p(z_1 \mid z_2, x^2, y^2, u^2, v^2) \tag{169}$$

From the definition of the manner in which observations are made, Eqs. (111) and (112), and the independence of η_1 and ξ_1, it must be that

$$p(x_1, y_1 \mid z_1, z_2, x^2, y^2, u^2, v^2) = p(x_1 \mid z_1) p(y_1 \mid z_1) \tag{170}$$

Also, from the definition of how the state evolves, Eq. (110), it follows that

$$p(z_1 \mid z_2, x^2, y^2, u^2, v^2) = p(z_1 \mid z_2, u_2, v_2) \tag{171}$$

Substituting Eqs. (167) through (171) back into Eq. (127) yields

$$J_1 = E\{\|\lambda_1\|_{c1}^2\} + \int \gamma_1(z_2, x^2, y^2, u^2, v^2) \times p(z_2, x^2, y^2, u^2, v^2)\, d(z_2, x^2, y^2, u^2, v^2) \tag{172}$$

where

$$\gamma_1(z_2, x^2, y^2, u^2, v^2) = \int \{\|k_1 z_1 + a_1 \bar{u}_1 + b_1 \bar{v}_1\|_{c1}^2 + \|\bar{u}_1\|_{d1}^2 - \|\bar{v}_1\|_{e1}^2\} \times p(x_1 \mid z_1)\, dx_1\, p(y_1 \mid z_1)\, dy_1 \times p(z_1 \mid z_2, u_2, v_2)\, dz_1 \tag{173}$$

Noting that

$$p(z_2, u_2, v_2) = \int p(z_2, x^2, y^2, u^2, v^2)\, d(x^2, y^2, u^3, v^3) \tag{174}$$

Eq. (164) can be rewritten as

$$J_2 = E\{\|\lambda_1\|_{c1}^2 + \|\lambda_2\|_{c2}^2\} + \underset{u_2}{\min}\ \underset{v_2}{\max} \int \{\|k_2 z_2 + a_2 u_2 + b_2 v_2\|_{c2}^2 + \|u_2\|_{d2}^2 - \|v_2\|_{e2}^2 + \gamma_1(z_2, x^2, y^2, u^2, v^2)\} p(z_2, x^2, y^2, u^2, v^2) \times d(z_2, x^2, y^2, u^2, v^2) \tag{175}$$

To find the game optimal control strategies at stage 2, the same procedure used to find the game optimal controls at stage 1 is applied. That is, assume pure control strategies exist, as in Eq. (121). Defining

$$I_2(\tilde{u}_2, \tilde{v}_2) = E\{\|\lambda_1\|_{c1}^2 + \|\lambda_2\|_{c2}^2\} + \int \{\|k_2 z_2 + a_2 \tilde{u}_2 + b_2 \tilde{v}_2\|_{c2}^2 + \|\tilde{u}_2\|_{d2}^2 - \|\tilde{v}_2\|_{e2}^2 + \gamma_1(z_2, x^2, y^2, \tilde{u}_2, u^3, \tilde{v}_2, v^3)\} p(z_2, x^2, y^2, u^3, v^3) \times d(z_2, x^2, y^2, u^3, v^3) \tag{176}$$

analogous to Eq. (128), use the saddle point condition in both directions

$$I_2(\bar{u}_2 + \varepsilon\delta(x^2, u^3), \bar{v}_2) - J_2 \geqslant 0 \tag{177}$$

$$I_2(\bar{u}_2, \bar{v}_2 + \varepsilon\, \Delta(y^2, v^3)) - J_2 \leqslant 0 \tag{178}$$

Linear transformations similar to those given in Eqs. (140) through (150) are used to generate a pair of simultaneous linear operator equations which are then solved simultaneously to find $\bar{u}_2$ and $\bar{v}_2$.

At this point, the procedure has become perfectly general. The procedure at any stage is then given by

$$J_i = E\left\{\sum_{j=1}^{i} \|\lambda_j\|_{cj}^2\right\} + \min_{u_i} \max_{v_i} \int \{\|k_i z_i + a_i u_i + b_i v_i\|_{ci}^2 + \|u_i\|_d^2 - \|v_i\|_{ei}^2 + \gamma_{i-1}(z_i, x^i, y^i, u^i, v^i)\} p(z_i, x^i, y^i, u^i, v^i) \times d(z_i, x^i, y^i, u^i, v^i) \tag{179}$$

where

$$\gamma_{i-1}(z_i, x^i, y^i, u^i, v^i) = \int \{\|k_{i-1} z_{i-1} + a_{i-1}\bar{u}_{i-1} + b_{i-1}\bar{v}_{i-1}\|_{ci-1}^2 + \|\bar{u}_{i-1}\|_{di-1}^2 - \|v_{i-1}\|_{ei-1}^2 + \gamma_{i-2}(z_{i-1}, x^{i-1}, y^{i-1}, \bar{u}_{i-1}, u^i, \bar{v}_{i-1}, v^i)\} \times p(z_{i-1}, x^{i-1}, y^{i-1}, u^i, v^i)\, d(z_{i-1}, x^{i-1}, u^i, v^i) \tag{180}$$

At each point the saddle point conditions

$$I_i(\bar{u}_i + \varepsilon\delta(x^i, u^{i+1}), \bar{v}_i) - J_i \geqslant 0 \tag{181}$$

$$I_i(\bar{u}_i, \bar{v}_i + \varepsilon\, \Delta(y^i, v^{i-1})) - J_i \leqslant 0 \tag{182}$$

are employed to generate the necessary conditions for game optimal strategies.

While the outline of the optimization problem is straightforward, the actual evaluation of the strategies, even for the easiest case of Gaussian random variables, is extremely tedious.

D. Generation of the Required Probability Density Functions

Some of the required probability density functions are quite easy to express (*37*). For example, from Eqs. (2) and (3), using the notation discussed in Section III, B.

$$p(x_i \mid z_i) = \|x_i - G_i z_i\|^2_{\sigma_{\eta i}^{-2}} \tag{183}$$

$$p(y_i \mid z_i) = \|y_i - H_i z_i\|^2_{\sigma_{\xi i}^{-2}} \tag{184}$$

Also, from (110),

$$p(z_i \mid z_{i+1}, u_{i+1}, v_{i+1}) = \|z_i - k_{i+1} z_{i+1} - a_{i+1} u_{i+1} - b_{i+1} v_{i+1}\|^2_{\sigma_{\lambda i+1}^{-2}} \tag{185}$$

The remaining conditional probabilities can be found recursively by using the chain rule for conditional densities in combination with Bayes's rule (*37*).

An auxiliary conditional density function is first found

$$\begin{aligned} p(z_i, x^i, y^i \mid u^{i+1}, v^{i+1}) &= \int p(z_i, z_{i+1}, x^i, y^i \mid u^{i+1}, v^{i+1})\, dz_{i+1} \\ &= \int p(z_i, x_i, y_i \mid z_{i+1}, x^{i+1}, y^{i+1}, u^{i+1}, v^{i+1}) \\ &\quad \times p(z_{i+1}, x^{i+1}, y^{i+1} \mid u^{i+1}, v^{i+1})\, dz_{i+1} \end{aligned} \tag{186}$$

But

$$\begin{aligned} &p(z_i, x_i, y_i \mid z_{i+1}, x^{i+1}, y^{i+1}, u^{i+1}, v^{i+1}) \\ &\quad = p(x_i, y_i \mid z_i, z_{i+1}, x^{i+1}, y^{i+1}, u^{i+1}, v^{i+1}) \\ &\quad \times p(z_i \mid z_{i+1}, x^{i+1}, y^{i+1}, u^{i+1}, v^{i+1}) \\ &\quad = p(x_i \mid z_i) p(y_i \mid z_i) p(z_i \mid z_{i+1}, u_{i+1}, v_{i+1}) \end{aligned} \tag{187}$$

where Eqs. (183) through (185) are the justification for saying that the conditional densities of x_i and y_i, given z_i, depend on nothing else and that the conditional density for z_i, given z_{i+1}, u_{i+1}, and v_{i+1} is not changed if more information is available.

Also, it is easy to see that

$$p(z_{i+1}, x^{i+1}, y^{i+1} \mid u^{i+1}, v^{i+1}) = p(z_{i+1}, x^{i+1}, y^{i+1} \mid u^{i+2}, v^{i+2}) \tag{188}$$

since the value of a control chosen at the $(i+1)$ st stage can yield no information concerning either the state or an observation of the state. It must be reitereated that these conditional densities do *not* involve any assumptions concerning the optimality of controls chosen in the past. In particular, for purposes of estimation—which is what the conditional densities actually represent—no assumptions concerning strategies are required. When the probability density of one or more random variables is conditioned on one or more values of another variable, these conditioning variables enter the density function only as specific values. In this case, it means that one need only specify a set, any set, of values for u^{i+1} and v^{i+1} and then evaluate $p(z_{i+1}, x^{i+1}, y^{i+1} | u^{i+1}, v^{i+1})$. When this is done, it can be seen that the values for u_{i+1} and v_{i+1} do not appear in the conditional density function.

Making use of Eqs. (186) and (187) allows the rewriting of Eq. (186) as

$$p(z_i, x^i, y^i | u^{i+1}, v^{i+1}) = \int p(x_i | z_i) p(y_i | z_i) p(z_i | z_{i+1}, u_{i+1}, v_{i+1}) \times p(z_{i+1}, x^{i+1}, y^{i+1} | u^{i+2}, v^{i+2})\, dz_{i+1} \tag{189}$$

which is the desired recursion relationship for $p(z_i, x^i, y^i | u^{i+1}, v^{i+1})$. To start Eq. (189) off, note that

$$\begin{aligned} p(z_N, x^N, y^N | u^{N+1}, v^{N+1}) &= p(z_N, x_N, y_N) \\ &= p(z_N, y_N | z_N) p(z_N) \\ &= p(x_N | z_N) p(y_N | z_N) p(z_N) \end{aligned} \tag{190}$$

where the first two conditional densities are given by Eqs. (183) and (184) and the last one is given by Eq. (118). Thus it is possible to compute $p(z_i, x^i, y^i | u^{i+1}, v^{i+1})$ for $i = 1, 2, \ldots, N$.

The required conditional probability densities are then

$$p(z_i | x^i, y^i, u^{i+1}, v^{i+1}) = \frac{p(z_i, x^i, y^i | u^{i+1}, v^{i+1})}{\int p(z_i, x^i, y^i | u^{i+1}, v^{i+1})\, dz_i} \tag{191}$$

$$p(y^i | x^i, u^{i+1}, v^{i+1}) = \frac{\int p(z_i, x^i, y^i | u^{i+1}, v^{i+1})\, dz_i}{\int p(z_i, x^i, y^i | u^{i+1}, v^{i+1})\, d(z_i, y^i)} \tag{192}$$

$$p(x^i | y^i, u^{i+1}, v^{i+1}) = \frac{\int p(z_i, x^i, y^i | u^{i+1}, v^{i+1})\, dz_i}{\int p(z_i, x^i, y^i | u^{i+1}, v^{i+1})\, d(z_i, x^i)} \tag{193}$$

The last two sets of conditional densities—$p(v^i | x^{i-1}, u^i)$ and $p(u^i | y^{i-1}, v^i)$—must be handled somewhat differently.

$$p(v^i | x^{i-1}, u^i) = \frac{p(x_{i-1}, v_i, v^{i+1} | x^i, u^i)}{\int p(x_{i-1}, v_i, v^{i+1} | x^i, u^i)\, dv^i} \tag{194}$$

where

$$p(x_{i-1}, v_i, v^{i+1} | x^i, u^i) = p(x_{i-1}, v_i | x^i, u^i, v^{i+1}) p(v^{i+1} | x^i, u^i) \tag{195}$$

Looking first at the second conditional probability density of the right side of Eq. (195), it is clear that

$$p(v^{i+1} | x^i, u^i) = p(v^{i+1} \mathrm{l} x^i, u^{i+1}) \tag{196}$$

since knowledge of the value of a later control, for either player, can have no effect, can yield no information, on the estimate of the value for an earlier control unless there is some *a priori* known functional or statistical relationship.

The first conditional probability density on the right side of Eq. (195) can be written as

$$p(x_{i-1}, v_i \mid x^i, u^i, v^{i+1}) = p(x_{i-1} \mid x^i, u^i, v^i) p(v_i \mid x^i, u^i, v^{i+1}) \tag{197}$$

The first conditional density on the right side of Eq. (197) presents no real conceptual difficulties. It is generated by

$$p(x_{i-1} \mid x^i, u^i, v^i) = \frac{\int p(z_{i-1}, x^{i-1}, y^{i-1} \mid u^i, v^i)\, d(z_{i-1}, y^{i-1})}{\int p(z_{i-1}, x^{i-1}, y^{i-1} \mid u^i, v^i)\, d(z_{i-1}, x_{i-1}, y^{i-1})} \tag{198}$$

The second conditional density on the right side of Eq. (197) is not as straightforward. In fact,

$$p(v_i \mid x^i, u^i, v^{i+1}) = p(v_i) \tag{199}$$

To understand what is meant by Eq. (199), a clear understanding of the principle of optimality is required. Roughly, it states that no matter what has occurred in the past, the best that can be done is to choose the controls in an optimal fashion in the future. With regard to the present problem, it means that a player need not (actually should not) assume that his opponent has used an optimal strategy or even that his opponent has used any nonrandom strategy whatsoever. Naturally, each player has a complete record of his own observations and past controls, but, even were he to be given a complete list of his opponent's control values, v^{i+1}, in the absence of any strategy which relates the opponent's control strategy to his (the opponent's) observations or to any other set of data, they can provide no hint as to what v_i will be. The only information that the opposing player can count on is data concerning physical bounds on the magnitude of the control available at the ith stage. Accordingly, the *a priori* probability density for v_i is actually a uniform distribution over the physical limits known to exist. It should be stressed that this does not mean that one player believes that his opponent should have or would have chosen his ith control from a uniform distribution; rather, it reflects the very limited knowledge available to a player about his opponent's real choice. It is merely the best, reliable information present.

Because this problem is addressed to Gaussian random variables, it makes sense to approximate the uniform distribution over a bounded set of values by a Gaussian distribution over an infinite set of values. A reasonable choice would be one with the same mean as the uniform distribution and with a variance such that the bounds of the uniform distribution are equal to plus and minus one standard deviation of the Gaussian distribution. Such a choice yields a relatively constant probability density function over the bounds of the uniform distribution. (The choice of a Guassian random variable, instead of the uniform, is done only for the convenience associated with them. Theoretically, there is no reason why the uniform distribution should not be used.)

If no information as to capability is available, then the obvious choice for Eq. (199) is a density whose variance is, in the limit, infinite. Working with such variances leads to no difficulties.

Substituting Eqs. (195), (196), (197), and (199) back into Eq. (194) leads to the required recursive information

$$p(v^i \mid x^{i-1}, u^i) = \frac{p(v_i)p(x_{i-1} \mid x^i, u^i, v^i)p(v^{i+1} \mid x^i, u^{i+1})}{\int p(v_i)p(x_{i-1} \mid x^i, u^i, v^i)p(v^{i+1} \mid x^i, u^{i+1})\, dv^i} \tag{200}$$

where Eq. (198) is used to compute $p(x_{i-1} \mid x^i, u^i, v^i)$. To start Eq. (200), set

$$p(v^{N+1} \mid xx^N, {}^{N+1}) = p(v_{N+1} \mid x_N, u_{N+1}) = \delta(v_{N+1}) \tag{201}$$

where $\delta(v_{N+1})$ is the Dirac delta function.

E. Example

The amount of work involved in trying to solve an N-stage game (even where N equals two) in an analytic manner is tremendous. Accordingly a more restricted, two-stage, scalar game will be considered.

In the general problem the game optimal control strategies will involve all information available to each player. In effect, the information was used to better define the state at each stage. While not obvious, the key piece of information is the assumed *a priori* distribution representing physical limitations on the opposing player's available control magnitude. These assumptions allow a player to generate an *a priori* estimate of the state each stage, which is then combined with the current observation to produce the *a posteriori* estimate of the state.

What happens if the two players have no knowledge of their opponent's capabilities? In this case, the *a priori* control distribution may be taken as one which, in the limit, has infinite variance. The result is a particularly simple separation solution; the game optimal control strategy at each stage, except the Nth where an *a priori* distribution of the state is assumed avilable, is the deterministic control strategy with current observation taking the place of the true state. At the Nth stage, a more usual strategy (involving noise variances) is used.

To show that such is actually the case, let us examine a two-stage game where a different set of linear transformations is used to define the necessary conditions. Instead of Eq. (134), consider the following:

$$\begin{aligned} p(z_1, x^1, y^1, u^2, v^2) &= p(y_1 \mid z_1, x^1, y_2, u_2, v_2)p(z_1, x^1, y_2, u_2, v_2) \\ &= p(y_1 \mid z_1)p(y_2, v_2 \mid z_1, x^1, u_2)p(z_1 \mid x^1, u_2)p(x^1, u_2) \\ &= p(y_1 \mid z_1)p(y_2 \mid z_1, x^1, u_2, v_2)p(v_2 \mid z_1, x^1, u_2) \\ &\quad \times p(z_1 \mid x^1, u_2)p(x_1, u_2). \end{aligned} \tag{202}$$

where the independence of the observation noise justifies the statement that $p(y_1 \mid z_1, x^1, y_2, u_2, v_2) = p(y_1 \mid z_1)$. Using this decomposition of the joint density does not lead to any nice characterization of the resulting conditional densities as does the decomposition used in Eq. (134) although it is equally valid. Its virtue, as is seen later, rests in the conditioning of z_1 upon x^1 and u_2, the information available to Player II. In this case, the past is discarded and, because of the decomposition, the actual evaluation of the functional form of the control strategies becomes almost trivial.

All random variables are assumed to be Gaussian. Both players know the mean and variance of each random variable. Denoting each distribution by $N(\mu, \sigma^2)$, where μ is the mean and σ^2 the variance, the required *a priori* probability densities are

$$z_N : N(m, \sigma_z^{\,2}) \tag{203}$$

$$\lambda_i : N(0, \sigma_{\lambda i}^2) \tag{204}$$

$$\eta_i : N(0, \sigma_{\eta i}^2) \tag{205}$$

$$\xi_i : N(0, \sigma_{\xi i}^2) \tag{206}$$

$$v_2 : N(\tilde{v}_2, \sigma_{v2}^2);\ \sigma_{v2}^2 \to \infty \tag{207}$$

$$u_2 : N(\tilde{u}_2, \sigma_{u2}^2);\ \sigma_{u2}^2 \to \infty \tag{208}$$

($\tilde{v}_2$ and $\tilde{u}_2$ here are merely the *a priori* means of the control capability and, for most problems, would be zero.) Both players know (203) through (208).

Using (203) through (208) and the formulas developed in Section III, D, it is a straightforward task to generate the required conditional probability densities.

System dynamics and observations are given by (110), (111), and (112) with

$$G_i = H_i = 1 \tag{209}$$

To write out the conditional densities required to evaluate the transformations, a number of auxiliary variables are defined

$$A = 1/\sigma_{\eta 2}^2 + 1/\sigma_{\xi 2}^2 + 1/\sigma_z{}^2 + k_2{}^2/\sigma_{\lambda 2}^2 \tag{210}$$

$$D = 1/\sigma_{\lambda 2}^2 \tag{211}$$

$$E = 1/\sigma_{\eta 2}^2 \tag{212}$$

$$F = 1/\sigma_{\xi 2}^2 \tag{213}$$

$$G = k_2/\sigma_{\eta 1}^2 \tag{214}$$

$$L = 1/\sigma_{\lambda 2}^2 \tag{215}$$

$$M = 1/\sigma_{\xi 1}^2 \tag{216}$$

$$N = m/\sigma_z{}^2 \tag{217}$$

$$O = k_2 a_2/\sigma_{\lambda 2}^2 \tag{218}$$

$$P = k_2 b_2/\sigma_{\lambda 2}^2 \tag{219}$$

$$Q = a_2/\sigma_{\lambda 2}^2 \tag{220}$$

$$R = b_2/\sigma_{\lambda 2}^2 \tag{221}$$

Using Eqs. (202) through (221) the control strategies are

$$\bar{u}_1 = -\frac{a_1 c_1 k_1}{a_1{}^2 c_1 + d_1} \times \left[1 - \frac{a_1{}^2 b_1{}^2 c_1{}^2}{(a_1{}^2 c_1 + d_1)(b_1{}^2 c_1 - e_1)} T_{14} T_{13} T_{12} T_{11} T_{18} T_{17} T_{16} T_{15}\right]^{-1} T_{14} \times \left[1 + \frac{b_1{}^2 c_1}{e_1 - b_1{}^2 c_1} T_{13} T_{12} T_{11} T_{18}\right] z_1 \tag{222}$$

$$\bar{v}_1 = \frac{b_1 c_1 k_1}{e_1 - b_1{}^2 c_1} \left[1 - \frac{a_1{}^2 b_1{}^2 c_1{}^2}{(a_1{}^2 c_1 + d_1)(b_1{}^2 c_1 - e_1)} T_{18} T_{17} T_{16} T_{15} T_{14} T_{13} T_{12} T_{11}\right]^{-1} T_{18} \times \left[1 - \frac{a_1{}^2 c_1}{a_1{}^2 c_1 + d_1} T_{17} T_{10} T_{15} T_{14}\right] z_1 \tag{223}$$

where

$$\beta(z_1, x^1, u_2, v_2) = T_{11}\alpha(y_2) = \int \alpha(y_2) p(y_2 | z_1, x^1, u_2, v_2)\, dy_2 \tag{224}$$

$$\beta(z_1, x^1, u_2) = T_{12}\alpha(v_2) = \int \alpha(v_2) p(v_2 | z_1, x^1, u_2)\, dv_2 \tag{225}$$

$$\beta(z_1) = T_{13}\alpha(y_1) = \int \alpha(y_1) p(y_1 | z_1)\, dy_1 \tag{226}$$

$$\beta(x^1, u_2) = T_{14}\,\alpha(z_1) = \int \alpha(z_1)\,p(z_1 \mid x^1, u_2)\,dz_1 \tag{227}$$

$$\beta(z_1, y^1, u_2 v_2) = T_{15}\,\sigma(x_2) = \int \alpha(x_2)\,p(x_2 \mid z_1, y^1, u_1, v_2)\,dx_2 \tag{228}$$

$$\beta(z_1, y^1, v_2) = T_{16}\,\alpha(u_2) = \int (u_2)\,p(u_2 \mid z_1, y^1, v_2)\,du_2 \tag{229}$$

$$\beta(z_1) = T_{17}\,\alpha(x_1) = \int \alpha(x_1)\,p(x_1 \mid z_1)\,dx_1 \tag{230}$$

$$\beta(y^1, v_2) = T_{18}\,\alpha(z_1) = \int \alpha(z_1)\,p(z_1 \mid y^1, v_2)\,dz_1 \tag{231}$$

and all transformations have their domain and range in the appropriate Hilbert space. It is clear that these are not the same transformations defined in Eqs. (140) through (151), although they are an equivalent set.

The required conditional densities are (remembering that probability densities are given as twice the negative of the exponent):

$$T_{11} : p(y_2 \mid z_1, x^1, u_2, v_2) = -\frac{F^2 - AF}{A}\left\{y_2 + \frac{Ex_2 + Gz + N - Ou_2 - Pv_2}{F - A}\right\}^2 \tag{232}$$

$$T_{12} : p(v_2 \mid z_1, x^1, u_2) = \frac{b_2{}^2[G^2 + (F - A)D]}{G^2(F - A)(L + D)}$$
$$\times \left\{v_2 - \left[\frac{1}{b_2}\,z_1 - \frac{a^2}{b_2}\,u_2 + \frac{EP}{b_2{}^2[G^2 + (F - A)D]}\,x_2 + \frac{G_N}{b_2[G^2 + (F - A)D]}\right]\right\}^2 \tag{233}$$

$$T_{13} : p(y_1 \mid z_1) = M\{y_1 - z_1\}^2 \tag{234}$$

$$T_{14} : p(z_1 \mid x^1, u_2) = L\{z_1 - x_1\}^2 \tag{235}$$

$$T_{15} : p(x_2 \mid z_1, y^1, u_2, v_2) = -\frac{E^2 - AE}{A}\left\{x_2 + \frac{Fy_2 + Gz_1 + N - Ou_2 - Pv_2}{E - A}\right\}^2 \tag{236}$$

$$T_{16} : p(u_2 \mid z_1, y^1, v_2) = \frac{a_2{}^2[G^2 + (E - A)D]}{G^2 + (E - A)(M + D)}$$
$$\times \left\{u_2 - \left[\frac{1}{a_2}\,z_1 - \frac{b_2}{a_2}\,v_2 + \frac{FO}{a_2{}^2[G^2 + (E - A)D]}\,x_2 + \frac{GN}{a_2[G^2 + (E - A)D]}\right]\right\}^2 \tag{237}$$

$$T_{17} : p(x_1 \mid z_1) = L\{x_1 - z_1\}^2 \tag{238}$$

$$T_{18} : p(z_1 \mid y^1, v_2) = M\{z_1 - y_1\}^2 \tag{239}$$

The conditional densities for the state (235) and (239) involve only the observation at stage 1 because the entire past has been lost, as it were, by the assumption of infinite variance on the opposing player's control at stage 2. In concept, this is similar to the way in which a Kalman filter is initialized (*39*). The practical result is to place all weighting on the current observation. It is the best estimate of the state at that point.

Now consider (222). Using (232) through (239) it follows that

$$T_{14}\left[1+\frac{b_1{}^2c_1}{e_1-b_1{}^2e_1}T_{13}T_{12}T_{11}T_{18}\right]z_1=\left[1+\frac{b_1{}^2c_1}{e_1-b_1{}^2c}\right]x_1 \tag{240}$$

$$T_{18}T_{17}T_{16}T_{15}T_{14}T_{13}T_{12}T_{11}z_1=x_1 \tag{241}$$

so that

$$\bar{u}_1=-\frac{a_1c_1e_1k_1}{(a_1{}^2c_1+d_1)(e_1-b_1{}^2c_1)+a_1{}^2b_1{}^2c_1}x_1 \tag{242}$$

In the same manner, it is easy to show that

$$\bar{v}_1=\frac{b_1c_1d_1k_1}{(a_1{}^2c_1+d_1)(e_1-b_1{}^2c_1)+a_1{}^2b_1{}^2c_1}y_1 \tag{243}$$

Note that (242) and (243) are precisely the control strategies (detailed in Section II) for the deterministic case.

It is a straightforward task to use (173) to show that

$$\begin{aligned}J_2=c_1\sigma^2_{\lambda 1}+c_2\sigma^2_{\lambda 2}&+\frac{a_1{}^2c_1{}^2e_1{}^2k_1{}^2(a_1{}^2c_1+d_1)\sigma^2_{\eta 1}-b_1{}^2c_1{}^2d_1{}^2k_1{}^2(e_1-b_1{}^2c_1)\sigma^2_{\xi 1}}{[(a_1{}^2c_1+d_1)(e_1-b_1{}^2c_1)+a_1{}^2b_1{}^2c_1{}^2]^2}\\&+\frac{c_1d_1e_1k_1{}^2}{(a_1{}^2c_1+d_1)(e_1-b_1{}^2c_1\{+a_1{}^2b_1{}^2c_1}\sigma^2_{\lambda 2}\\&+\min_{u_2}\max_{v_2}\int\left\{\left[c_2+\frac{c_1d_1e_1k_1{}^2}{(a_1{}^2c_1+d_1)(e_1-b_1{}^2c_1)+a_1{}^2b_1{}^2c_1{}^2}\right]\right.\\&\left.\times(k_2z_2+a_2u_2+b_2v_2)^2+d_2u_2{}^2-e_2v_2{}^2\right\}\\&\times p(z_2,u_2,v_2)\,d(z_2,u_2,v_2)\end{aligned} \tag{244}$$

The game optimal control strategies for (244) are easy to find and so are not derived here.

F. Concluding Comments

A major factor in the solution of the multistage stochastic differential game is the shared knowledge of the two players. Both players know the value for all parameters of the dynamical equations and the payoff. All density functions are fully known to both sides. Given this type of structural knowledge, it should be clear that other types of strategies involving other information sets could as easily be used.

Admissible control strategies, other than those specified by (126) can be handled in a similar manner. The main difference, practically speaking, is in the form of the linear transformations that arise from a consideration of the necessary conditions. Some examples are considered in Section IV.

IV. Single-Stage Stochastic Differential Games

A. Introduction

Section III derived all the theory required to solve multistage stochastic differential games having pure strategies. This section is limited to examples of single-stage scalar games involving Gaussian random variables. Consequently, the theory already in hand is used.

This section has two purposes: (1) to show that the solutions to the single-stage game have a closed form solution (which may or may not be true for the multistage case), and (2) to exhibit the game optimal control strategies that result when different assumptions are made concerning the information available to each player (different admissible strategies).

All subscripts referring to the stage number are absent since there can be no ambiguity. Further, shorthand notation, which is obvious in context, is introduced as required for convenience.

Finally, in each of the following examples the maximizing player (player I) is assumed to have only noisy observations of the state.

If the $c\sigma_\lambda{}^2$ term is neglected, then

$$J = \min_u \max_v \int \{c(kz + au + bv)^2 + du^2 - ev^2\} p(z, x, y, u, v)\, d(z, x, y, u, v) \tag{245}$$

or, since

$$p(z, x, y, u, v) = p(u, v \mid z, x, y)\, p(z, x, y) \tag{246}$$

$$J = \int \{c(kz + a\bar{u} + b\bar{v})^2 + d\bar{u}^2 - e\bar{v}^2\}\, p(z, x, y)\, d(z, x, y) \tag{247}$$

where $\bar{u}$ and $\bar{v}$ are the game optimal admissible control strategies.

Defining

$$I = (\tilde{u}, \tilde{v}) = \int \{c(kz + a\tilde{u} + b\tilde{v})^2 + d\tilde{u}^2 - e\tilde{v}^2\}\, p(z, x, y)\, d(z, x, y) \tag{248}$$

the saddle point conditions are

$$I(\bar{u}+\varepsilon\delta, \bar{v}) - I(\bar{u}, \bar{v}) = 2\int \{ackz + (a^2c+d)\bar{u} + abc\bar{v}\}\, \varepsilon\delta p(z, x, y)\, d(z, x, y) + \int \{a^2c+d\}\, e^2\delta^2 p(z, x, y)\, d(z, x, y) \geqslant 0 \tag{249}$$

$$I(\bar{u}, \bar{v}+\varepsilon\Delta) - I(\bar{u}, \bar{v}) = 2\int \{bckz + abc\bar{u} - (e-b^2c)\bar{v}\}\varepsilon\Delta p(z, x, y)\, d(z, x, y) - \int \{e-b^2c\}\, \varepsilon^2\Delta^2 p(z, x, y)\, d(z, x, y) \leqslant 0 \tag{250}$$

In the following, it is assumed that

$$a^2c + d > 0 \tag{251}$$

$$e - b^2c > 0 \tag{252}$$

so that the game optimal control strategies are found from the simultaneous solution of

$$\int \{ackz + (a^2c+d)\bar{u} + abc\bar{v}\}\, \varepsilon\delta p(z, x, y)\, d(z, x, y) = 0 \tag{253}$$

$$\int \{bckz + abc\bar{u} - (e-b^2c)\bar{v}\}\, \varepsilon\Delta p(z, x, y)\, d(z, x, y) = 0 \tag{254}$$

About all that can be said at this point is that ε is a small number (not zero) and that Δ is any real function of y. Until admissible strategies are defined for player II, it is impossible to say what δ is a function of, although, in all cases, it is assumed to be a real quantity.

As in Section III, it is assumed that both players know the structure of the game, the class of admissible strategies, the values of all system parameters, and the mean and variances of all distributions.

B. Example I. The Minimizing Player Has Noisy Observations

Example 1 is the single-stage case which corresponds to the derivations and examples of Section III. In this case,

$$p(u, v \mid z, x, y) = \delta(u - \bar{u}(x))\delta(v - \bar{v}(y)) \tag{255}$$

so that it is convenient to decompose $p(z, x, y)$ into

$$p(z, x, y) = p(z \mid x, y)\, p(y \mid x)\, p(x) \tag{256}$$

and

$$p(z, x, y) = p(z \mid x, y)\, p(x \mid y)\, p(y) \tag{257}$$

Defining the following linear transformations

$$\beta(x, y) = T_1\alpha(z) = \int \alpha(z)\, p(z \mid x, y)\, dz \tag{258}$$

$$\beta(x) = T_2\,\alpha(y) = \int \alpha(y)\, p(y \mid x)\, dy \tag{259}$$

$$\beta(y) = T_3\,\alpha(x) = \int \alpha(x)\, p(x \mid y)\, dx \tag{260}$$

(with suitable domain and range, of course) the necessary conditions for game optimal control strategies are (253) and (254)

$$ackT_2T_1z + (a^2c + d)\bar{u} + abcT_2\bar{v} = 0 \tag{261}$$

$$bckT_3T_1z + abcT_3\bar{u} - (e - b^2c)\bar{v} = 0 \tag{262}$$

so that

$$\bar{u} = -\frac{ack}{a^2c+d}\left[1 - \frac{a^2b^2c^2}{(a^2c+d)(b^2c-e)}T_2T_3\right]^{-1} T_2\left[1 + \frac{b^2c}{e-b^2c}T_3\right]T_1z \tag{263}$$

$$\bar{v} = \frac{bck}{e-b^2c}\left[1 - \frac{a^2b^2c^2}{(a^2c+d)(b^2c-e)}T_3T_2\right]^{-1} T_3\left[1 - \frac{a^2c}{a^2c+d}T_2\right]T_1z \tag{264}$$

The required conditional densities are

$$T_1 : p(z|x, y) = \frac{\sigma_\xi{}^2\sigma_z{}^2 + \sigma_\eta{}^2\sigma_z{}^2 + \sigma_\eta{}^2\sigma_\xi{}^2}{\sigma_\eta{}^2\sigma_\xi{}^2\sigma_z{}^2}\left\{z - \frac{\sigma_\xi{}^2\sigma_z{}^2x + \sigma_\eta{}^2\sigma_z{}^2y + \sigma_\eta{}^2\sigma_\xi{}^2m}{\sigma_\eta{}^2\sigma_z{}^2 + \sigma_\eta{}^2\sigma_z{}^2 + \sigma_\eta{}^2\sigma_\xi{}^2}\right\}^2 \tag{265}$$

$$T_2 : p(y|x) = \frac{\sigma_z{}^2 + \sigma_\eta{}^2}{\sigma_\xi{}^2\sigma_z{}^2 + \sigma_\eta{}^2\sigma_z{}^2 + \sigma_\eta{}^2\sigma_\xi{}^2}\left\{y - \frac{\sigma_z{}^2x + \sigma_\eta{}^2m}{\sigma_z{}^2 + \sigma_\eta{}^2}\right\}^2 \tag{266}$$

$$T_3 : p(x|y) = \frac{\sigma_z{}^2 + \sigma_\xi{}^2}{\sigma_\xi{}^2\sigma_z{}^2 + \sigma_\eta{}^2\sigma_z{}^2 + \sigma_\eta{}^2\sigma_\xi{}^2}\left\{x - \frac{\sigma_z{}^2y + \sigma_\xi{}^2m}{\sigma_z{}^2 + \sigma_\xi{}^2}\right\}^2 \tag{267}$$

Rewriting (263) through (267) as

$$T_1 : p(z|x, y) = \alpha_1\{z - \theta_1x - \theta_2y - \theta_3\}^2 \tag{268}$$

$$T_2 : p(y|x) = \alpha_2\{y - \theta_4x - \theta_5\}^2 \tag{269}$$

$$T_3 : p(x|y) = \alpha_3\{x - \theta_6y - \theta_7\}^2 \tag{270}$$

it follows that

$$T_1z = \theta_1x + \theta_2y + \theta_3 \tag{271}$$

where the θ_i and α_i have the obvious values.

$$\begin{aligned}\left[1 + \frac{b^2c}{e-b^2c}T_3\right]T_1z &= \theta_1x + \theta_2y + \theta_3 + \frac{b^2c}{e-b^2c}\left[\theta_1(\theta_6y + \theta_7) + \theta_2y + \theta_3\right] \\ &= \theta_1x + \left[\left(1 + \frac{b^2c}{e-b^2c}\right)\theta_2 + \frac{b^2c}{e-b^2c}\theta_1\theta_6\right]y + \theta_3 \\ &\quad + \frac{b^2c}{e-b^2c}(\theta_1\theta_7 + \theta_3) \\ &= \theta_1x + \theta_8y + \theta_9\end{aligned} \tag{272}$$

$$T_2\left[1+\frac{b^2c}{e-b^2c}\,T_3\right]T_1z=\theta_1x+\theta_8(\theta_4x+\theta_5)+\theta_9$$
$$=(\theta_1+\theta_8\theta_4)x+\theta_8\theta_5+\theta_9$$
$$=\theta_{10}x+\theta_{11} \tag{273}$$

When the inverse is expanded, terms involving powers of T_2T_3 appear which operate on Eq. (273)

$$T_3x=\theta_6y+\theta_7 \tag{274}$$
$$T_2T_3=\theta_6(\theta_4x+\theta_5)+\theta_7$$
$$=\theta_6\theta_4x+\theta_6\theta_5+\theta_7$$
$$=\theta_{12}x+\theta_{13} \tag{275}$$

Thus, if

$$WT=\frac{a^2b^2c^2}{(a^2c+d)(b^2c-e)}\,T_2T_3 \tag{276}$$
$$\|WT\|<1 \tag{277}$$

then

$$[1-WT_2T_3]^{-1}T_2\left[1+\frac{b^2c}{e-b^2c}\,T_3\right]T_1z$$
$$=\theta_{10}x+\theta_{11}+W[\theta_{10}(\theta_{12}x+\theta_{13})+\theta_{11}]$$
$$+W^2[\theta_{10}\theta_{12}(\theta_{12}x+\theta_{13})+\theta_{10}\theta_{13}+\theta_{11}]$$
$$+W^3[\theta_{10}\theta_{12}^2(\theta_{12}x+\theta_{13})+\theta_{10}\theta_{12}\theta_{13}+\theta_{10}\theta_{13}+\theta_{11}]$$
$$+W^4[\theta_{10}\theta_{12}^3(\theta_{12}x+\theta_{13})+\theta_{10}\theta_{12}^2\theta_{13}+\theta_{10}\theta_{12}\theta_{13}+\theta_{10}\theta_{13}+\theta_{11}]$$
$$+W^5[\theta_{10}\theta_{12}^4(\theta_{12}x+\theta_{13})+\theta_{10}\theta_{12}^3\theta_{13}+\theta_{10}\theta_{12}^2\theta_{13}+\theta_{10}\theta_{12}\theta_{13}$$
$$+\theta_{10}\theta_{13}+\theta_{11}]+\cdot$$
$$=\theta_{10}x[1+W\theta_{12}+W^2\theta_{12}^2+W^3\theta_{12}^3+W^4\theta_{12}^4+W^5\theta_{12}^5+\cdots]$$
$$+\theta_{11}[1+W+W^2+W^3+W^4+W^5+\cdots]$$
$$+W\theta_{10}\theta_{13}[1+W+W^2+W^3+W^4+\cdots+\theta_{12}(1+W+W^2$$
$$+W^3+\cdots)$$
$$+W^2\theta_{12}^2(1+W+W^2+\cdots)+\cdots]$$
$$=\frac{\theta_{10}}{1-W\theta_{12}}\,x+\frac{\theta_{11}}{1-W}+\frac{W\theta_{10}\theta_{13}}{(1-W)(1-W\theta_{12})} \tag{278}$$

so that

$$\bar{u} = -\frac{ack}{a^2c+d}\left[\frac{\theta_{10}}{1-W\theta_{12}}x + \frac{\theta_{11}}{1-W} + \frac{W\theta_{10}\theta_{13}}{(1-W)(1-W\theta_{12})}\right] \tag{279}$$

where

$$\theta_{10} = \left[1 + \frac{b^2c}{e-b^2c}\frac{\sigma_z^2}{\sigma_z^2+\sigma_\xi^2}\right]\frac{\sigma_z^2}{\sigma_z^2+\sigma_\eta^2} \tag{280}$$

$$\theta_{11} = \frac{m}{\sigma_z^2+\sigma_\eta^2}\left[\sigma_\eta^2 + \frac{b^2c}{e-b^2c}\frac{\sigma_\xi^2\sigma_z^2+\sigma_\eta^2\sigma_z^2+\sigma_\eta^2\sigma_\xi^2}{\sigma_z^2+\sigma_\xi^2}\right] \tag{281}$$

$$\theta_{12} = \left(\frac{\sigma_z^2}{\sigma_z^2+\sigma_\eta^2}\right)\left(\frac{\sigma_z^2}{\sigma_z^2+\sigma_\xi^2}\right) \tag{282}$$

$$\theta_{13} = \left(\frac{\sigma_z^2}{\sigma_z^2+\sigma_\xi^2}\right)\left(\frac{m\sigma_\eta^2}{\sigma_z^2+\sigma_\eta^2}\right) + \frac{m\sigma_\xi^2}{\sigma_z^2+\sigma_\xi^2} \tag{283}$$

[Note that

$$|W\theta_{12}| < 1 \tag{284}$$

so that the infinite series involving $W\theta_{12}$ in Eq. (278) converge with the sum being given by a closed form solution.]

A similar exercise leads to

$$\bar{v} = \frac{bck}{e-b^2c}\left[\frac{\theta_{14}}{1-W\theta_{16}}y + \frac{\theta_{15}}{1-W} + \frac{W\theta_{14}\theta_{17}}{(1-W)(1-W\theta_{16})}\right] \tag{285}$$

where

$$\theta_{14} = \left[1 - \frac{a^2c}{a^2c+d}\frac{\sigma_z^2}{\sigma_z^2+\sigma_\eta^2}\right]\frac{\sigma_z^2}{\sigma_z^2+\sigma_\xi^2} \tag{286}$$

$$\theta_{15} = \frac{m}{\sigma_z^2+\sigma_\xi^2}\left[\sigma_\xi^2 - \frac{a^2c}{a^2c+d}\frac{\sigma_\xi^2\sigma_z^2+\sigma_\eta^2\sigma_z^2+\sigma_\eta^2\sigma_\xi^2}{\sigma_z^2+\sigma_\eta^2}\right] \tag{287}$$

$$\theta_{16} = \left(\frac{\sigma_z^2}{\sigma_z^2+{}_1\eta^2}\right)\left(\frac{\sigma_z^2}{\sigma_z^2+\sigma_\xi^2}\right) \tag{288}$$

$$\theta_{17} = \left(\frac{\sigma_z^2}{\sigma_z^2+\sigma_\eta^2}\right)\left(\frac{m\sigma_\xi^2}{\sigma_z^2+\sigma_\xi^2}\right) + \frac{m\sigma_\eta^2}{\sigma_z^2+\sigma_\eta^2} \tag{289}$$

A comparison of (279) and (285) with the example of a single-stage game, with control strategies specified to be linear (*40*), shows that (except for a typographical error) the two solutions are identical if the mean of the *a priori* estimate of the state is zero ($m = 0$). However, this example proves, by construction of the solution, that (under the assumptions of linear dynamics, quadratic payoff function, Gaussian random variables, and noisy observations for both players) there is no nonlinear pure control strategy that can do better.

Consider what happens when player I is unable to affect the outcome of the game ($b = 0$). In this case, the single-stage game degenerates to a single-stage minimization problem with solution given by

$$\bar{u} = -\frac{ack}{a^2c + d}\left(\frac{\sigma_z^{\,2}\alpha + \sigma_\eta^{\,2}m}{\sigma_z^{\,2} + \sigma_\eta^{\,2}}\right) \tag{290}$$

where the terms within the parentheses comprise the minimum variance estimate of the true state—an example of the well-known separation property of this class of stochastic control problems (*36*). Note that this happy situation does not exist in (279) since system parameters and both players' observation noise variances are inextricably mixed together. In other words, even in this simplest of stochastic differential games, a separation theorem does not exist.

Setting the observation noise variances to zero (perfect observations) leads directly to the deterministic solution found in Section II.

If only one of the players, say player II, has perfect observations, then the control strategies are still given by (279) and (285) except that

$$\sigma_\eta^{\,2} = 0 \tag{291}$$

In this case, player II's control strategy is not identical with the deterministic one of Section II. Player II's game optimal strategy still involves terms reflecting the noisy nature of player I's observations. Again, there is no separation theorem.

C. Example II. The Minimizing Player Has Perfect Observations and Knows the Maximizing Player's Observation

This single-stage game corresponds, in terms of information content, to the work presented by Behn and Ho (*41*). In this case,

$$p(u, v \mid z, x, y) = \delta(u - \bar{u}(z, y))\delta(v - \bar{v}(y)) \tag{292}$$

where x has been dropped from consideration since x is identical to z at all times (perfect information). Instead of Eq. (257), the remaining joint density can be written

$$p(z, y) = p(z \mid y)p(y) \tag{293}$$

so that only one linear transformation is required

$$\beta(y) = T\alpha(z) = \int \alpha(z)p(z \mid y)\, dz \tag{294}$$

which results in

$$ackz + (a^2c + d)\bar{u} + abc\bar{v} = 0 \tag{295}$$

$$bckTz + abcT\bar{u} - (e - b^2c)\bar{v} = 0 \tag{296}$$

Solving Eqs. (295) and (296) simultaneously leads to

$$\bar{u} = -\frac{ack}{a^2c + d}\, z - \frac{abc}{a^2c + d}\left[\frac{bcdk}{(a^2c + d)(e - b^2c) + a^2b^2e^2}\right] Tz \tag{297}$$

$$\bar{v} = \frac{bcdk}{(a^2c + d)(c - b^2c) + a^2b^2c^2}\, Tz \tag{298}$$

Since the conditional mean of z given y is precisely the minimum variance estimate of the state, $\hat{z}$, Eq. (298) indicates that, at last, there is a separation theorem for the maximizing player. If the error $\tilde{z}$ between the true state z and the best estimate of the state $\hat{z}$ is introduced, then Eq. (297) can be rewritten as

$$\bar{u} = -\frac{acdk}{(a^2c + d)(e - b^2c) + a^2b^2c^2}\, z + \frac{abc}{a^2c + d}\left[\frac{bcdk}{(a^2c + d)(e - b^2c) + a^2b^2c^2}\right] \tilde{z} \tag{299}$$

where

$$\tilde{z} = z - \hat{z} \tag{300}$$

Equation (299) shows that player II's optimal control strategy can be broken into parts: one part which is identical to that used in the fully deterministic case, and a second part which is proportional to the error in player I's estimate of the true state. As usual, a linear control strategy results.

This example could be extended to the multistage case, if desired, but the results would not match those obtained by Behn and Ho (*41*). Even though both players have linear control strategies under either formulation, the imposition of the requirement that the strategies be linear changes the essential character of the solution; a great deal more information is available to both players if they know the form (the structure) of the strategies. In effect, the variance of the estimate of the opposing player's past controls is reduced since mere capability must no longer be considered alone. Instead, the estimate depends on the ability of each player to estimate his opponent's observation—a situation which is much easier to handle.

V. Future Work

The work presented in this article leads one inevitably to consider future areas of research.

For games of perfect information, the question of what combinations of payoff function and dynamics lead to pure strategies is a natural one to ask. It also would be useful to know under what conditions randomized strategies exist and how they are to be found.

The corresponding questions for continuous time games are also worth asking. Does it, in fact, make any sense to talk about randomized strategies when a new control must be chosen at every instant of time?

Much work remains to be done for stochastic games. Simple extensions of the work done herein would include the closed form solution, if one exists, for the multistage vector game of Section III. Numerical solutions should be of interest in any event.

Also, the solution to continuous time differential games, of the type studied in Section III, would be interesting. It is not immediately clear that the same use of conditional probability densities and simple linear operators would produce answers.

Still, in the realm of pure strategies, it would be useful to extend the results to nonlinear problems and to payoff functions that are not quadratic. With regard to randomized strategies, is it possible to apply these techniques to stochastic games or must new ones be developed?

A great deal of information concerning the structure of the problem is assumed available to both players. Further work might consider the effect of less information or information in the form of probability densities. In the same vein, it would be interesting to know if there is a suitable corollary to adaptive control in the game situation.

Obviously, there is a great deal of work yet to be done.

References

1. R. Isaacs, Differential games. I, Introduction. Research Memorandum, RM-1391. RAND Corp. Santa Monica, Calif., Nov. 30, 1954.
2. R. Isaacs, Differential Games. II. The definition and formulation. Research Memorandum, RM-1399. RAND Corp., Santa Monica, Calif., Nov. 30, 1954.
3. R. Isaacs, Differential games. III. The basic principles of the solution process. Research Memorandum, RM-1411. RAND Corp., Santa Monica, Calif., December 21, 1954.
4. R. Isaacs, Differential games. IV. Mainly examples. Research Memorandum, RM-1486. RAND Corp., Santa Monica, Calif., March 25, 1955.
5. R. Isaacs, "Differential Games." Wiley, New York, 1965.

6. M. Dresher, A. W. Tucker, and P. Wolfe (eds.), "Contributions to the Theory of Games," Vol. III, Princeton Univ. Press, Princeton, New Jersey, 1964.
7. M. Dresher, L. S. Shapley, and A. W. Tucker (eds.), "Advances in Game Theory." Princeton Univ. Press, Princeton, New Jersey, 1964.
8. A. V. Balakrishnan and L. W. Neustadt (eds.), "Mathematical Theory of Control." Academic Press, New York, 1967.
9. E. N. Simakova, Differential games. *Autom. Remote Control* **27**, No. 11, 1980–1998 (1966).
10. Y. C. Ho, Book review of differential games. *IEEE Trans. Autom. Control* **AC-10**, No. 4, 501–503 (1965).
11. B. H. Billik, Some optimal low-acceleration rendezvous maneuvers. *AIAA J.* **2**, No. 3, 510–516 (1964).
12. Y. C. Ho, A. E. Bryson, Jr., and S. Baron, Differential games and optimal pursuit—evasion strategies. *IEEE Trans. Autom. Control* **AC-10**, No. 4, 385–389 (1965).
13. R. E. Wong, Some aerospace differential games. *J. Spacecraft Rockets* **4**, No. 11, 1460–1465 (1967).
14. P. A. Meschler, On a goal-keeping differential game. *IEEE Trans. Autom. Control* **AC-12**, No. 1, 15–21 (1967).
15. R. Chattopadhyay, On differential games. *Int. J. Control* **6**, No. 3, 287–295 (1967).
16. Y. C. Ho, Optimal terminal maneuver and evasion strategy. *J. SIAM Control* **4**, No. 3, 421–428 (1966).
17. J. L. Speyer, A stochastic differential game with controllable statistical parameters. *IEEE Trans. Systems Sci. Cybernetics* **SSC-3**, No. 1, 17–20 (1967).
18. R. D. Behn and Y. C. Ho, On a class of linear stochastic differential games. *IEEE Trans. Autom. Control* **AC-10**, No. 3 227–240 (1967).
18a. Proceedings of the First International Conference on the Theory and Practice of Differential Games, Amherst, Mass., Sept. 1969.
19. J. von Neumann and O. Morgenstern, "Theory of Games and Economic Behavior," 2nd ed. Princeton Univ. Press, Princeton, New Jersey, 1947.
20. J. C. C. McKinsey, "Introduction to the Theory of Games." McGraw-Hill, New York, 1952.
21. R. D. Luce and H. Raiffa, "Games and Decisions, Introduction and Critical Survey." Wiley, New York, 1957.
22. M. Dresher, "Games of Strategy: Theory and Applications." Prentice-Hall, Englewood Cliffs, New Jersey, 1961.
23. G. Owen, "Game Theory." Saunders, Philadelphia, Pennsylvania, 1968.
24. W. H. Fleming, The convergence problem for differential games. *J. Math. Anal. Applications* **3**, No. 1, 102–116 (1961).
25. L. D. Berkovitz and M. Dresher, A game-theory analysis of tactical air war. *Operations Res.* **7**, No. 5, 599–620 (1959).
26. L. D. Berkovitz and M. Dresher, A multimove infinite game with linear payoff. *Pacific J. Math. 10*, No. 3, 743–765 (1960).
27. L. D. Berkovitz and M. Dresher, Allocation of two types of aircraft in tactical air war: A game-theoretic analysis. *Operations Res.* **8**, No. 5, 694–706 (1960).
28. L. D. Berkovitz, A variational approach to differential games. *In* "Advances in Game Theory" (M. Dresher, A. W. Tucker, and P. Wolfe, eds.), Princeton Univ. Press, Princeton, New Jersey, 1964.
29. R. E. Bellman, "Dynamic Programming." Princeton Univ. Press, Princeton, New Jersey, 1957.
30. G. A. Bliss, "Lectures on the Calculus of Variations," Univ. of Chicago Press, Chicago, Illinois, 1946.

31. F. T. SMITH, An introduction to the application of dynamic programimng to linear control systems. Research Memorandum, RM-3526-PR. RAND Corp., Santa Monica, Calif., February, 1963.
32. M. D. CILETTI, On a class of deterministic differential games with imperfect information. Tech. Rep., No. EE-679. Dept. Elect. Eng., Notre Dame Univ., December 1, 1967.
33. W. A. PORTER, On function space pursuit—evasion games. *J. SIAM Control* **5**, No. 4, 555–574 (9167).
34. H. F. BOHNENBLUST, S. KARLIN, and L. S. SHAPLEY, Games with continuous, convex pay-off. *Contrib. Theory Games* **1**, 181–192 (1950).
35. P. A. MESCHLER, Differential game-theoretic analysis of maneuvering threats. Tech. Memorandum, No. 346/1. Defense Res. Corp., June, 1966.
36. M. AOKI, "Optimization of Stochastic Systems." Academic Press, New York, 1967.
37. A. PAPOULIS, "Probability, Random Variables, and Stochastic Processes." McGraw-Hill, New York, 1965.
38. W. A. PORTER, "Modern Foundations of Systems Engineering," Macmillan, New York, 1966.
39. P. B. LIEBELT, "An Introduction to Optimal Estimation," Addison-Wesley, Reading, Massachusetts, 1967.
40. W. W. WILLMAN, Formal solutions for a class of stochastic pursuit—evasion games. Tech. Rep., No 575. Division Eng. Appl. Phys., Harvard Univ., November, 1968.
41. R. D. BEHN and Y. C. HO, On a class of linear stochastic differential games. Tech. Rep., No. 542. Division Eng. Appl. Phys., Harvard Univ., October, 1967.

Optimal Control Applications in Economic Systems

L. F. BUCHANAN

General Dynamics Corporation, Electro Dynamic Division
Pomona Operation, Pomona, California

AND

F. E. NORTON

Graduate School of Business Administration
University of California
Los Angeles, California

I. Introduction

The control of dynamic systems has always been the interest of control systems engineering. The power of feedback to produce improved system performance in the presence of disturbances and varying open-loop parameters is well known. The development of feedback control theory has progressed from the original single loop analysis methods for system stability through the root-locus and describing function techniques to the current optimal control theory which includes multidimensional systems.

These significant advances in control systems theory provide a new plateau of capability for analysis and synthesis of much broader classes of control systems. Economic systems constitutes one of the broader areas of dynamic systems of interest to control systems engineers and will be discussed here.

The concept of economic systems is a very broad one. It may encompass an entire nation's economy, including its fundamental subsystems, such as the household sector, business sector, governmental sector, and financial sector, and their interdependence, or may be limited to a detailed specification of one of its individual decision-making units, such as a business firm. The first type of economic system involves of necessity a high degree of aggregation and is known as the area of *macroeconomics*. The second type of economic system involves the detailed structure of a decision-making unit or even a single process within a unit, such as a production system of an individual business firm. The latter type involves much less aggregation and is an aspect of *microeconomics*.

Recent developments in control theory make possible many applications both in the macroeconomic and microeconomic areas of economics. This is true since both areas are concerned with the efficient use of economic resources over time. The objective is usually to maximize utility or profits over time with respect to certain decision variables. Applications in the microeconomic areas are to be found in the literature of operations analysis (*1*) or managerial economics (*2*, *3*). To date, most of the development has taken the form of optimization of specific processes often within a larger decision-making unit. Applications in the macroeconomic area are just beginning. While some recent theoretical applications in macroeconomic growth theory are of interest (*4*, *5*), they are a long way from practical application in terms of governmental policy making. The application of control theory to the other aspect of macroeconomics, namely, income and employment theory, is also in its initial stages but is more likely to make a near-term impact on public policies. It is the purpose of this article to make a contribution to this last area.

The development of econometrics—theoretical and statistical knowledge—as applied to macroeconomics had laid the foundation for the application of modern control theory to overall practical economic policy problems. Large scale systems involving up to several hundred equations are now in existence, where parameters are estimated by sophisticated statistical techniques. This complexity is feasible largely because of the increasing data processing capability of digital computers.

While the general tendency has been toward overly complicated models, the efforts have yielded significant improvements in economic theory and application. The net result is the existence of a large number of econometric models of national economies that cover a wide spectrum of complexities and areas of interest which are available for our investigations. Some of the recently developed econometric models are the Brookings Model (*6–8*), the Wharton Model (*9*), the FRB–MIT Model (*10*), and the OBE Models (*11, 12*).

It is important for control systems engineers who are usually concerned with the design and/or analysis of feedback control for physical systems to recognize and understand the modeling–theory building problem encountered by economists and econometricians with respect to the nation's economy. In the first place, their system dynamics include and are influenced to a great extent by the attitudes and behavior of people. Thus, questions of measurability, predictability, and consistency are continually of concern. In the second place, economists are not usually permitted the luxury that physical scientists and engineers enjoy of testing their hypotheses with actual experiments on the system which they want to understand and/or control. This is because of two important realities: (a) the impact of the test results on the social welfare of the nation would be disastrous as the test conditions are driven to either substantiate or negate a given hypothesis, and (b) the overall political process through which national economic policies are established is so cumbersome that such testing would be most difficult and probably impossible to conduct even if condition (a) did not exist.

Tustin first noted that the problem of determining macroeconomic policies is a feedback control problem in 1953 (*13*). Work along this direction was also done by Phillips in 1954 and 1957 (*14, 15*). However, feedback control theory at that time was unable to handle multidimensional systems to any useful degree. Thus the efforts of Tustin and Phillips were quite limited in their application, since they required simplification of the economic model to the point of questionable value. More recently, Van Eijk and Sandee (*16*), Holt (*17, 18*), and Theil (*19*) have applied more modern analysis to macroeconomic systems without correlating to control systems aspects of the problem. However, the advances in control theory, computational capabilities, and econometrics in the last two decades provide a basis for revisiting the problem of determining control policies of a national economy in its natural habitat—as a problem in determining optimal control policies for a dynamic, multidimensional system. Modern control theory thus provides the framework for structuring this complex problem.

It is the purpose of this article to present the results of some recent research in this area. In the process, we will not only determine optimal control policies for a dynamic macroeconomic model, but will also discover areas in which further econometric research must be accomplished before one can intelligently discuss "optimal" economic policies in a practical sense. As a result of framing the problem in optimal control format, each of the various elements and functions of the optimization problem is brought clearly into focus with respect to the other and thus areas where insufficient information exists become clear. This is a prerequisite for application of modern control theory to large scale econometric models.

The model of the macroeconomic systems used here is a dynamic set of difference equations which exhibit those economic characteristics generally thought to be important by economists as causing the economy's overall performance. Thus the difference equations are the structural relations of the economy based upon economic theory and constitute the primary mechanism of market economies similar to the United States economy. Yet it is not so complex as to lose tractability. The model is an eleven-dimensional system, which includes a monetary system and the feedback effect of the accumulation of stocks on the demand for durable goods of various kinds. It is a quarterly model. The control vector has two components, a portion of government purchases and a portion of the money supply.

This macroeconomic model is converted into control system format, and the dynamic properties of the open-loop system are studied for two representative sets of parameters.

The optimization problem is formulated through a quadratic social welfare functional, which includes a penalty function on control variable activity. The optimal control policies are obtained by dynamic programming techniques. The digital computer was used to obtain numerical solutions of the optimal feedback control policies for the two sets of system parameters. It is shown that the optimal control policies change significantly between the two sets of system parameters and also as a function of the length of time into the future over which it is desired to optimize.

The magnitude of the control activity penalty function was varied over two orders of magnitude since no econometric data were available on this important function.

A digital computer study of the system performance with and without the optimal controller was made with stochastic signals imposed on the flow variables. It is shown that the payoff to society from optimal control is potentially quite large and is strongly related to the penalty function placed on control vector activity.

It is concluded that modern control theory is fundamental to the problem of overall economic policy determination for macroeconomic systems. It provides the natural framework for attacking the problem. Moreover, further areas of necessary research are brought into focus by such an approach.

II. The Macroeconomic Model in Econometric Format

The macroeconomic model which provides the framework for this study was constructed by Norton and lies somewhere in complexity between analytical macroeconomic models and large scale econometric macroeconomic models, such as the Brookings model (*6–8*). While the Gross National Product (GNP) model system formulated is based upon the Keynesian central model and draws on the work of Samuelson (*20*), Hicks (*21*), Kaldor (*22*), Goodwin (*23*), Duesenberry (*24*), Slutsky (*25*), and Frisch (*26*), it is elaborated to include some of the mechanisms recently thought to be important in explaining the overall performance of market economics. The objective in designing the model was to emphasize those properties that economists believe to be strategic in causing economic fluctuations and growth without introducing unnecessary complexity. It was important that the model be capable of being handled by modern control theory in its current state.[1] Although the model is a substantial step from the real world, this very fact should make it easier to focus on the problem of optimal fiscal and monetary policies to achieve overall economic goals since the model does reflect the fundamental performance of the economy.

THE MACROECONOMIC MODEL. The macroeconomic model system formulated to study the problem of optimal economic policies is given below. It determines aggregate demand and thus actual $\mathscr{GNP}$.

$$\mathscr{GNP}(j) = \mathscr{C}^{NA}(j) + \mathscr{C}^{A}(j) + \mathscr{R}(j) + \mathscr{I}(j) + \Delta\mathscr{H}(j) + \mathscr{F}(j) + \mathscr{G}(j) \tag{1}$$

$$\mathscr{C}^{NA}(j) = c_0 + c_1\mathscr{GNP}(j-1) - c_2\,\imath(j-1) + c_3\mathscr{C}^{NA}(j-1) + w_1(j) \tag{2}$$

$$\mathscr{C}^{A}(j) = a_0 + a_1\mathscr{GNP}(j-1) - a_2\imath(j-1) - a_3\mathscr{K}_a(j-1) + w_2(j) \tag{3}$$

$$\mathscr{R}(j) = d_0 + d_1\mathscr{GNP}(j-1) - d_2\,\imath(j-1) - d_3\mathscr{K}_h(j-1) + d_4\,\mathscr{E}(j-1) \tag{4}$$

$$\mathscr{I}(j) = b_0 + b_1\mathscr{GNP}(j-1) - b_2\,\imath(j-1) - b_3\mathscr{K}_p(j-1) + b_4\,\mathscr{E}(j-1) + w_4(j) \tag{5}$$

$$\Delta\mathscr{H}(j) = h_0 + h_1\mathscr{GNP}(j-1) - h_2\,\imath(j-1) - h_3\mathscr{H}(j-1) + w_5(j) \tag{6}$$

$$\mathscr{G}(j) = \mathscr{G}_0(j) + G(j) \tag{7}$$

$$\mathscr{F}(j) = \mathscr{F}(j-1) + w_6(j) \tag{8}$$

$$\mathscr{K}_a(j) = \tfrac{1}{4}\mathscr{C}^{A}(j) + (1 - \tfrac{1}{4}\alpha)\mathscr{K}_a(j-1) \tag{9}$$

[1] The primary simplifications of the macroeconomic model were in linearization of the more complex equations including removal of limits on the state variables.

$$\mathscr{K}_h(j) = \tfrac{1}{4}\mathscr{R}(j) + (1 - \tfrac{1}{4}\beta)\mathscr{K}_h(j-1) \tag{10}$$

$$\mathscr{K}_p(j) = \tfrac{1}{4}\mathscr{I}(j) + (1 - \tfrac{1}{4}\delta)\mathscr{K}_p(j-1) \tag{11}$$

$$\mathscr{H}(j) = \tfrac{1}{4}\Delta\mathscr{H}(j) + \mathscr{H}(j-1) \tag{12}$$

$$\imath(j) = v_0 + v_1\mathscr{GNP}(j) - v_2\mathscr{M}(j) \tag{13}$$

$$\mathscr{M}(j) = \mathscr{M}_0(j) + M(j) \tag{14}$$

The notation of the variables used in Eqs. (1) through (14) is listed below.

$\mathscr{GNP}$	Gross National Product
$\mathscr{C}^{NA}$	Non-automobile expenditures
$\mathscr{C}^{A}$	Automobile expenditures
$\mathscr{R}$	Residential construction
$\mathscr{I}$	Plant and equipment expenditures
$\Delta\mathscr{H}$	Change in business inventories
$\mathscr{G}$	Government purchases of goods and services
$\mathscr{G}_0$	Long-term trend of government purchases of goods and services
G	Variation of Federal government purchases of goods and services from the trend value, a portion of which is a policy or control variable
$\mathscr{F}$	Net exports of goods and services
$\mathscr{M}$	Supply of money
$\mathscr{M}_0$	Long term trend of the money supply
M	Variation of the money supply from the trend value, a portion of which is a policy or control variable
$\imath$	Interest rate
$\mathscr{E}$	Full employment labor input
$\mathscr{K}_a$	Automobile stock
$\mathscr{K}_h$	Housing stock
$\mathscr{K}_p$	Plant and equipment stock
$\mathscr{H}$	Inventories
w_i	Random disturbances
j	Index on the quarterly sampling times
α	Annual automobile stock replacement rate
β	Annual housing stock replacement rate
δ	Annual plant and equipment stock replacement rate

The statistical characteristics of the noise disturbance terms (the w_i's) are assumed for this paper to be as follows:

$$\text{Expectation of } w_i(j) = E[w_i(j)] = 0 \tag{15}$$

$$\text{Standard deviation of } w_i(j) = \sigma_{w_i}(j) < \infty \tag{16}$$

$$\text{Time correlation} = \rho_{w_i(j),\, w_{i(j-1)}} = 0 \tag{17}$$

$$\text{Variable correlation} = \rho_{w_i(j),\, w_{k(j)}} = 0 \tag{18}$$

As will be noted, the model system is basically Keynesian, but dynamic rather than static in character. It has, however, a number of additional properties. Overall demand for output is disaggregated along the lines of gross national product on the expenditure side with separate equations for each aggregate demand component. A monetary subsystem of the Keynesian variety is included.[2] The growth of the system is dependent on population and labor force growth. All the behavior equations are subject to stochastic disturbances.

A few comments may be in order regarding the explicit and implicit properties of the model. Equation (1) merely defines $\mathcal{GNP}$ as the sum of its components. Equations (2) to (6) are the basic aggregate demand equations. It is well known that the durable consumer expenditures behave differently than other components of consumer expenditure. Perhaps the most important part of durable consumer expenditures from this point of view is that of automobile expenditures. In view of the studies of Suits (*27*) and Chow (*28*, *29*), we have treated automobile expenditures separately from other consumer expenditures. The equation for non-automobile consumer expenditures (2) is based upon a "modified" consumption function related in part to the studies of Brown (*30*), Klein and Goldberger (*31*), and Friedman (*32*) with a lagged non-automobile consumer expenditure term. The interest rate has been included in the "modified" consumption function because it may influence expenditures on durable goods other than automobiles.[3] Since various types of consumer expenditures, probably as well as residential construction, are ultimately related to household decisions, these categories of expenditures should be directly influenced by disposable income, that is, spendable income after taxes in the hands of households, rather than gross national product. In fact, the formulation we have adopted using gross national product instead of disposable income in these equations presupposes a linear "disposable income function," relating disposable income to gross national product. This, in turn, implies given linear depreciation, indirect business tax, corporate profits, corporate profits tax, corporate savings, social insurance contributions, transfer payment, and personal tax functions.[4]

If all of these structural relations pertaining to income flows are given, there is a unique relation between disposable income and gross national

[2] However, we assume a linear liquidity preference function with respect to both gross national income and the interest rate. Thus no liquidity trap exists.

[3] The modified consumption function upon which Eq. (2) is partly based is $\mathcal{C}^{NA}[y_d(j-1), \imath(j-1), \mathcal{C}^{NA}(j-1)]$, where y_d is disposable income.

[4] These are the relations determining the values of the major variables that must be added to or subtracted from gross national product to arrive at disposable income. Other "minor" variables are assumed to be truncated into these major variables for purposes of simplification.

product.[5] For reasons explained later, we assume the tax and transfer payment structure including all tax rates to be given. Thus fiscal policy decisions are limited to the manipulation of that part of Federal government purchases of goods and services which is controllable, namely, a portion of G.

Equations (3) for automobile expenditures, (4) for residential construction, (5) for plant and equipment expenditures, and (6) for inventory investment all involve an adjustment mechanism and are related in a rough way to the econometric studies of Chow (*28*, *29*) Muth (*33*), Lee (*34*), Chenery (*35*), and Darling (*36*), respectively. This may be illustrated by deriving Eq. (4) for residential construction, which is representative of these subsystems. The *desired* stock of housing at the end of the jth period is

$$\mathscr{K}_h^*(j) = f[\mathscr{GNP}(j-1), \imath(j-1), \mathscr{E}(j-1), p(j)] \tag{19}$$

where $p(j)$ is a noise term, or using a linear approximation

$$\mathscr{K}_h^*(j) = \gamma_0 + \gamma_1 \mathscr{GNP}(j-1) + \gamma_2 r(j-1) + \gamma_3 \mathscr{E}(j-1) + \gamma_4 p(j)$$
$$\gamma_0 \gtrless 0, \gamma_1 > 0, \gamma_2 < 0, \gamma_3 > 0, \gamma_4 > 0 \tag{20}$$

The adjustment mechanism is

$$\mathscr{R} = g[\mathscr{K}_h^*(j) - \mathscr{K}_h(j-1)] + \beta \mathscr{K}_h(j-1) \tag{21}$$

or specifying proportional correction of adjustment as an approximation,

$$\mathscr{R} = \rho[\mathscr{K}_h^*(j) - \mathscr{K}_h(j-1)] + \beta \mathscr{K}_h(j-1) \qquad 0 < \rho < 1; \qquad 0 < \beta < 1 \tag{22}$$

The first term of this equation accounts for expansion of the housing stock and the second term for its replacement. If the desired stock of housing at the end of the jth period is greater than the actual stock at the end of the $(j-1)$st period, a fraction ρ of the difference will be put in place in the period in question. A fraction β of the actual housing stock is assumed to be replaced during the period. The sum of expansion plus replacement gives total residential construction. Substitution of Eq. (20) into (22) gives Eq. (4) with a redefinition of parameters. Thus, all the aggregate demand equations for final output pertaining to durable goods contain a flexible accelerator among other mechanisms.

It will be noted that the full employment input $\mathscr{E}$ enters both the housing equation (4) and the plant and equipment equation (5). This is an

[5] For example, if the modified consumption function in terms of disposable income is $\mathscr{C}^{NA}[\mathscr{Y}_d(j-1), \imath(j-1), \mathscr{C}^{NA}(j-1)]$ and under the assumptions specified there is a "disposable income function" $\mathscr{Y}_d[\mathscr{GNP}(j)]$ then Eq. (2) is derived as $\mathscr{C}^{NA}[\mathscr{Y}_d(\mathscr{GNP}(j-1)), \imath(j-1), \mathscr{C}^{NA}(j-1)]$.

exogenous forcing function. In the former equation it stands as a proxy for population, while in the latter it stands for the influence of the size of the labor force on investment opportunities in plant and equipment.

The final aggregate demand equations are those pertaining to government purchases of goods and services (7) and net exports of goods and services (8). Since net exports of goods and services is such a small proportion of $\mathscr{GNP}$, no structural equation is specified for it. It is arbitrarily defined in (8) to depend upon its previous value plus a stochastic disturbance.

While the dynamic macroeconomic model is based on quarterly sampling periods, the flow variables (which are the components of the total aggregate demand) are given in equivalent annual rates. The factor of $\frac{1}{4}$ is introduced into the stock equations to obtain the proper accumulation of stock for the quarterly sampled system.

Equations (9) to (12) define how certain stock variables change over time as the result of expenditures, on the one hand, and the annual replacement rates, α, β, and δ on the other. Equation (13) is the interest rate equation which is derived from the demand for money equation and the supply of money.[6]

$\mathscr{G}$ and $\mathscr{M}$ are merely exogenous variables in this linear open-loop system, but portions of each do constitute the two components of the control vector and hence will ultimately be part of the control system.

Finally, all the behavioral equations of the linear system are subject to stochastic disturbances. The w_i are assumed to be normally distributed random shocks with the properties specified; namely, zero mean, finite variance, zero autocorrelation, and zero intercorrelation, although in fact they may take other distribution forms. This brings into the analysis in a systematic way the element thought to be very significant as a cause of economic instability by Slutsky (*25*) and Frisch (*26*).

III. The Macroeconomic Model in Modern Control System Format

The synthesis of the optimal controller for the economy will be accomplished by making a perturbation analysis of the dynamic behavior of the economic system as it is perturbed from its long term trend. Specifically, we write

$$\mathscr{GNP} = \mathscr{GNP}_0 + GNP \qquad (23)$$

[6] That is, the liquidity preference function or demand for money function is $\mathscr{L}[\mathscr{GNP}(j), \imath(j)]$ while the supply of money $\mathscr{M}(j)$ is considered an exogenous variable. When the demand for and the supply of money are equated, we have $\imath[\mathscr{GNP}(j), \mathscr{M}(j)]$.

where $\mathscr{GNP}_0$ is the long term trend value of $\mathscr{GNP}$, and GNP is the perturbation of $\mathscr{GNP}$ from the long term trend value. The perturbation variable for the other variables are similarly defined. For example,

$$\mathscr{C}^{NA} = \mathscr{C}_0^{NA} + C^{NA} \tag{24}$$

where $\mathscr{C}_0^{NA}$ is the long term trend value of non-automotive consumption, and C^{NA} is the perturbation (or deviation) of non-automotive consumption from the long term trend value.

From Eq. (1) we may write two similar equations which, when taken together, are equivalent to Eq. (1).

$$\mathscr{GNP}_0(j) = \mathscr{C}_0^{NA}(j) + \mathscr{C}_0{}^A(j) + \mathscr{R}_0(j) + \mathscr{I}_0(j) + \Delta\mathscr{H}_0(j) + \mathscr{F}_0(j) + \mathscr{G}_0(j) \tag{25}$$

and

$$GNP = C^{NA}(j) + C^A(j) + R(j) + I(j) + \Delta H(j) + F(j) + G(j) \tag{26}$$

where Eq. (25) is the trend equation and Eq. (26) is the perturbation equation.

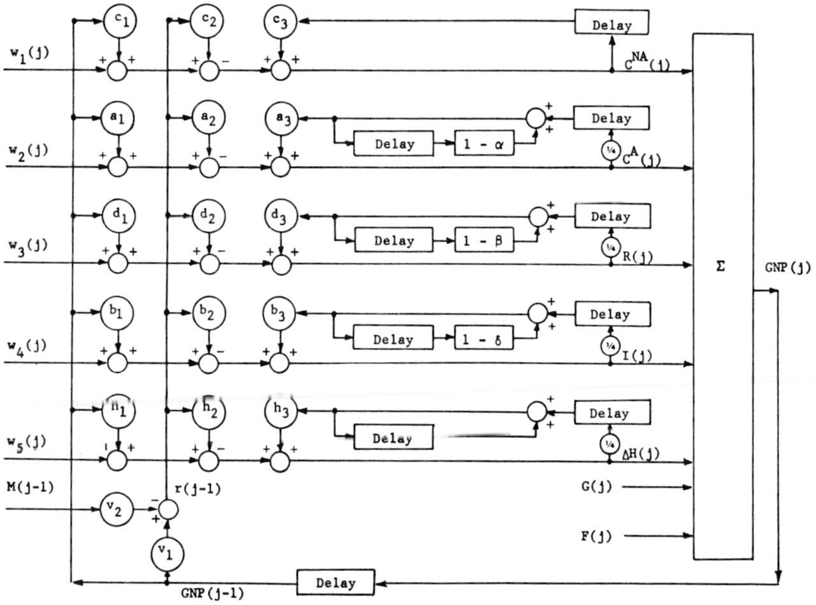

FIG. 1. Block diagram of the perturbed open-loop model economy.

In a similar manner, we may write both a trend equation and a perturbation equation for each of the equations of the macroeconomic model. Since the model is linear and superposition holds, this introduces no approximation other than those already made in the basic construction of the model.

Thus, for example, Eq. (2) becomes

$$\mathscr{C}_0^{NA}(j) + c_0 = c_1 \mathscr{G}\mathscr{N}\mathscr{P}_0(j-1) - c_2\, \imath_0(j-1) + c_3 \mathscr{C}_0^{NA}(j-1) \tag{27}$$

and

$$C^{NA}(j) = c_1 GNP(j-1) - c_2\, \imath(j-1) + c_3\, C^{NA}(j-1) + w_1(j) \tag{28}$$

Note that the random disturbances become part of the perturbed system.

The perturbed system of equations, therefore, is the same as that of Eqs. (1) through (6) and (9) through (13) with script variables replaced by the perturbation variables and the constants (i.e., $c_0 = a_0 = d_0 = b_0 = h_0 = v_0 = 0$) and/or trend value set equal to zero.

The economic policy problem is then separated into two parts: that of the long term trend characteristics and that of the perturbation system which describes the deviations from the trend values. While the long term trend behavior is certainly of interest, and is also amenable to optimal control analysis, we will limit this paper to a discussion of the behavior of the perturbation system.

To apply modern control theory to this problem, we must, first of all, rearrange the mathematics of the perturbation system to state-variable representation in multidimensional space.

We begin by constructing a block diagram of the perturbed equations. This is shown in Fig. 1. From it we note that Eqs. (1) and (13) can be substituted into Eqs. (2), (3), (4), (5), and (6) and thus eliminate *GNP* and r from the open-loop system dynamics.[7] Let the vectors $\mathbf{x}^1$ and $\mathbf{y}$ be[8]

$$\mathbf{x}^1(j) = [C^A(j), R(j), I(j), \Delta H(j)]^T \tag{29}$$

and

$$\mathbf{y}(j) = [K_a(j), K_h(j), K_p(j), H(j)]^T \tag{30}$$

[7] We point out that the *GNP* equation really describes what in control theory is called an observational system and thus is important in establishing the system output, but it is not part of the state vector of the dynamic system.

[8] Superscript T indicates the transpose of the matrix or vector.

Then we have the set of equations

$$\mathbf{x}^1(j) = \begin{bmatrix} a_1 - a_2 v_1 & a_1 - a_2 v_1 & a_1 - a_2 v_1 & a_1 - a_2 v_1 \\ d_1 - d_2 v_1 & d_1 - d_2 v_1 & d_1 - d_2 v_1 & d_1 - d_2 v_1 \\ b_1 - b_2 v_1 & b_1 - b_2 v_1 & b_1 - b_2 v_1 & b_1 - b_2 v_1 \\ h_1 - h_2 v_1 & h_1 - h_2 v_1 & h_1 - h_2 v_1 & h_1 - h_2 v_1 \end{bmatrix} \mathbf{x}^1(j-1)$$

$$+ \begin{bmatrix} a_1 - a_2 v_1 \\ d_1 - d_2 v_1 \\ b_1 - b_2 v_1 \\ h_1 - h_2 v \end{bmatrix} [G(j-1) + F(j-1) + C^{NA}(j-1)]$$

$$+ \begin{bmatrix} a_2 v_2 \\ d_2 v_2 \\ b_2 v_2 \\ h_2 v_2 \end{bmatrix} M(j-1) - \begin{bmatrix} a_3 & 0 & 0 & 0 \\ 0 & d_3 & 0 & 0 \\ 0 & 0 & b_3 & 0 \\ 0 & 0 & 0 & h_3 \end{bmatrix} \mathbf{y}(j-1) + \mathbf{W}(j) \quad (31)$$

$$\mathbf{y}(j) = \begin{bmatrix} 1 - \frac{1}{4}\alpha & 0 & 0 & 0 \\ 0 & 1 - \frac{1}{4}\beta & 0 & 0 \\ 0 & 0 & 1 - \frac{1}{4}\delta & 0 \\ 0 & 0 & 0 & 1 \end{bmatrix} \mathbf{y}(j-1) + \tfrac{1}{4}\mathbf{x}^1(j) \quad (32)$$

and

$$C^{NA}(j) = (c_1 + c_3 - c_2 v_1) C^{NA}(j-1) + c_2 v_2 M(j-1)$$
$$+ (c_1 - c_2 v_1)[C^A(j-1) + R(j-1) + I(j) + \Delta H(j-1)$$
$$+ G(j-1) + F(j-1)] + w_1(j-1) \quad (33)$$

Define the matrices A^1, B^1, and D, by the following equations:

$$\mathbf{x}^1(j) = A^1 \mathbf{x}^1(j-1) - B^1 \mathbf{y}(j-1) + \cdots \quad (34)$$

$$\mathbf{y}(j) = D\mathbf{y}(j-1) + \tfrac{1}{4}\mathbf{x}^1(j) \quad (35)$$

We wish to stack the $\mathbf{x}^1$ vector on top of the $\mathbf{y}$ vector to get a state vector and a corresponding recursive equation. However, Eqs. (34) and (35) are not amenable to this since (35) gives $\mathbf{y}$ at sample time j in terms of $\mathbf{x}^1$ also at sample time j. To solve this problem, we define a new vector Ψ by the relationship[9]

$$\mathbf{y}(j) = \tfrac{1}{4}\mathbf{x}^1(j) + \Psi(j) \quad (36)$$

[9] An alternative approach is to substitute Eq. (34) into (35) for $\mathbf{x}^1(j)$. This gives a more complex transition matrix, however, and the approach taken here is preferred.

From (35) and using (36), we have

$$\mathbf{y}(j) = D\mathbf{y}(j-1) + \tfrac{1}{4}\mathbf{x}^1(j)$$
$$= D[\tfrac{1}{4}\mathbf{x}^1(j-1) + \Psi(j-1)] + \tfrac{1}{4}\mathbf{x}^1(j) \tag{37}$$
$$= \tfrac{1}{4}\mathbf{x}^1(j) + \Psi(j) \tag{38}$$

We can use the last equality to give us a recursive equation in $\Psi(j)$, since $\mathbf{x}^1(j)$ cancels out.

$$\Psi(j) = \tfrac{1}{4}D\mathbf{x}^1(j-1) + D\Psi(j-1) \tag{39}$$

Just for the record, the new vector Ψ is given by

$$\Psi(j) = \begin{bmatrix} (1-\tfrac{1}{4}\alpha) & K_a(j-1) \\ (1-\tfrac{1}{4}\beta) & K_h(j-1) \\ (1-\tfrac{1}{4}\delta) & K_p(j-1) \\ & H(j-1) \end{bmatrix} \tag{40}$$

To be consistent, substitute (37) in (34) to obtain

$$\mathbf{x}^1(j) = [A^1 - \tfrac{1}{4}B^1]\mathbf{x}^1(j-1) - B^1\Psi(j-1) + \cdots \tag{41}$$

So now let $\mathbf{x}^2(j)$ be the vector:

$$\mathbf{x}^2 = \begin{bmatrix} \mathbf{x}^1 \\ \Psi \end{bmatrix} \tag{42}$$

and we have

$$\mathbf{x}^2(j) = \begin{bmatrix} A^1 - \tfrac{1}{4}B^1 & -B^1 \\ \tfrac{1}{4}D & D \end{bmatrix} \mathbf{x}^2(j-1) + \cdots \tag{43}$$

where the remaining terms are obvious from Eq. (31). Now add on the C^{NA} component to the vector $\mathbf{x}^2$ to get the following state vector for the open-loop system

$$\mathbf{x}(j) = \begin{bmatrix} C^{NA}(j) \\ \mathbf{x}^2(j) \end{bmatrix} \tag{44}$$

The single vector equation which replaces Eqs. (31), (32), and (33) is then given as

$$\mathbf{x}(j) = A\mathbf{x}(j-1) + \alpha_1[G(j-1) + F(j-1)] + \alpha_2 M(j-1) + \mathbf{W}(j) \tag{45}$$

where the α_i are matrices, A is the transition matrix for the system, G, F, and M are scalar forcing functions, and $\mathbf{W}$ is a noise vector. The matrices are explicitly given as

$$A = \begin{bmatrix} c_1 + c_3 - c_2 v_1 & c_1 - c_2 v_1 & c_1 - c_2 v_1 & c_1 - c_2 v_1 & c_1 - c_2 v_1 & 0 & 0 & 0 & 0 \\ a_1 - a_2 v_1 & a_1 - \frac{1}{4} a_3 - a_2 v_1 & a_1 - a_2 v_1 & a_1 - a_2 v_1 & a_1 - a_2 v_1 & -a_3 & 0 & 0 & 0 \\ d_1 - d_2 v_1 & d_1 - d_2 v_1 & d_1 - \frac{1}{4} d_3 - d_2 v_1 & d_1 - d_2 v_1 & d_1 - d_2 v_1 & 0 & -d_3 & 0 & 0 \\ b_1 - b_2 v_1 & b_1 - b_2 v_1 & b_1 - b_2 v_1 & b_1 - \frac{1}{4} b_3 - b_2 v_1 & b_1 - b_2 v_1 & 0 & 0 & -b_3 & 0 \\ h_1 - h_2 v_1 & h_1 - h_2 v_1 & h_1 - h_2 v_1 & h_1 - h_2 v_1 & h_1 - \frac{1}{4} h_3 - h_2 v_1 & 0 & 0 & 0 & -h_3 \\ 0 & \frac{1}{4}(1 - \frac{1}{4}\alpha) & 0 & 0 & 0 & 1 - \frac{1}{4}\alpha & 0 & 0 & 0 \\ 0 & 0 & \frac{1}{4}(1 - \frac{1}{4}\beta) & 0 & 0 & 0 & 1 - \frac{1}{4}\beta & 0 & 0 \\ 0 & 0 & 0 & \frac{1}{4}(1 - \frac{1}{4}\delta) & 0 & 0 & 0 & 1 - \frac{1}{4}\delta & 0 \\ 0 & 0 & 0 & 0 & \frac{1}{4} & 0 & 0 & 0 & 1 \end{bmatrix} \qquad (46)$$

$$\alpha_1^T = [c_1 - c_2 v_1; a_1 - a_2 v_1; d_1 - d_2 v_1; b_1 - b_2 v_1; h_1 - h_2 v_1; 0; 0; 0; 0] \quad (47)$$

$$\alpha_2^T = [c_2 v_2 ; a_2 v_2 ; d_2 v_2 ; b_2 v_2 ; h_2 v_2 ; 0; 0; 0; 0] \quad (48)$$

There is one additional modification to make to Eq. (45) before it is in the usual control theory form. The control function for coupling into the system in order to control its output must be clearly established.

Let the deviation of government purchases G from the trend value $\mathcal{G}_0$ be divided into two components

$$G = G_c + G_s \quad (49)$$

where G_c is that portion of the total deviation which can be changed by executive action for purposes of control of the perturbation of the economy, and G_s is that portion of the total deviation which is uncontrollable by executive action. In a similar manner, let the deviation of the money supply M from the trend value $\mathcal{M}_0$ be divided into two components

$$M = M_c + M_s \quad (50)$$

where M_c is that portion of the total deviation which can be changed by the Federal Reserve system for purposes of control of the perturbation of the economy, and M_s is that portion of the total deviation which is uncontrollable by executive action.

Now let the control vector $\mathbf{u}(j)$, be defined as

$$\mathbf{u}^T(j) = [G_c(j), M_c(j)] \quad (51)$$

With this modification, Eq. (45) then becomes

$$\mathbf{x}(j) = A\mathbf{x}(j-1) + B\mathbf{u}(j-1) + \alpha_1[F(j-1) + G_s(j-1)] + \alpha_2 M_s(j-1) + \mathbf{W}(j) \quad (52)$$

where $B = [\alpha_1, \alpha_2]$.

A study of the block diagram in Fig. 1 together with the elements of the A transition matrix indicates how the dynamic performance of the GNP model system depends upon its parameters. Also, the α_1 and α_2 matrices show how the policy or control variables couple into the system to influence its dynamic behavior.

It will be useful to identify the principal parameters of the system as belonging to five sets:

(1) *Income effect set*

$$\frac{\partial C^{NA}(j)}{\partial GNP(j-1)} = c_1, \quad \frac{\partial C^{A}(j)}{\partial GNP(j-1)} = a_1, \quad \frac{\partial R(j)}{\partial GNP(j-1)} = d_1,$$

$$\frac{\partial I(j)}{\partial GNP(j-1)} = b_1, \quad \frac{\partial \Delta H(j)}{\partial GNP(j-1)} = h_1, \quad \frac{\partial r(j)}{\partial GNP(j)} = v_1$$

(2) *Interest effect set*

$$\frac{\partial C^{NA}(j)}{\partial r(j-1)} = c_2, \qquad \frac{\partial C^{A}(j)}{\partial r(j-1)} = a_2, \qquad \frac{\partial R(j)}{\partial r(j-1)} = d_2,$$

$$\frac{\partial I(j)}{\partial r(j-1)} = b_2, \qquad \frac{\partial \Delta H(j)}{\partial r(j-1)} = h_2$$

(3) *Monetary effect set*

$$\frac{\partial r(j)}{\partial M(j)} = v_2$$

(4) *Stock effect set*

$$\frac{\partial C^{A}(j)}{\partial K_a(j-1)} = a_3, \qquad \frac{\partial R(j)}{\partial K_h(j-1)} = d_3, \qquad \frac{\partial I(j)}{\partial K_p(j-1)} = b_3,$$

$$\frac{\partial \Delta H(j)}{\partial H(j-1)} = h_3$$

(5) *Inertia effect set*

$$\frac{\partial C^{NA}(j)}{\partial C^{NA}(j-1)} = c_3$$

The elements of the A matrix involving more than one parameter are of two types, namely, those in the principal diagonal (such as $c_1 + c_3 - c_2 v_1$, $a_1 - a_2 v_1 - \frac{1}{4} a_3$), and all others (such as $a_1 - a_2 v_1$, $d_1 - d_2 v_1$). These elements correspond to the channels of influence represented in the block diagram. A rise in $GNP\,(j-1)$ will lead to a positive income effect on the aggregate demand components, but this will be partially offset by a negative interest effect on those components through the positive income effect on the interest rate. Elements like $a_1 - a_2 v_1$ represent these channels of influence. They are also the channels through which $G(j-1)$ influence the system as shown in the matrix α_1. The element $c_1 + c_3 - c_2 v_1$ embodies all the previous influences plus the inertia effect pertaining to non-automobile expenditures. Furthermore, as the aggregate demand components rise, a negative stock effect will influence them with a delay. Elements of the type $a_1 - \frac{1}{4} a_3 - a_2 v_1$ and $-a_3$ account for this influence. The matrix α_2 indicates that $M(j-1)$ influences the system via the product of the interest effect and the monetary effect. Thus, the values of elements of the A matrix are fundamental to the dynamic behavior of the GNP model system, which includes its stability, response time constants, and steady-state gains.

IV. Numerical Analysis of the Open-Loop System

In this section representative values for the parameters of the complete open-loop macroeconomic system have been employed to quantitatively examine some of the fundamental characteristics of the system.

Two sets of representative parameters will be studied. The first set, called the *a priori* set, was determined primarily from econometric studies relating to the individual dynamical equations of Section II. The second set was obtained from a least-squares-fit of the equations in Section II to the economic data from 1950 to 1965 (*37*).

The problem of parameter estimation always involves many subtle issues. Here the main objective was to estimate the *potential* leverage or multiplier effect of the policy or control variables, G and M in the model system. Unfortunately, the period 1950–1965 is deficient in one very important respect: traditional monetary policy was not pursued until after the Treasury–Federal Reserve Accord in March, 1951, and even then not very actively until almost 1955. Consequently, an estimate of the potential interest and monentary effects cannot be based upon the actual variation in money supply and the interest rate during this period. For this reason, it was decided to develop a set of *a priori* parameter values based, where possible, on previous econometric studies relating to the individual equations. These studies include those referred to in Section II in connection with the description of the GNP model system and consist of the work of Bronfrenbrenner and Mayer (*38*), Chow (*28, 29*), Christ (*39*), Darling (*36*), Gehrels and Wiggins (*40*), Jorgenson (*41*), Ando, Brown, Kareken, and Solow (*42*), Klein (*43*), Latane (*44, 45*), Lee (*34*), and Muth (*33*). In many instances these econometric studies covered the entire interwar period or longer. Because of the different periods and the data involved, the approach followed was to use the partial elasticity coefficients from such studies pertaining to the variables included in this macroeconomic model and to translate them into parameter values on the basis of that data.[10] In a few instances, it was necessary to depart from this procedure and to specify purely *a priori* parameter values.

The postwar economic environment also possessed other characteristics which make parameter estimation tenuous. While most of the backlog demand for household and business firm durable goods which had built up during World War II (when these goods were not in production) had

[10] If $y = y(x_1, x_2, \ldots, x_3)$, where y is the dependent variable and x_i $(i = 1, \ldots, s)$ are the independent variables, the partial elasticity coefficient is $\eta y/x_i = (x_i/y)(\partial y/\partial x_i)$. Since the model system considered consists of linear equations, the parameter is $\partial y/\partial x_i = \eta y/x_i(y/x_i)$. Data are used to represent y and x_i.

been eliminated by the beginning of the Korean War in mid-1950, a substantial shortage of housing remained. Furthermore, the Korean War led to priorities and allocations of scarce materials, price and wage control, and selected housing and consumer installment credit controls. These developments probably caused some changes in the structural equations of the economy and introduced discontinuities. Thus the presumption of basic continuity which underlies all methods of parameter estimation may not have been sufficiently fulfilled.

The alternative least-squares parameter estimates were of the single equation variety. No attempt was made to deal with the problem of identification or to employ equation system estimation procedures. This was because the purpose of this section is to show how modern control theory can contribute to "good" economic policy decisions in the framework of a macroeconomic system embodying most of the strategic mechanisms thought to account for the performance of the real world economy. While the macroeconomic system used should reproduce the main profiles of economic development over time, one cannot expect replication with fidelity. To achieve the latter would call for a large scale econometric model, and it is important to establish initially an understanding of fundamental issues before attempting analysis of the more complex situation.

TABLE I

PARAMETER VALUES FOR NUMERICAL ANALYSIS

Parameter	a_1	a_2	a_3	b_1	b_2	b_3
A Priori Set	0.138	2.0	0.230	0.13	10.0	0.24
Least-Squares Set	0.077	2.85	0.103	0.148	2.12	0.0823
	c_1	c_2	c_3	d_1	d_2	d_3
A Priori Set	0.05	0	0.70	0.122	2.44	0.115
Least-Squares Set	0.186	0	0.703	0.0293	1.08	0.016
	h_1	h_2	h_3	v_1	v_2	
A Priori Set	0.063	0.48	0.30	0.01	0.02	
Least-Squares Set	0.116	1.93	0.481	0.0105	0.008	
	α	β	δ			
A Priori Set	0.25	0.035	0.093			
Least-Squares Set	0.330	0.047	0.14			

The approach taken here is to determine the difference in the control system behavior for the two sets of parameters. In this section the open-loop dynamics are studied for each set of parameters. Later this approach will be continued by determining the change in the optimal control policy which results from the change in the parameters. It is noted that the result is significant and recommendations for further research are then made based on these results.

The two sets of parameters are given in Table I.

A. Eigenvalues of the Open-Loop System

The stability of the system and its characteristic time constants can be inferred from its eigenvalues. These were determined on a digital computer for the A matrix. They are given in Table II and are plotted on the complex "z" plane in Figs. 2 and 3.

TABLE II

OPEN-LOOP EIGENVALUES

A Priori Set	Least-Squares Set
0.958	0.984
0.920	0.927
0.910	0.890
$0.828 + j\,0.016$	$0.926 + j\,0.053$
$0.828 - j\,0.016$	$0.926 + j\,0.053$
0.296	0.223
0.026	0
0	0
0	0

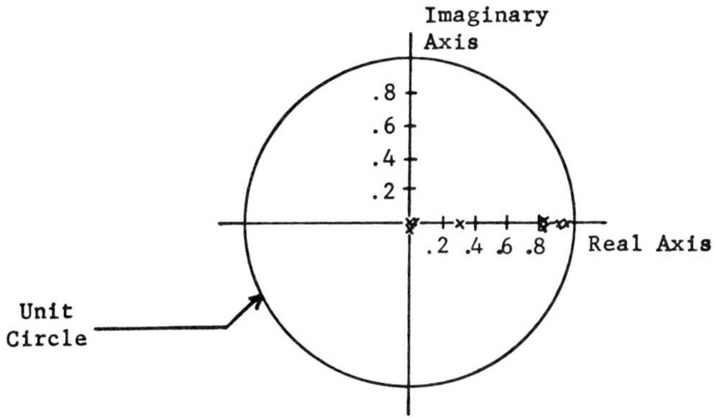

FIG. 2. Open-loop eigenvalues—*a priori* set.

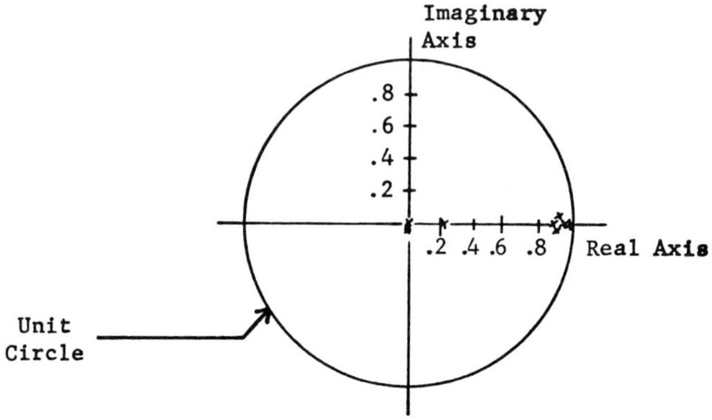

FIG. 3. Open-loop eigenvalues—least-squares set.

It is observed that the open-loop system is stable (all roots are inside the unit circle) and that the predominant time constants are those closest to the unit circle. For the *a priori* case the predominant response would be from the root at $z = 0.958$, although the other roots are not significantly removed from 0.958 to be much faster in response time.

B. Transient Response and Weighting Functions of the Open-Loop System

The mathematical model represents a set of linear perturbation equations describing local variations in the state from the trend values. The superposition theorem can be applied to the perturbation dynamics since they are linear. Thus, it is possible to establish the total perturbation response of the system to a combined input by summing the responses obtained from the inputs applied one at a time.

To obtain a general understanding for the system dynamics, step functions were applied, one at a time, to each of the flow components of the state vector. This then would give the basic system response for each of these terms.

The response to step functions were obtained from a digital simulation. Typical results are given in Figs. 4 through 9 for the *a priori* set.

It is observed that (1) the open-loop system is stable in either case in accordance with the eigenvalues of Table II and (2) characteristic time constants are around 3 to 5 years.

Figure 10 presents the response of the *a priori* open-loop system to a step change in G or M. Figure 11 presents the similar response data for the least-squares system parameters. A significant change in the transient

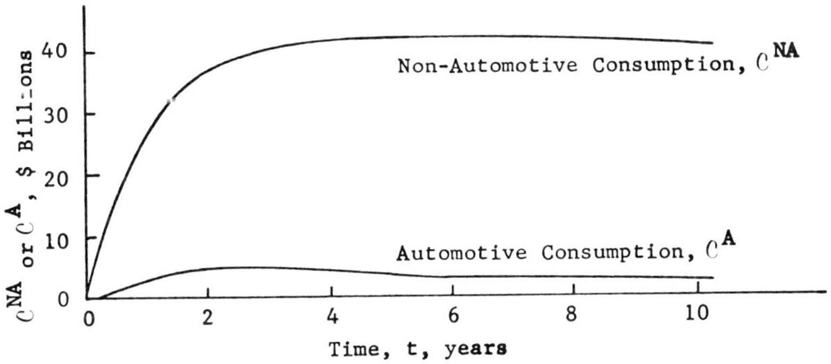

FIG. 4. System response to a $10 billion step change of non-automotive consumption.

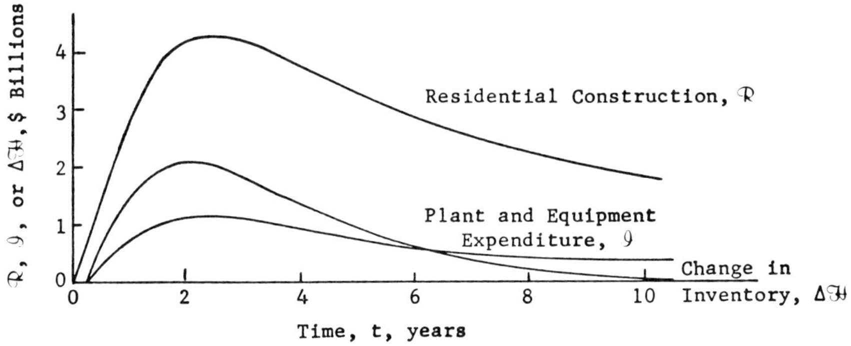

FIG. 5. System response to a $10 billion step change of non-automotive consumption.

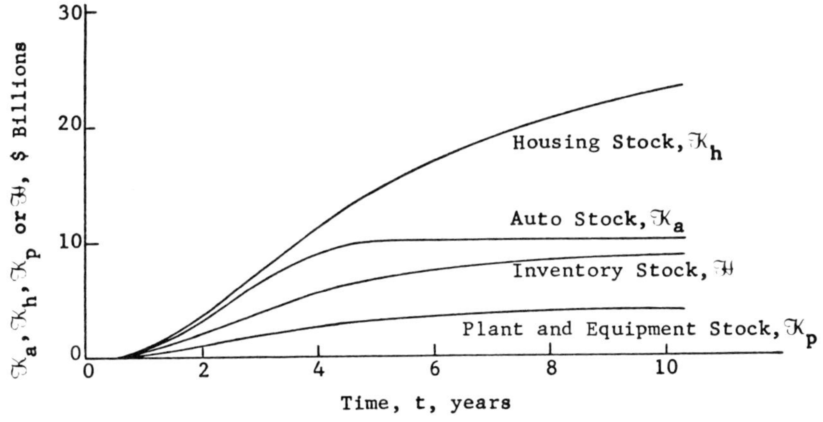

FIG. 6. System response to a $10 billion step change of non-automotive consumption.

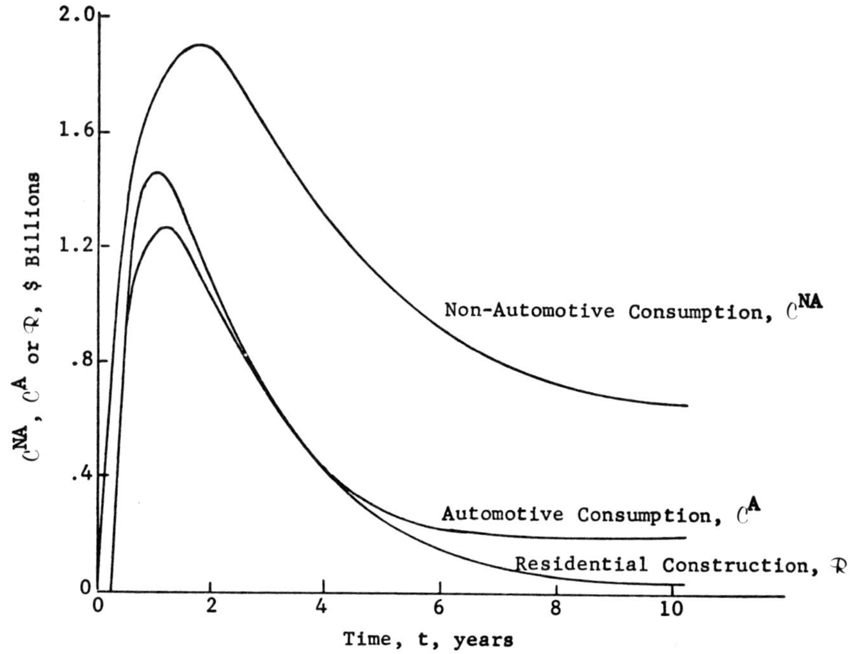

FIG. 7. System response to a $10 billion step change of plant and equipment investment.

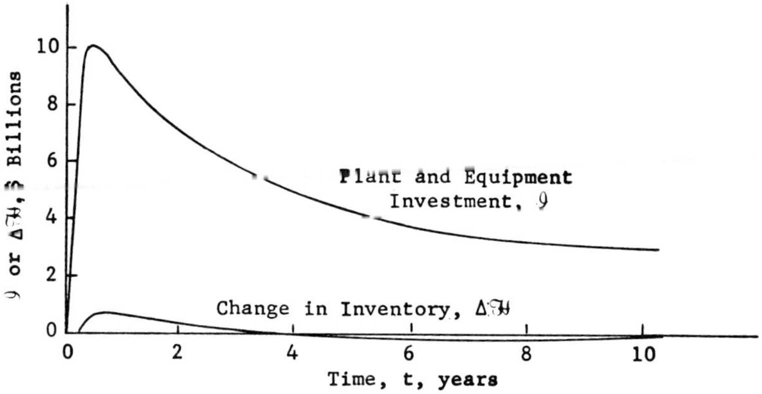

FIG. 8. System response to a $10 billion step change of plant and equipment investment.

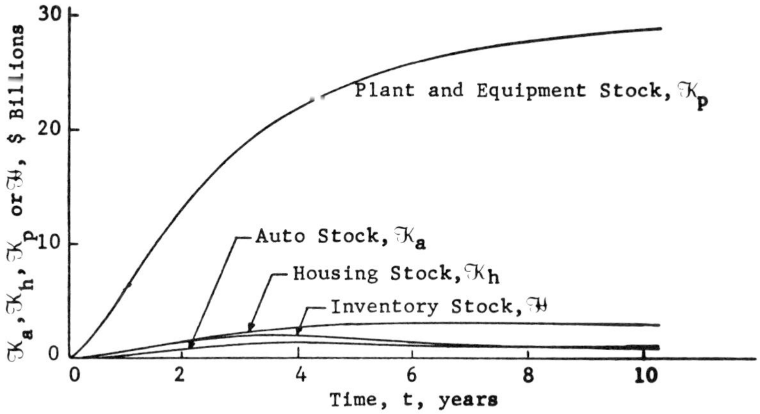

FIG. 9. System response to a \$10 billion step change of plant and equipment investment.

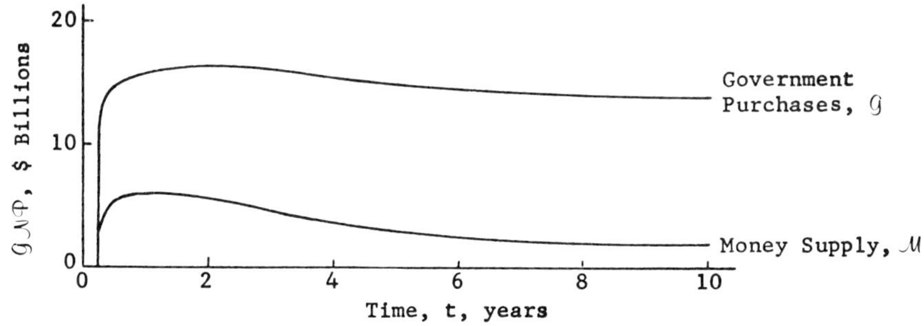

FIG. 10. Gross national product response to a \$10 billion step change in control variable—*a priori* set.

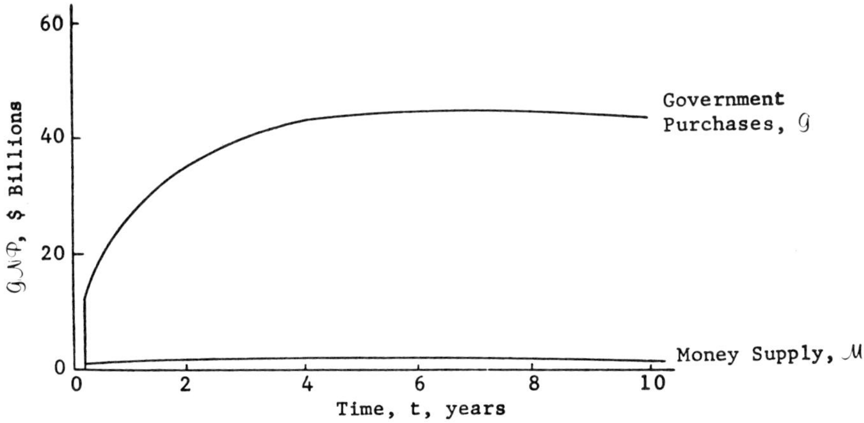

FIG. 11. Gross national product response to a \$10 billion step change in control variable—least-squares set.

characteristics as well as in the steady-state gain is noted. Thus these two figures represent the dynamic multipliers of the macroeconomic model with respect to the policy variables.

The increase in gain between the *a priori* and the least-squares system for controllable government purchases is primarily due to the reduction in the stock effect on investment b_3 and the increase in the inertia effect on consumption c_3. A similar increase in the gain for the money supply was not observed mainly because of the approximate factor of 3 reduction in both the interest effect on investment b_2 and in the monetary effect v_2 which compensates for the effect of most of the changes in b_3 and c_3.

C. Response to Random Noise

The behavior of the open-loop *a priori* system to random noise was also investigated.

The first question that arises is "What kind of random noise?" To get a rough estimate of typical levels of noise, it was necessary to obtain economic data on the variables for some period of time. Quarterly data on the flow variables were obtained for the years 1947 through 1965 in constant 1958 dollars.

A rough measure of typical levels of noise to be used in this study was then obtained by constructing trend lines through the data and estimating the standard deviation of the randomness about that trend line. The results obtained are given in Table III. These data should be taken as "order of magnitude data." No attempt has been made at this time to determine the shape of the appropriate power spectral density functions. It was just assumed to be zero mean Gaussian noise which is uncorrelated from sample to sample.

TABLE III

ESTIMATES OF THE RANDOMNESS OF THE VARIABLES OF THE SYSTEM

Variable	F	G	C^{NA}	C^{A}	R	I
Standard deviation	2.8	2.5	3	1.5	2	1.5

Random noise in accordance with Table III was then used as the forcing function to the perturbation dynamics of the *a priori* system.

Typical results on GNP are shown in Fig. 12. Note the rough oscillations of approximately a 7-year period. This is interesting and could indicate that the system dynamics are underdamped (and hence oscillatory)

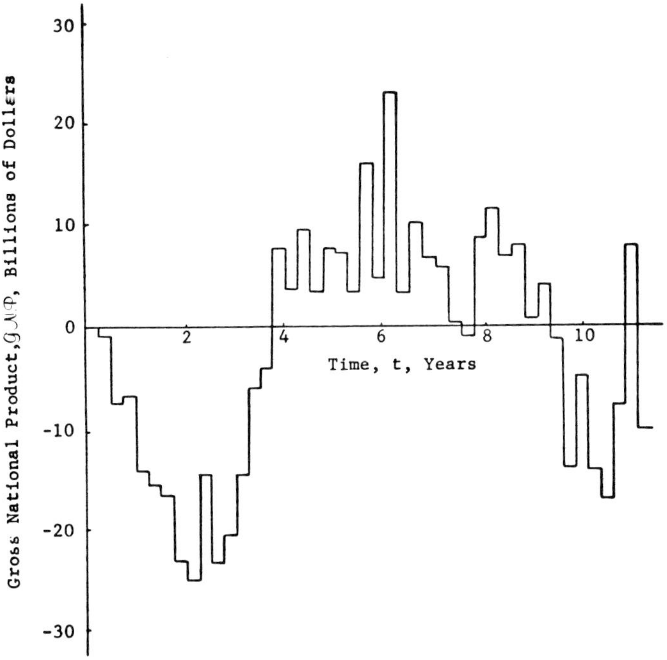

FIG. 12. Typical gross national product response to random noise.

at this frequency, but this does not agree with the location of the eigenvalues. It is in agreement with the transient responses, however, when the random noise is considered as a series of impulses exciting the weighting functions depicted previously with their characteristic time constants filtering out the higher frequency components.

It also should be noted that this is open-loop behavior and does not include any feedback control through G and M.

V. Optimal Control

This section initially discusses the policy problem. This includes the form of the desired output of the economy ($\mathscr{GNP}^*$) as well as the criterion functional for optimization. This is followed by the derivation of the optimal control policies for the dynamic model.

A. The Policy Problem

The most generally accepted overall economic goals for a market economy similar to that of the United States are those of full employment and price stability. It is assumed that the policy makers want to manipulate fiscal and monetary policies in such a way as to achieve performance as closely as possible to full employment and price stability over time.

The notion of price stability used here may be defined as including up to about $1\frac{1}{2}$ to 2% measured rise in prices, since the market basket price indexes have an upward bias because they do not allow for substitution effects and product quality improvement. From a welfare point of view, the measured price increase overstates the inflation. Full employment may be defined as including frictional unemployment in the neighborhood of 3 to 5% of the labor force.[11] This is considered to be the minimal unemployment necessary to provide for occupational and geographic mobility in the labor market. Phillips (*46*), Schultze (*47*), Samuelson and Solow (*48*), and Klein and Bodkin (*49*), among others, have investigated the relation between the percentage change in money wage rates and the unemployment rate. While the empirical evidence submitted in these studies is subject to varying interpretations, it is assumed that full employment and price stability as defined above are capable of simultaneous attainment. Productivity trends are such that the tradeoff between the rate of change of the money wage rate and the unemployment rate make these economic goals compatible.[12] Some past econometric studies of the price change–unemployment tradeoff have been reviewed and extended by Bodkin, Bond, Reuber, and Robinson (*50*).

Thus the potential output $\mathscr{GNP}^*$[13] can be specified as the value of output that the economy can achieve in any period at full employment without inflation. If actual output $\mathscr{GNP}$ exceeds the potential output $\mathscr{GNP}^*$ inflation of the demand-pull variety results.[14] On the other hand, a level of $\mathscr{GNP}$ below the potential output $\mathscr{GNP}^*$ leads to unemployment.

The production function for the economy which determines potential output is given by the Cobb–Douglas production function as

$$\mathscr{GNP}^*(j) = \lambda_0 \mathscr{K}_p^{\lambda_1}(j-1)\mathscr{E}^{(1-\lambda_1)}(j-1) \tag{53}$$

[11] Full employment labor input = labor force—frictional unemployment. Actually, allowance should be made for changes in the length of the work week over time and therefore be concerned with the potential labor-hour input. This refinement will not be introduced here.

[12] That is, the set of values for the two economic goals reflecting community preferences as interpreted by policy-makers lie on the "modified" Phillips curve expressing the relation between the percentage change in prices and the unemployment ratio, which takes account of long-term productivity gains.

[13] Both potential and actual output are measured in terms of real gross national product.

[14] It is assumed that there is no autonomous wage-push or profit-push inflation. Moreover, it is assumed that any demand-pull inflation that that takes place does not feed back and invalidate the behavioral equations specified as generating aggregate demand.

where $K_p(j-1)$ is real plant and equipment stock at the end of the $(j-1)$st quarter, $\mathscr{E}(j-1)$ is full employment labor input at the end of the $(j-1)$st quarter, and λ_0, λ_1 are parameters.

Making a Taylor's series expansion of the production function in the region of the nominal values of $\mathscr{K}_p$, we have[15]

$$\mathscr{GNP}^* = \mathscr{GNP}_0^* + \left.\frac{\partial \mathscr{GNP}^*}{\partial \mathscr{K}_p}\right|_{\mathscr{K}p=\mathscr{K}p0} (\mathscr{K}_p - \mathscr{K}_{po}) + \text{higher order terms} \tag{54}$$

Ignoring the higher order terms gives

$$\mathscr{GNP}^*(j) = \mathscr{GNP}_0^*(j) + n\mathscr{K}_p(j-1) \tag{55}$$

where

$$\mathrm{n} = \left.\frac{\partial \mathscr{GNP}^*}{\partial \mathscr{K}_p}\right|_{\mathscr{K}p=\mathscr{K}p0}$$

The error introduced by neglecting the higher order terms was investigated for the region of interest on $\mathscr{K}_p$ and found to be negligible compared to the stochastic disturbances on the economic behavior.

Thus, the long term trend equation for the production function is $\mathscr{GNP}_0^*(j)$, and the perturbation equation for the production function is

$$GNP^*(j) = \mathrm{n}K_p(j-1) \tag{56}$$

The criterion functional is

$$J(u) = \sum_{j-1}^{N} \{[GNP^*(j) - GNP(j)]^2 + \mathbf{u}^T(j-1)R\mathbf{u}(j-1)\} \tag{57}$$

where N is the total number of periods over which optimization is to take place, and R is the matrix penalty function on the activity of the control vector. This is the quadratic social welfare functional which is desired to be minimized subject to the constraints imposed by the model system, which determines actual output. It reflects the disutility over time resulting from the deviations of actual output from potential output which imply periods of unemployment or inflation and includes a disutility component which arises from the activity of the control function.[16]

Although the policy mix might contain numerous types of economic policies to achieve the overall economic goals, it remains true that the role of fiscal and monetary policies is likely to remain dominant. Here it is

[15] We do not perturb ξ since the perturbations of the labor force from the trend value are assumed to be negligible.

[16] If there were no penalty function on the activity of the control vector, then the optimal problem would have the trivial solution of setting G_c and M_c at each quarter such that the error is always zero.

assumed that discretionary fiscal policy actions by the Federal government will be limited to manipulation of Federal government purchases of goods and services. The entire perturbation of Federal, state, and local government purchases of goods and services $G(j)$ from the long term trend values $\mathcal{G}_0(j)$ is not under the control of Federal government executive action. Accordingly, $G(j)$ has been divided into two parts: (1) $G_c(j)$, the controllable portion, and (2) $G_s(j)$, the stochastic or random portion which is uncontrollable by executive action. It is assumed then that $G_c(j)$ is a policy or control variable that can be varied from quarter to quarter. Therefore, $G(j) = G_c(j) + G_s(j)$.

It might be maintained that tax and transfer payment policy changes are more flexible than government purchases changes and therefore more suitable as policy instruments. However, the impact on the economy of such changes would be much the same as in the case of changes in government purchases, except the initial impact would be on disposable income via changes in tax or transfer payment functions rather than on aggregate demand directly. Here, for simplicity, we assume that tax and transfer payment policies are given. However, their automatic fiscal stabilizing effects remain.

The other policy or control variable is taken to be a portion $M_c(j)$ of the variation $M(j)$ of the money supply from the trend value. Thus $M(j) = M_c(j) + M_s(j)$, where $M_s(j)$ is that random portion of the perturbation of the money supply from its trend value that the Federal Reserve system cannot control by executive action. To explain the determination of the actual money supply, it would be necessary to consider the portfolio policies of the member banks of the Federal Reserve system and how they respond to changes in the yield and risk on earning assets. This would become an involved analysis by itself which is largely a separate problem, and hence not further discussed here.

The criterion functional includes a penalty component because too much variation of the policy or control variables over time may have adverse welfare effects by itself. When control activity causes increasing disutility in accordance with the quadratic utility functional, this calls for limitation on such variation and in the limit no change in policies or control activity whatsoever.

Large and frequent variation of $G_c(j)$ may mean that Federal programs for which such expenditures are made can make very little contribution to the welfare of the community apart from regulating aggregate demand. The efficiency of many programs is apt to suffer if such changes in expenditure are required. Moreover, excessive variation in $M_c(j)$ may create debt management problems for the Federal treasury and destabilize adversely the portfolios of private financial institutions.

How important these considerations are can only be determined on the basis of careful study. The formulation adopted here, however, makes possible the assignment of separate penalties to the two forms of control activity in case that should be desirable. As the penalty for control activity is raised, the magnitude of optimal control is reduced with respect to movements of the endogenous variables of the model system.

The policy decision-making process is envisaged as follows: At the end of the $(k-1)$st quarter of a calendar year $K_p(k-1)$, the stock of real plant and equipment is known. Thus the potential output $GNP^*(j)$ is known for the immediately following quarter. $K_p(k-1)$ is determined by the entire past performance of the system. The policy decision is to choose values of $M_c(k)$, the money supply, and $G_c(k)$, Federal government purchases of goods and services subject to control, so that actual output $GNP(k)$ will deviate from potential output $GNP^*(k)$ only in accordance with minimization of the quadratic social welfare functional criterion.

Thus we seek to determine the optimal economic policies or an optimal control law, given a macroeconomic model of the economy, which determines actual output $GNP(k)$ and whose production function determines potential output $GNP^*(k)$ and the welfare functional. Figure 13 indicates the basic control loop under investigation. Our problem is to determine the mathematical relations which describe the optimum controller block in terms of minimization of social disutility over time. These mathematical relations then give us the optimum economic policies or decision rule $\hat{\mathbf{u}}$ as a function of the current error $\varepsilon = (GNP^* - GNP)$, and the current state of the open-loop system $\mathbf{x}$.

B. Determination of the Optimal Control Policies

It is desired to find that control function $\hat{\mathbf{u}}(k)$, from all possible $\mathbf{u}(k)$, which minimizes the discrete functional given by Eq. (57). $\hat{\mathbf{u}}(k)$ is then the optimal control law or policy for the macroeconomic system [represented by Eq. (52)] in that if it were implemented, it would minimize Eq. (57).

Utilizing Eqs. (26) and (56), the error function becomes

$$\begin{aligned}\varepsilon(j) = GNP^*(j) - GNP(j) = \mathrm{n}K_p(j-1) - C^{NA}(j) - C^{A}(j)\\ - R(j) - I(j) - \Delta H(j) - G_c(j) - G_s(j) - F(j)\end{aligned} \tag{58}$$

Note that $(1-\frac{1}{4}\delta)K_p(j-1)$ is a component of the state vector $\mathbf{x}(j)$. Let

$$\mathrm{n}_1 = \frac{\mathrm{n}}{(1-\frac{1}{4}\delta)} \tag{59}$$

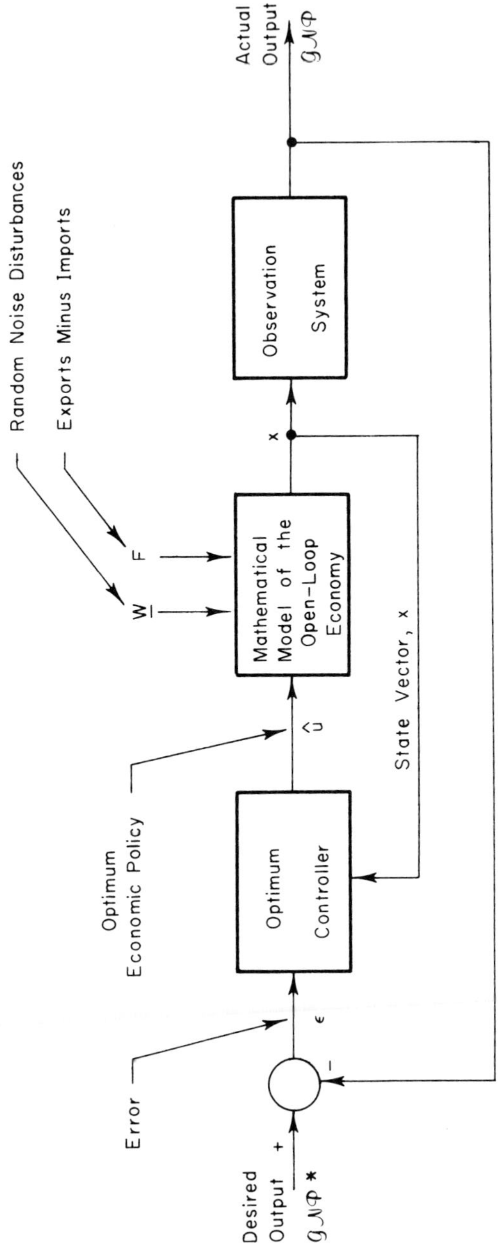

FIG. 13. Block diagram of the basic system.

and define a new state vector

$$\mathbf{z}^T(j) = [\mathbf{x}^T(j), G_s(j), F(j)] \tag{60}$$

$$\varepsilon^2(j) = (GNP^* - GNP)^2 = \mathbf{z}^T(j)Q\mathbf{z}(j) + \mathbf{u}^T(j)R_1\mathbf{u}(j) - \mathbf{u}^T(j)P\mathbf{z}(j) \tag{61}$$

and the matrices are

$$Q = \begin{bmatrix} 1 & 1 & 1 & 1 & 1 & 0 & 0 & -n_1 & 0 & 1 & 1 \\ 1 & 1 & 1 & 1 & 1 & 0 & 0 & -n_1 & 0 & 1 & 1 \\ 1 & 1 & 1 & 1 & 1 & 0 & 0 & -n_1 & 0 & 1 & 1 \\ 1 & 1 & 1 & 1 & 1 & 0 & 0 & -n_1 & 0 & 1 & 1 \\ 1 & 1 & 1 & 1 & 1 & 0 & 0 & -n_1 & 0 & 1 & 1 \\ 0 & 0 & 0 & 0 & 0 & 0 & 0 & 0 & 0 & 0 & 0 \\ 0 & 0 & 0 & 0 & 0 & 0 & 0 & 0 & 0 & 0 & 0 \\ -n_1 & -n_1 & -n_1 & -n_1 & -n_1 & 0 & 0 & n_1^2 & 0 & -n_1 & -n_1 \\ 0 & 0 & 0 & 0 & 0 & 0 & 0 & 0 & 0 & 0 & 0 \\ 1 & 1 & 1 & 1 & 1 & 0 & 0 & -n_1 & 0 & 1 & 1 \\ 1 & 1 & 1 & 1 & 1 & 0 & 0 & -n_1 & 0 & 1 & 1 \end{bmatrix} \tag{62}$$

$$P = 2\begin{bmatrix} -1 & -1 & -1 & -1 & -1 & 0 & 0 & n_1 & 0 & -1 & -1 \\ 0 & 0 & 0 & 0 & 0 & 0 & 0 & 0 & 0 & 1 & 0 \end{bmatrix} \tag{63}$$

$$R_1 = \begin{bmatrix} 1 & 0 \\ 0 & 0 \end{bmatrix} \tag{64}$$

The functional which we wish to minimize, Eq. (57), can now be written as

$$J(u) = \sum_{n-1}^{N} \mathbf{z}^T(j)Q\mathbf{z}(j) - \mathbf{u}^T(j)P\mathbf{z}(j) + \mathbf{u}^T(j)R_1\mathbf{u}(j) + \mathbf{u}^T(j-1)R\mathbf{u}(j-1) \tag{65}$$

and our problem is to find the control function $\mathbf{u}(j)$ which minimizes (65) subject to the constraints of the system dynamics as given by Eq. (52). However, Eq. (52) must first be modified to be consistent with the new state vector defined by Eq. (60).

$$\mathbf{z}(j) = \beta_1\mathbf{z}(j-1) + \beta_2\mathbf{u}(j-1) + \mathbf{V}(j) \tag{66}$$

where the β's are the matrices given by

$$\beta_1 = \begin{bmatrix} [A] & & & & & & & & [\alpha_1] & [\alpha_1] \\ 0 & 0 & 0 & 0 & 0 & 0 & 0 & 0 & 0 & 1 & 0 \\ 0 & 0 & 0 & 0 & 0 & 0 & 0 & 0 & 0 & 0 & 1 \end{bmatrix} \tag{67}$$

$$\beta_2 = \begin{bmatrix} [B] \\ 0 \quad 0 \\ 0 \quad 0 \end{bmatrix} \tag{68}$$

$$\mathbf{V}^T = [W^T, v_{10}, v_{11}] \tag{69}$$

The problem is now consistently formulated. The optimal control policies could be obtained utilizing either the calculus of variations, Pontriagin's maximum principle, or dynamic programming. Dynamic programming (*51*) was used to determine the optimal policies of the form

$$\hat{\mathbf{u}}(k) = K(N-k)\mathbf{z}(k) \tag{70}$$

VI. Numerical Solution of the Optimal Control Policy

The optimal control law is given as a matrix of gains which transform the state of the system at the kth quarter $\mathbf{x}(k)$ into the optimal control vector $\hat{\mathbf{u}}(k)$ to be used during that quarter. Since the control vector has two components G_c and M_c, and since the state vector has eleven components, the optimal gain matrix $K(N-k)$ has two rows and eleven columns. Also note that the optimal gain matrix is a function of the number of quarters in the future over which we wish to optimize, $N-k$, which is called "time-to-go" in many systems.

Thus a solution to the optimal control problem is obtained when the optimal gain matrix $K(N-k)$ is determined for time-to-go from $N-k=1$ to $N-k \to \infty$. The long term optimal policy $(N-k \to \infty)$, is constant because the dynamics of the system are not significant over this time span and the optimal control policy depends only on the steady-state gain of the system.

This section presents the results of a numerical solution of the resulting Matrix–Ricatti equation and the optimal control policy. Since

$$\hat{\mathbf{u}}(j) = K(N-k)\mathbf{z}(k) \tag{70}$$

the optimal feedback gain to multiply the nth component of the state vector to obtain its contribution to the first component of the control vector G_c is

$$\partial\hat{G}_c/\partial z_n = k_{1,n}(N-k) \tag{71}$$

Likewise,

$$\partial\hat{M}_c/\partial z_n = k_{2,n}(N-k) \tag{72}$$

where $k_{m,n}(N-k)$ is the element of the $K(N-k)$ which is on the mth row and the nth column.

Specifically, the optimal control policy then is

$$\hat{\mathbf{u}}(k) = \begin{bmatrix} \hat{G}_c(k) \\ \hat{M}_c(k) \end{bmatrix} = \begin{bmatrix} \frac{\partial \hat{G}_c}{\partial C^{NA}}(N-k), \frac{\partial \hat{G}_c}{\partial C^{A}}(N-k), \frac{\partial \hat{G}_c}{\partial R}(N-k), \\ \frac{\partial \hat{M}_c}{\partial C^{NA}}(N-k), \frac{\partial \hat{M}_c}{\partial C^{A}}(N-k), \frac{\partial \hat{M}_c}{\partial R}(N-k), \end{bmatrix}$$

$$\frac{\partial \hat{G}_c}{\partial I}(N-k), \frac{\partial \hat{G}_c}{\partial \Delta H}(N-k), \frac{\partial \hat{G}_c}{\partial \Psi_1}(N-k), \frac{\partial \hat{G}_c}{\partial \Psi_2}(N-k),$$

$$\frac{\partial \hat{M}_c}{\partial I}(N-k), \frac{\partial \hat{M}_c}{\partial \Delta H}(N-k), \frac{\partial \hat{M}_c}{\partial \Psi_1}(N-k), \frac{\partial \hat{M}_c}{\partial \Psi_2}(N-k),$$

$$\begin{matrix} \frac{\partial \hat{G}_c}{\partial \Psi_3}(N-k), \frac{\partial \hat{G}_c}{\partial \Psi_4}(N-k), \frac{\partial \hat{G}_c}{\partial G_s}(N-k), \frac{\partial \hat{G}_c}{\partial F}(N-k) \\ \frac{\partial \hat{M}_c}{\partial \Psi_3}(N-k), \frac{\partial \hat{M}_c}{\partial \Psi_4}(N-k), \frac{\partial \hat{M}_c}{\partial G_s}(N-k), \frac{\partial \hat{M}_c}{\partial F}(N-k) \end{matrix} \Bigg] \mathbf{z}(k) \qquad (73)$$

Thus the optimal economic policies or optimal economic decision rules which are sought are a function of the state variables of the entire system including those entering the welfare functional through the production function. The state variables include the endogenous aggregate demand variables, $C^{NA}(k)$, $C^{A}(k)$, $R(k)$, $I(k)$, and $\Delta H(k)$, the endogenous stock variables $K_a(k)$, $K_h(k)$, $K_p(k)$, and $H(k)$, and the exogenous variables G_s and F of the model system. The matrix equation (70) specifies the appropriate policy decisions with respect to the policy or control variables $G_c(k)$ and $M_c(k)$ if the performance of the model system is to be optimized over a time horizon of $N-k$ quarters. This information takes into account the dynamics of the model system as well as the stochastic disturbances (characteristics as assumed earlier) that may impinge upon it.

The two sets of system parameters given in Table I were used to obtain two different optimal economic control policies, one for each system. The values for n_1 in the production function was taken in both cases to be $n_1 = 0.37$.

No data could be found for estimating the penalty function for control activity, primarily since the problem has not been formulated in this manner before. Therefore a brief sensitivity analysis was conducted using an assumed form of the penalty function as

$$R = \sigma \begin{bmatrix} 1 & 0 \\ 0 & 1 \end{bmatrix} = \sigma I \qquad (74)$$

where σ is a scalar and I is the identity matrix. Thus equal weighting was given to activity of each component of the control vector. The effect of the level of the penalty function was studied by considering values of the scalar σ which ranged over two orders of magnitude; i.e., values of σ studied were $\sigma = 0.1$, 0.5, 1.0, 5, and 10.[17]

A. Optimal Feedback Gains

In general, the shape of the optimal feedback gains did not appreciably change with σ although the magnitude did. Figures 14 through 21 show the optimal gains as functions of time-to-go $N-k$ for $\sigma = 1$. Careful study of these results reveals some very interesting phenomena.

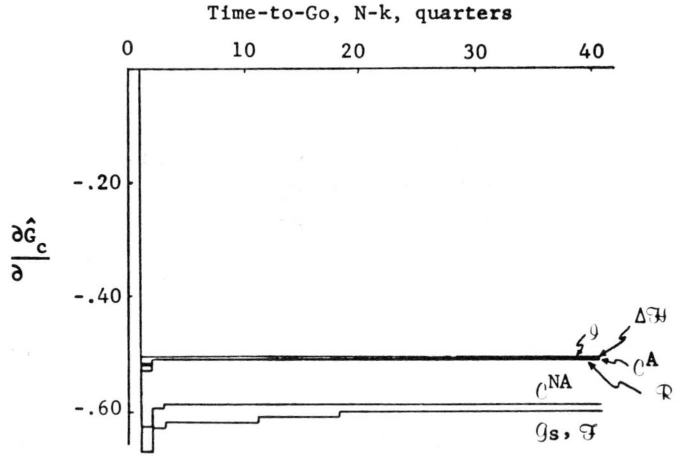

FIG. 14. Optimal feedback gains from flow variables to controllable government purchases—*a priori* set, $\sigma = 1.0$.

An interpretation of the algebraic signs of the elements in the $K(N-k)$ matrix is quite complicated because not only are the channels of the open-loop system involved, as shown in Fig. 1, but also the additional channels provided by the production function in the welfare functional when the control loop is included. These algebraic signs are occasionally the result of the influence of a given variable on the aggregate demand side and the aggregate supply side of the closed-loop system which incorporates

[17] See Buchanan and Stubberud (*52*) for further discussion of different types of penalty functions.

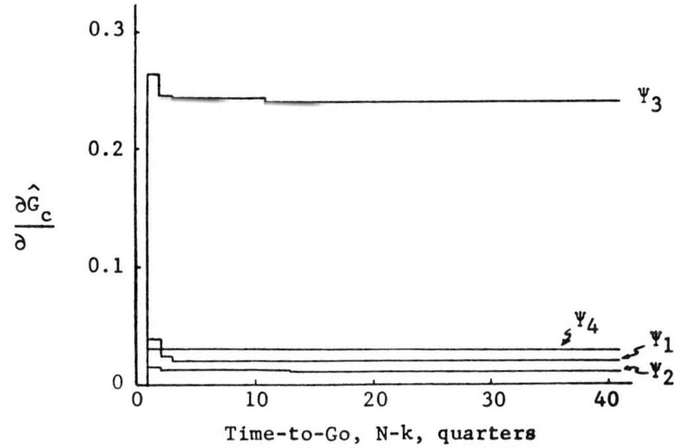

FIG. 15. Optimal feedback gains from stock variables to controllable government purchases—*a priori* set, $\sigma = 1.0$.

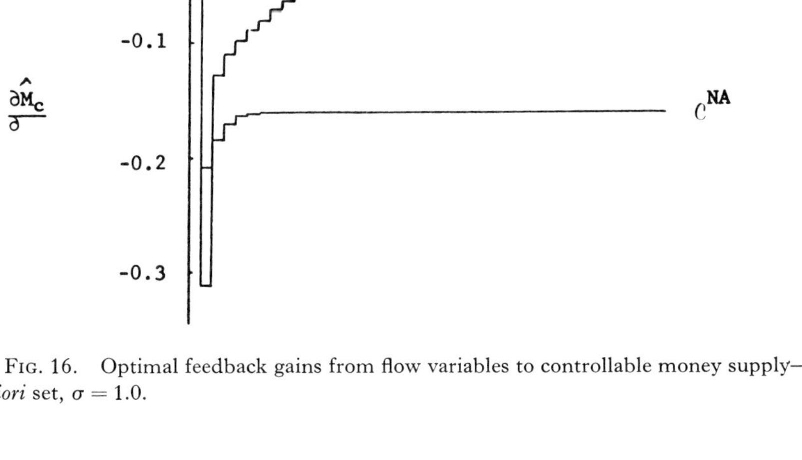

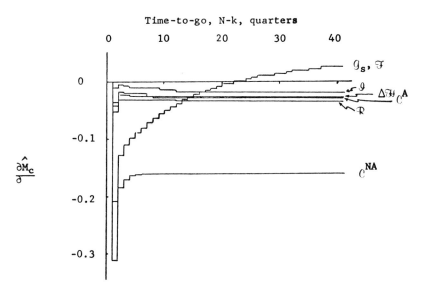

FIG. 16. Optimal feedback gains from flow variables to controllable money supply—*a priori* set, $\sigma = 1.0$.

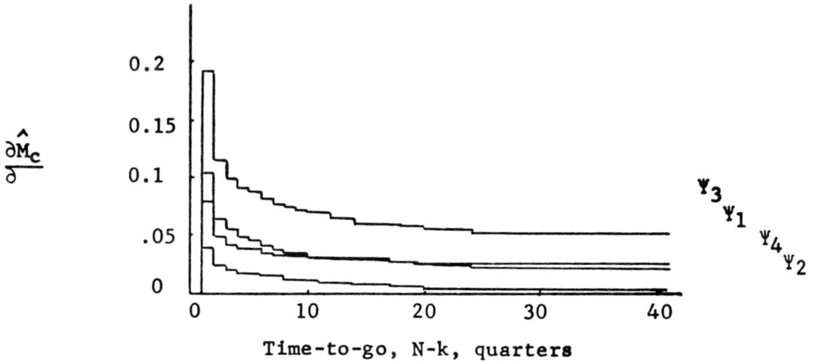

FIG. 17. Optimal feedback gains from stock variables to controllable money supply—*a priori* set, $\sigma = 1.0$.

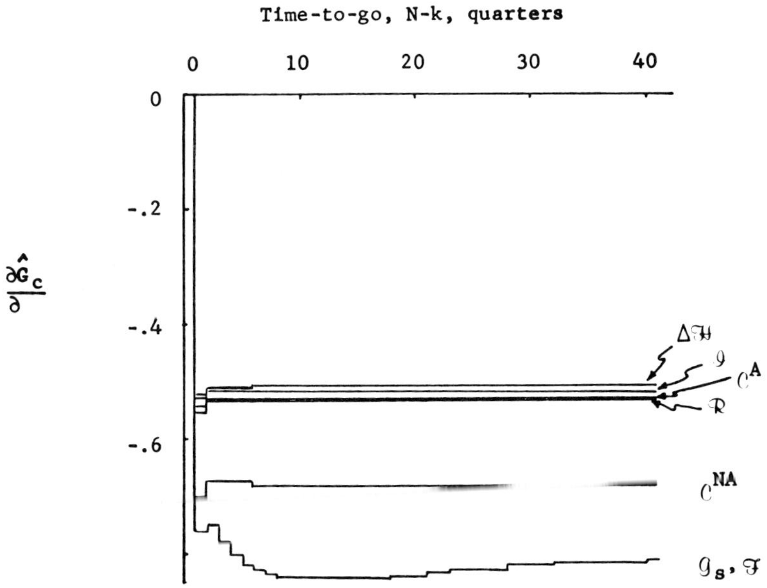

FIG. 18. Optimal feedback gains from flow variables to controllable government purchases—least-squares set, $\sigma = 1.0$.

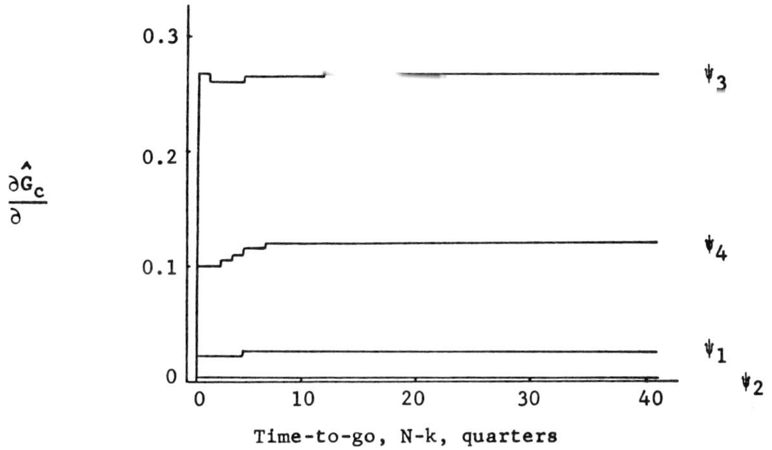

FIG. 19. Optimal feedback gains from stock variables to controllable government purchases—least-squares set, $\sigma = 1.0$.

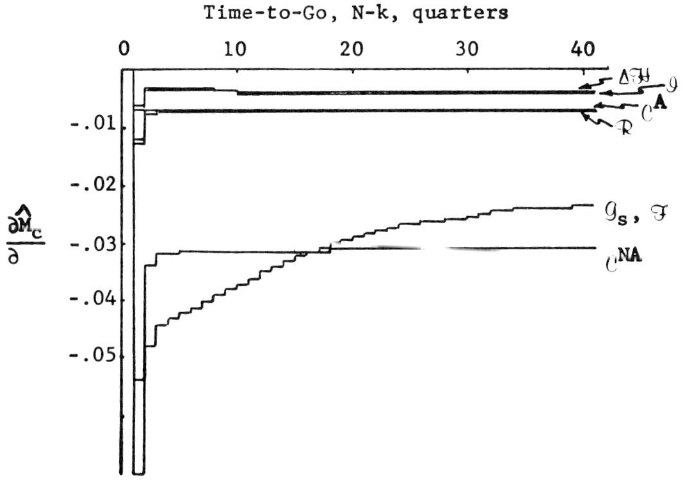

FIG. 20. Optimal feedback gains from flow variables to controllable money supply—least-squares set, $\sigma = 1.0$.

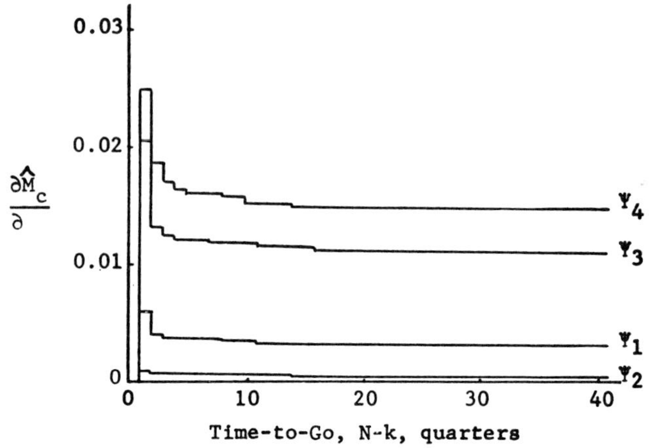

FIG. 21. Optimal feedback gains from stock variable to controllable money supply—least-squares set, $\sigma = 1.0$.

the controller. For simplicity, only the long-term optimal control policy ($N \to \infty$) for $\sigma = 1.0$ for the *a priori* system will be discussed.

$$\hat{\mathbf{u}}(k) = \begin{bmatrix} \hat{G}_c(k) \\ \hat{M}_c(k) \end{bmatrix} = \begin{bmatrix} -.582, & -.509, & -.512, & -.501, & -.507, & .0225, & .010, & .240, & .0284, & -.581, & -.581 \\ -.157, & -.0290, & -.0352, & -0.192, & -.030, & .0262, & .0138, & .0519, & .0218, & .079, & .079 \end{bmatrix} \mathbf{z}(k) \quad (75)$$

It is clear that

$$\frac{\partial \hat{G}_c(j)}{\partial C^{NA}(j)} < 0; \quad \frac{\partial \hat{G}_c(j)}{\partial C^{A}(j)} < 0; \quad \frac{\partial \hat{G}_c(j)}{\partial R(j)} < 0; \quad \frac{\partial \hat{G}_c(j)}{\partial I(j)} < 0; \quad \frac{\partial \hat{G}_c(j)}{\partial \Delta H(j)} < 0$$

since an increase in $C^{NA}(j)$, $C^{A}(j)$, $R(j)$, or $\Delta H(j)$ increases aggregate demand and calls for a decrease in $G_c(j)$ as an offset. Also

$$\frac{\partial \hat{G}_c(j)}{\partial K_a(j)} > 0; \quad \frac{\partial \hat{G}_c(j)}{\partial K_h(j)} > 0; \quad \frac{\partial \hat{G}_c(j)}{\partial K_p(j)} > 0; \quad \frac{\partial \hat{G}_c(j)}{\partial H(j)} > 0$$

since a rise in $K_a(j)$, $K_h(j)$, $K_p(j)$, or $H(j)$ will tend to lower aggregate demand and therefore $\hat{G}_c(j)$ should be raised.

By reasoning analogous to that used earlier,

$$\frac{\partial \hat{M}_c(k)}{\partial_C NA_{(k)}} < 0; \quad \frac{\partial \hat{M}_c(k)}{\partial_C A_{(k)}} < 0; \quad \frac{\partial \hat{M}_c(k)}{\partial R(k)} < 0; \quad \frac{\partial \hat{M}_c(k)}{\partial I(k)} < 0; \quad \frac{\partial \hat{M}_c(k)}{\partial \Delta H(k)} < 0$$

In each instance an increase in these variables raises aggregate demand. Therefore $M_c(k)$ should be reduced. Moreover,

$$\frac{\partial \hat{M}_c(k)}{\partial K_a(k)} > 0; \qquad \frac{\partial \hat{M}_c(k)}{\partial K_n(k)} > 0, \qquad \frac{\partial \hat{M}_c(k)}{\partial K_p(k)} > 0; \qquad \frac{\partial \hat{M}_c(k)}{\partial H(k)} > 0$$

since a rise in these stock variables tends to reduce aggregate demand and dictates an increase in $\hat{M}_c(k)$.

Further research must be conducted to choose where the set of parameters which best fits the particular economy under investigation lies on the scale between the *a priori* set and the least-squares set.

If one concludes that the dynamics of the particular economy of concern is best described by the *a priori* set, then some very interesting questions arise. These are mostly concerned with the length of time in the future where the optimal policy changes significantly compared to the immediate goals of the economic performance. However, these philosophical questions are outside the domain of this paper and therefore will not be pursued further here.

An analysis was made to determine the parameters of the open-loop system which most markedly affect this result. It was found that the most significant parameters were the capital stock effect b_3 and the inertia effect c_3, especially as the inertia effect approached unity.

Optimal gains as functions of time-to-go $N - k$, similar to the previous results except for $\sigma = 0.1$ were also determined. Comparison of these results with those of Figs. 14 through 21 reveals that, in general, the shape of the optimal gains are similar for both values of σ but with increased magnitude for the smaller value of σ. This is reasonable since a tighter feedback control system results. This general effect is shown in Fig. 22 for the optimal steady-state feedback gain from investment to controllable government purchase $\partial \hat{G}_c / \partial I$. Thus each component of the optimal feedback gain matrix is the result of a complex weighting process which depends not only on the open-loop system dynamics and the production function chosen for desired output, but also, to a large extent, on the penalty function placed on the control activity.

The significant changes in optimal economic policy which occur for just a change in the magnitude σ of a particular form of the penalty function emphasize the need for quantitative research on penalty functions for macroeconomic systems.

The primary method of evaluating the operation of the optimal controller, however, is to simulate the system behavior on a digital computer with and without the controller in operation (in contrast to these analyses). Such a study was accomplished and is reported in the next section.

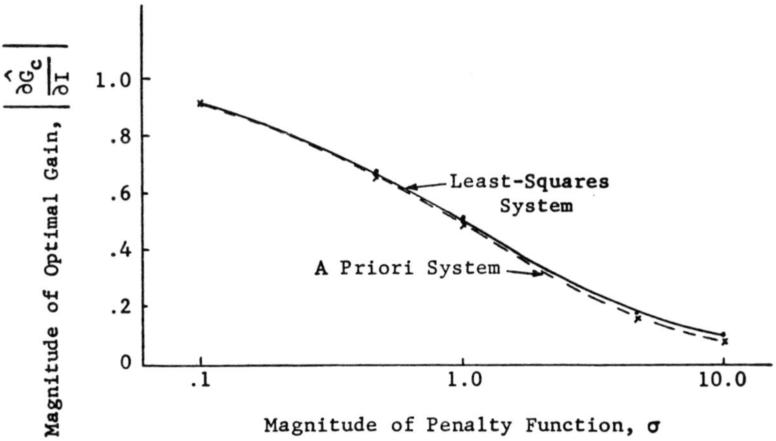

FIG. 22. Magnitude of optimal gains versus magnitude of penalty function.

B. Closed-Loop Results

A digital simulation of the closed-loop system was constructed utilizing the optimal feedback gains determined from the solutions of the Matrix–Ricatti equation for two orders of magnitude change on the magnitude of the penalty function on control activity σ for each of the two sets of system parameters. For simplicity, only the long term ($N - k \to \infty$) optimal control systems were simulated. Random noise was introduced as an exogenous forcing function to the system in accordance with Table III. Each noise run was for one hundred quarters (25 years) to be certain that long-term conditions had been reached. Ten noise runs were made for each data point.

Figure 23 presents the average and standard deviation of the value of the cost functional as a function of the magnitude of the control activity penalty function σ for the *a priori* set of open-loop system parameters. Figure 24 shows similar data for the least-squares open-loop system parameters. Specifically, the mean value of the cost functional $\bar{J}$ was computed as

$$\hat{J} = \frac{1}{n} \sum_{j=1}^{N} [\mathbf{x}^T(j)Q\mathbf{x}(j) - \mathbf{u}^T(j-1)P\mathbf{x}(j-1) + \mathbf{u}^T(j-1)(R_1 + \sigma)\mathbf{u}(j-1)] \tag{76}$$

where $N = 100$.

Since ten runs were made for each condition, it was possible to calculate the average value of those ten data points and also estimate the standard deviation of the mean value of the cost functional from that average point.

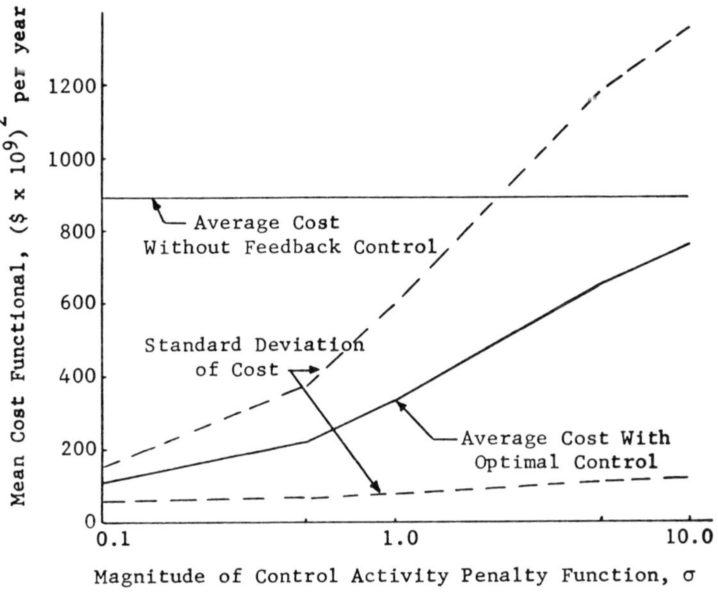

FIG. 23. Mean cost functional versus magnitude of the penalty function—*a priori* set.

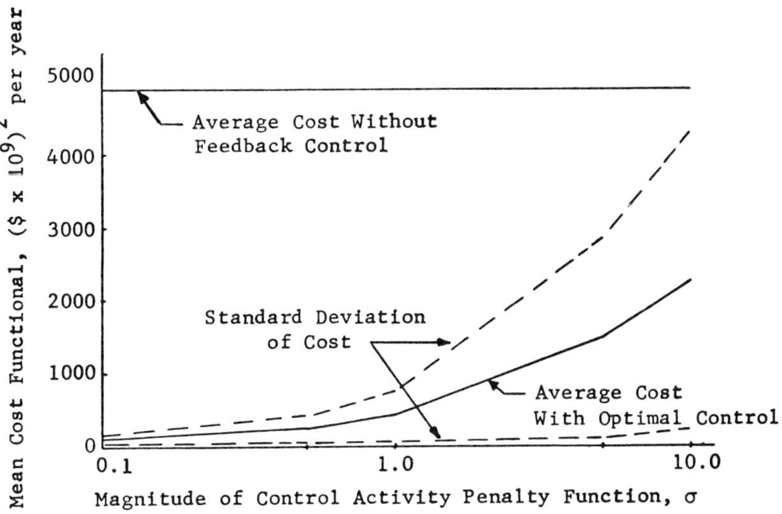

FIG. 24. Mean cost functional versus magnitude of the penalty function—least squares set.

It is important to note that ten data points is not a large sample size when interpreting the data shown in Figs. 23 and 24.

Also shown on Figs. 23 and 24 is similar data for the open-loop system (no feedback control), thus illustrating the value of optimal feedback control, especially for penalty function magnitudes of $\sigma \approx 0.1$.

For example, from Fig. 23 with $\sigma = 0.1$, the average mean cost per year is

Without control	850 ($\$ \times 10^9)^2$ per year
With optimal control	100 ($\$ \times 10^9)^2$ per year

which gives a reduction in dollars per year for the *a priori* system of a factor of

$$\rho_{\text{ap}} = \left(\frac{850}{100}\right)^{1/2} = 2.91$$

Another way to view the same result is to calculate the net reduction in the cost functional in dollars for a given period of time, say 25 years. The result is

$$[(850)^{1/2} - (100)^{1/2}]\, 25 = 480 \text{ billion dollars}$$

Thus the potential payoff for optimal control is clearly quite large.

A similar result is obtained for the optimal control of the least-squares system. In this case, again for $\sigma = 0.1$, the basic data for the average value of the cost functional per year are

Without control	4900 ($\$ \times 10^9)^2$ per year
With optimal control	150 ($\$ \times 10^9)^2$ per year

which gives a reduction in terms of equivalent dollars per year by a factor of

$$\rho_{Rs} = \frac{4900}{150} = 32.7$$

The corresponding net reduction in the cost functional over a period of 25 years is

$$[(4900)^{1/2} - (150)^{1/2}]\, 25 = 1460 \text{ billion dollars}$$

which is again quite a large potential payoff for optimal control.

However, a greater benefit of control is evident from the figures. Note that the scatter in the data is significantly reduced as the control effectiveness is increased (penalty function on control activity σ is reduced), thus indicating tighter control over the basic system dynamics and a resulting reduced sensitivity to disturbances and/or system parameter estimation.

VII. Conclusions and Recommendations

The primary conclusion of this chapter is that modern control theory is *fundamental* to the problem of economic policy determination for macro economic systems. It provides the natural framework for attacking the problem. Such an approach to the problem reveals areas which have a major impact on the choice of optimal economic policies, some of which have little, if any, definition in theoretical or quantitative terms. Thus further research is necessary before such optimal policies can be considered in a quantitative manner.

The extensions of control system theory in the past 15 years to multi-dimensional systems and to the optimal control of those multidimensional systems, in addition to the advances made by economists in the modeling of dynamic macroeconomic systems, are the primary reasons why this conclusion is possible today, but not so in the past. The potential payoff to society is large, as was shown for either set of system parameters.[18]

The optimal economic control policies which are ultimately obtained when the required research in the necessary areas is completed will probably contain some interesting changes from current theory. This is because of the significant changes in the optimal policies which occurred, both for the time in the future over which it is desired to optimize (time-to-go $N-k$) and for changes in the control penalty function and/or the open-loop system dynamics.

There is much further research to be accomplished before application of optimal control policies to the practical problems of fiscal and monetary decisions is made. However, the significant point to recognize is that *the problem is fundamentally a control problem.* Thus modern control theory as developed in the engineering sciences provides the framework for the further research necessary to make the techniques more useful.[19]

The primary areas for further research are grouped by the disciplines in which they most generally apply.

A. Control Systems Engineering Areas of Research

(1) Equation (2) for non-automotive consumption C^{NA} includes a lag from total income *GNP* to non-automotive consumption. This was done by Norton to make an easier transition to control theory. However, a better

[18] It is obvious that some feedback does exist in the current economic situation. Hence the actual payoff will be less than shown here.

[19] A quote from Lucretius seems in order here when he said, "I speak, not on my prejudices, but on the nature of things."

fit of the economic data is obtained if there are no lags between income and non-automotive consumption. That is, a better fit is obtained if

$$C^{NA}(j) = c_0 + c_1 GNP(j) - c_2 r(j-1) + c_3 C^{NA}(j-1)$$

This change in the structural equation should be amenable to control theory and its effect on the optimal policy should be examined.

(2) The numerical results show a significant change in the optimal control policy for the two different sets of open-loop system parameters. This strongly suggests that control system engineers should investigate the applicability of sensitivity control theory to minimize the sensitivity of the optimal control policy to the most significant parameters of the system which might not be well known (or are subject to change).

(3) The macroeconomic model used in this discussion was purposely chosen to be complex enough to account for the basic performance of a market economy like that of the United States economy, but yet simple enough to be tractable. The necessity of such a level of complexity is obvious. Yet the problem still remains of relating these results to the more detailed models such as the Brookings model of the United States. It appears that future research should be conducted both in the direction of correlating with the complex models and in the direction of optimal control using simpler models than that of this paper.

To correlate with the large scale econometric models, multilevel control theory appears to provide a useful framework for research (*53*, *54*).

B. Macroeconomics Areas of Research

(1) Recognizing the difficulties in macroeconomic parameter estimation, it is still necessary to observe that further research should be conducted to improve the estimates of the parameters, especially since the optimal control policy has been shown to significantly depend on these parameters.

(2) Perhaps not as widely recognized, but nevertheless of major importance, is research directed towards the determination of reasonable form and values for the penalty function to be placed on the control activity [R in Eq. (57)].

(3) In order to reasonably design any control system, a mathematical model of the stochastic characteristics of the variables is required. Such a noise model does not exist at this time. However, it would be very useful and research in this direction is recommended.

Many other areas of research in this general problem area are interesting and appear to be fruitful. However, these seem most promising as the next steps which should be made.

References

1. H. M. WAGNER, "Principles of Operations Research with Applications to Managerial Decisions." Prentice-Hall, Englewood Cliffs, New Jersey, 1969.
2. C. P. BONINI, "Simulation of Information and Decision Systems in the Firm." Prentice-Hall, Englewood Cliffs, New Jersey, 1963.
3. R. M. CYERT and J. G. MARCH, "A Behavioral Theory of the Firm." Prentice-Hall, Englewood Cliffs, New Jersey, 1963.
4. K. SHELL, ed., "Essays On the Theory of Optimal Economic Growth." M.I.T. Press, Cambridge, Massachusetts, 1967.
5. R. DORFMAN, An economic interpretation of optimal control theory. *Amer. Econ. Rev.* **54**, 817–831 (1969).
6. J. S. DUESENBERRY, G. FROMM, L. R. KLEIN, and E. KUH, eds., "The Brookings Quarterly Econometric Model of the U.S. Economy." Rand McNally, New York, and North-Holland Publ., Amsterdam, 1965.
7. G. FROMM and P. TAUBMAN, "Policy Simulations With An Econometric Model." The Brookings Institution, Washington, D.C., 1968.
8. J. S. DUESENBERRY, G. FROMM, J. R. KLEIN, and E. KUH, eds., "The Brookings Model: Some Further Results," Rand McNally, New York, and North-Holland Publ., Amsterdam, 1969.
9. M. K. EVANS and L. R. KLEIN, "The Wharton Econometric Forecasting Model." Univ. of Pennsylvania, Philadelphia, Pennsylvania, 1967.
10. F. DE LEEUW and E. GRAMLICH, The Federal Reserve—MIT econometric model. *Federal Reserve Bull.* **54**, 17–40 (1968).
11. M. LIEBENBERG, A. A. HIRSCH, and J. POPKIN, A quarterly econometric model of the United States: a progress report. *Survey Curr. Business* **46**, 13 ff. (1966).
12. L. C. THUROW, A fiscal policy model of the United States. *Survey Curr. Business* **49**, 45–64 (1969).
13. A. TUSTIN, "The Mechanism of Economic Systems." Harvard Univ. Press, Cambridge, Massachusetts, 1953.
14. A. W. PHILLIPS, Stabilization policy in a closed economy. *Econ. J.* **64**, 290–323 (1954).
15. A. W. PHILLIPS, Stabilization policy and the time-forms of lagged responses. *Econ. J.* **67**, 265–277 (1957).
16. C. J. VAN EIJK and J. SANDEE, Quantitative determination of an optimal economic policy. *Econometrica* **27**, 1–13, (1959).
17. C. HOLT, Linear decision rules for economic stabilization and growth. *Quart. J. Econ.* **76**, 21–45 (1962).
18. C. HOLT, Quantitative decision analysis and national policy: how can we bridge the gap? *In* "Quantitative Planning of Economic Policy" (B. G. Hickman, ed.), pp. 252–261. The Brookings Institution, Washington, D.C., 1965.
19. H. THEIL, "Optimal Decision Rules for Government and Industry," Rand McNally, Chicago, 1964.
20. P. A. SAMUELSON, Interactions between the multiplier analysis and the principles of acceleration. *Rev. Econ. Statist.* **21**, 75–78 (1939).
21. J. R. HICKS, "A Contribution to the Theory of the Trade Cycle." Oxford Univ. Press (Clarendon), London and New York, 1950.
22. N. KALDOR, A model of the trade cycle. *Econ. J.* **50**, 78–92 (1940).
23. R. M. GOODWIN, A model of cyclical growth. *In* "The Business Cycle in the Postwar World" (E. Lundberg, ed.), pp. 203–221. Macmillan, London, 1955.

24. J. S. Duesenberry, "Business Cycles and Economic Growth." McGraw-Hill, New York, 1958.
25. D. Slutsky, The summation of random causes as the source of cyclic processes. *Econometrica* **5**, 105–146 (1937).
26. R. Frisch, Propagation problems and impulse problems in dynamics. *In* "Economic Essays in Honor of Gustav Cassel." Allen and Unwin, London, 1933.
27. D. B. Suits, The demand for new automobiles in the U.S., 1929–56. *Rev. Econ. Statist.* **28**, 273–278 (1958).
28. G. C. Chow, "Demand for Automobiles in the United States," North-Holland Publ., Amsterdam, 1957.
29. G. C. Chow, Statistical demand functions for automobiles and their uses for forecasting. *In* "The Demand for Durable Goods" (A. C. Hargerger, ed.), pp. 149–178. Univ. of Chicago Press, Chicago, Illinois, 1960.
30. T. M. Brown, Habit, persistence and lags in consumer behavior. *Econometrica* **20**, 355–371 (1952).
31. L. R. Klein and A. S. Goldberger, "An Econometric Model of the United States, 1929–1952." North-Holland Publ., Amsterdam, 1955.
32. M. Friedman, "The Theory of the Consumption Function Princeton." Princeton Univ. Press, New Jersey, 1957.
33. R. F. Muth, The demand for non-farm housing. *In* "The Demand for Durable Goods" (A. C. Harberger, ed.), pp. 29–96. Univ. of Chicago Press, Chicago, Illinois, 1960.
34. T. H. Lee, The stock demand elasticities on non-farm housing. *Rev. Econ. Statist.* **46**, 82–89 (1964).
35. H. Chenery, Overcapacity and the acceleration principle. *Econometrica* **20**, 1–28 (1952).
36. P. G. Darling, Manufacturers' inventory investment 1947–1958: an application of acceleration analysis. *Amer. Econ. Rev.* **49**, 950–962 (1959).
37. D. L. Erickson, Sensitivity constrained optimal control policies for a dynamic model of the U.S. national economy. Ph.D dissertation, Dept. Eng., Univ. of California, Los Angeles, September, 1968.
38. M. Bronfenbrenner and T. Mayer, Liquidity functions in the American economy. *Econometrica* **27**, 810–834 (1960).
39. C. F. Christ, Interest rates and "Portfolio Selection" among liquid assets in the U.S. "Measurement of Economics," pp. 201–218. Stanford Univ. Press, Stanford, California, 1963.
40. F. Gehrels and S. Wiggins, Interest rates and fixed investments. *Amer. Econ. Rev.* **47**, 79–92 (1957).
41. D. W. Jorgenson, Capital theory and investment behavior. *Amer. Econ. Rev.* **53**, 247–259 (1963).
42. A. Ando, E. C. Brown, J. Kareken, and R. M. Solow, Lags in fiscal and monetary policy. "Stabilization Policies, Studies Prepared for the Commission on Money and Credit," pp. 1–164. Prentice-Hall, Englewood-Cliffs, New Jersey, 1963.
43. L. R. Klein, Studies in investment behavior, "Conference on Business Cycles," pp. 223–277. Nat. Bur. Econ. Res., New York, 1951.
44. H. A. Latane, Cash balances and the interest rate: a pragmatic approach. *Rev. Econ. Statist.* **58**, 451–461 (1954).
45. H. A. Latane, Income velocity and interest rates: a pragmatic approach. *Rev. Econ. Statist.* **42**, 445–449 (1966).
46. A. W. Phillips, The relation between unemployment and the rate of change of money wage rates in the United Kingdom, 1861–1947. *Economica* pp. 283–299 (November, 1958).

47. C. L. SCHULTZE, Recent inflation in the United States, Study Paper No. 1. "Study of Employment Growth and Price Level," Joint Economic Committee, U.S. Government Printing Office, Washington, D.C., 1959.

48. P. A. SAMUELSON and R. M. SOLOW, Analytical aspects of anti-inflation policy. *Amer. Econ. Rev.* **50**, 177–195 (1960).

49. L. R. KLEIN and R. G. BODKIN, Empirical aspects of the tradeoffs among three goals: high level employment, price stability, and economic growth. "Inflation, Growth and Employment, Studies Prepared for the Commission on Money and Credit," pp. 367–428. Prentice-Hall, Englewood-Cliffs, New Jersey, 1964.

50. R. G. BODKIN, E. P. BOND, G. L. REUBER, and T. R. ROBINSON, "Price Stability and High Employment: The Options for Canadian Economic Policy," Economic Council of Canada, Queen's Printer, Ottawa, 1967.

51. J. T. TOU, "Optimum Design of Digital Control Systems." Academic Press, New York, 1963.

52. L. F. BUCHANAN and A. R. STUBBERUD, Problems in optimal control of macroeconomic systems. *In* "Lecture Notes in Operations Research and Mathematical Economics: Computing Methods in Optimization Problems" (M. Beckman and H. P. Kunzi, eds.), pp. 30–42, Springer, New York, 1969.

53. D. A. WISMER, Optimal control of distributed parameter systems using multilevel techniques. Ph.D. in Engineering, Univ. of California, Los Angeles, 1966.

54. E. J. BAUMAN, Multi-level optimization techniques with applications to trajectory decomposition. Ph.D. in Engineering, Univ. of California, Los Angeles, 1966.

Numerical Solution of Nonlinear Equations and Nonlinear, Two-Point Boundary-Value Problems[1]

A. MIELE, S. NAQVI, A. V. LEVY, AND R. R. IYER

Department of Mechanical and Aerospace Engineering and Materials Science
Rice University, Houston, Texas

I. Description of the Problems

This paper presents general methods for solving nonlinear equations and nonlinear, two-point boundary value problems. The nature of these problems and the methods employed are given below.

A. Nonlinear Equations

In Section II, we present a general method for solving nonlinear, algebraic or transcendental, equations of the form

$$\phi(x) = 0 \tag{1}$$

[1] This research, supported by the National Science Foundation under Grant No. GP-18522, is a condensation of the investigations described by Miele *et al.* (*1*, *2*).

where x and ϕ are n-vectors. The method is based on the consideration of the performance index P defined as

$$P = \phi^T \phi \tag{2}$$

Clearly, P represents the cumulative error in the equations.

A *modified quasilinearization algorithm* is generated by requiring the first variation of the performance index δP to be negative. This algorithm differs from the *ordinary quasilinearization algorithm* because of the inclusion of the scaling factor or stepsize α in the system of variations. The main property of the modified quasilinearization algorithm is the descent property: if the stepsize α is sufficiently small, the reduction in P is guaranteed. Convergence to the desired solution is achieved when the inequality $P \leqslant \varepsilon$ is met, where ε is a small, preselected number.

The algorithm is represented by

$$\tilde{x} = x + \Delta x = x + \alpha A \tag{3}$$

where Δx denotes the variation leading from the nominal state x to the varied state $\tilde{x}$ and

$$A = \Delta x / \alpha \tag{4}$$

is the variation per unit stepsize.

The n components of the variation per unit stepsize A are governed by a system of n linear equations, which is solved by Gaussian elimination. Several numerical examples are presented. They illustrate (i) the simplicity as well as the rapidity of convergence of the modified quasilinearization algorithm and (ii) the importance of stepsize control.

B. Nonlinear, Two-Point Boundary-Value Problems

In Section III, we present a general method for solving nonlinear, differential equations of the form

$$\dot{x} - \phi(x, t) = 0, \qquad 0 \leqslant t \leqslant 1 \tag{5}$$

subject to boundary conditions of the form

$$f[x(0)] = 0, \qquad g[x(1)] = 0, \qquad h[x(0), x(1)] = 0 \tag{6}$$

Here, t is a scalar, x and ϕ are n-vectors, and f, g, h are p, q, r-vectors, with

$$p + q + r = n \tag{7}$$

The method is based on the consideration of the performance index P defined as

$$P = \int_0^1 (\dot{x} - \phi)^T (\dot{x} - \phi)\, dt + f^T f + g^T g + h^T h \tag{8}$$

Clearly, P is the cumulative error in the differential equations and the boundary conditions.

A modified quasilinearization algorithm is generated by requiring the first variation of the performance index δP to be negative. This algorithm differs from the ordinary quasilinearization algorithm because of the inclusion of the scaling factor or stepwise α in the system of variations. The main property of the modified quasilinearization algorithm is the descent property: if the stepsize α is sufficiently small, the reduction in P is guaranteed. Convergence to the desired solution is achieved when the inequality $P \leqslant \varepsilon$ is met, where ε is a small, preselected number.

The algorithm is represented by

$$\tilde{x}(t) = x(t) + \Delta x(t) = x(t) + \alpha A(t) \tag{9}$$

where $\Delta x(t)$ denotes the variation leading from the nominal state $x(t)$ to the varied state $\tilde{x}(t)$ and

$$A(t) = \Delta x(t)/\alpha \tag{10}$$

is the variation per unit stepsize.

The n components of the variation per unit stepsize $A(t)$ are governed by a system of n nonhomogeneous, linear differential equations subject to p separated initial conditions, q separated final conditions, and r mixed boundary conditions. This system is solved employing the *method of particular solutions*: $q + r + 1$ independent solutions are combined linearly, and the coefficients of the combination are determined so that the linear system is satisfied.

Several numerical examples are presented. They illustrate (i) the simplicity as well as the rapidity of convergence of the modified quasilinearization algorithm and (ii) the importance of stepsize control.

II. Solution of Nonlinear Equations

A. Introduction

In recent years, considerable attention has been devoted to the solution of nonlinear equations, algebraic or transcendental [see, for example, refs. (*3–12*)]. The most direct way to solve these equations is to employ quasilinearization, that is, to replace the nonlinear system by one that is linear in the perturbations about a nominal point. The resulting algorithm is called ordinary quasilinearization algorithm.

The main advantage of the ordinary quasilinearization algorithm is simplicity and rapidity of convergence if the nominal point is in the neighborhood of the solution point. There are cases, however, where ordinary quasilinearization diverges due to excessive magnitude of the variations. This is why it is convenient to imbed the linearized system into a more general system by means of the scaling factor α, $0 \leqslant \alpha \leqslant 1$, applied to each forcing term. The resulting algorithm is called modified quasilinearization algorithm.

At first glance, the above imbedding procedure may seem arbitrary. However, a rigorous conceptual justification can be given through the consideration of the performance index P: this is the cumulative error in the equations. By computing the first variation of P and requiring δP to be negative, one generates the modified quasilinearization algorithm. The main property of this algorithm is the descent property: if the stepsize α is sufficiently small, the reduction in P is guaranteed. In addition, the performance index P can also be employed as a convergence criterion: the algorithm is terminated when P becomes smaller than some preselected value.

B. Modified Quasilinearization

Consider a system described by the equation

$$\phi(x) = 0 \tag{11}$$

where x and ϕ are n-vectors. Assume that the first derivative of the function ϕ with respect to the vector x exists and is continuous. Also, assume that a solution to Eq. (11) exists. The problem is to find the vector x which solves Eq. (11).

Performance Index. In general, the system (11) is nonlinear, so that approximate methods must be employed. In this connection, let the performance index P be defined as[2]

$$P = \phi^T \phi \tag{12}$$

The scalar function P measures the error in the equation; therefore, $P = 0$ for any x satisfying Eq. (11), and $P > 0$ otherwise. When approximate methods are employed, they must ultimately lead to a state x such that

$$P \leqslant \varepsilon \tag{13}$$

where the quantity ε is a small, preselected number.

Modified Quasilinearization. Here, we present a modification of the quasilinearization algorithm which has a descent property in the per-

[2] The superscript T denotes the transpose of a matrix.

formance index P. Consider a nominal point x and a varied point $\tilde{x}$ such that

$$\tilde{x} = x + \Delta x \tag{14}$$

The passage from the nominal point to the varied point causes the performance index P to change. To first order, we see that

$$\delta P = 2\phi^T \delta\phi \tag{15}$$

where the symbol $\delta(\ldots)$ denotes the first variation.

Next, consider the system of variations defined by

$$\delta\phi = -\alpha\phi \tag{16}$$

where α is a scaling factor (or stepsize) in the range

$$0 \leqslant \alpha \leqslant 1 \tag{17}$$

Consequently, the first variation of the performance index P becomes

$$\delta P = -2\alpha\phi^T\phi \tag{18}$$

and, in the light of the definition (12), is equivalent to

$$\delta P = -2\alpha P \tag{19}$$

Note that, for any nominal point x not satisfying Eq. (11),

$$P > 0 \tag{20}$$

Therefore, for α positive, one has

$$\delta P < 0 \tag{21}$$

This is the basic descent property of the algorithm defined by Eq. (16): it guarantees that, if α is sufficiently small,

$$\tilde{P} < P \tag{22}$$

System of Variations. To first order, the change of the function ϕ is related to the change of the state Δx as follows:[3]

$$\delta\phi = \phi_x{}^T \Delta x \tag{23}$$

where the matrix ϕ_x is $n \times n$. Consequently, Eq. (16) can be rewritten as

$$\phi_x{}^T\Delta x + \alpha\phi = 0 \tag{24}$$

For a given value of α, Eq. (24) is equivalent to n scalar equations which are linear in the n components of the vector Δx. The associated algorithm is called modified quasilinearization algorithm.

[3] The matrix φ_x is defined so that its ith column is the gradient of the ith scalar component of φ with respect to the vector x.

For $\alpha = 1$, Eq. (24) becomes identical with that of ordinary quasilinearization, that is, the equation obtained by linearizing Eq. (11) about a nominal point x. While modified quasilinearization exhibits the descent property (21)–(22), this is not necessarily the case with ordinary quasilinearization. This means that, if Eq. (24) is employed with $\alpha = 1$, the performance index P may actually increase when passing from the nominal point x to the varied point $\tilde{x}$.

Coordinate Transformation. To simplify the problem, we introduce the auxiliary variable

$$A = \Delta x/\alpha \tag{25}$$

and rewrite Eq. (24) in the form

$$\phi_x{}^T A + \phi = 0 \tag{26}$$

This vector equation is equivalent to n scalar equations which are linear in the n components of the vector A. With A known and the stepsize α specified, the correction Δx is obtained from Eq. (25), and the varied point $\tilde{x}$ is computed from Eq. (14).

Determination of the Stepsize. After combining Eqs. (14) and (25), we obtain the relation

$$\tilde{x} = x + \alpha A \tag{27}$$

Since x is given and A is known from Eq. (26), Eq. (27) yields a one-parameter family of solutions, the parameter being the stepsize α. For this one-parameter family, the performance index P becomes a function of the form

$$P = P(\alpha) \tag{28}$$

At $\alpha = 0$, the slope of this function is negative and is given by

$$P_\alpha(0) = -2P(0) \tag{29}$$

The function (28) exhibits a relative minimum with respect to α, that is, a point where

$$P_\alpha(\alpha) = 0 \tag{30}$$

This point can be determined by means of a one-dimensional search (for example, using quadratic interpolation, cubic interpolation, or quasilinearization). Ideally, this procedure should be used iteratively until the modulus of the slope satisfies the following inequality:

$$|P_\alpha(\alpha)| \leqslant \theta \tag{31}$$

where θ is a small, preselected number.

Since the rigorous determination of α takes time on a computer, one might renounce solving Eq. (30) with a particular degree of precision and determine the stepsize in a noniterative fashion. To this effect, we first assign the value

$$\alpha = 1 \tag{32}$$

to the stepsize; this corresponds to full quasilinearization of Eq. (11) and is the value which would solve Eq. (30) exactly, should Eq. (11) be linear. Of course, the stepsize (32) is acceptable only if

$$P(\alpha) < P(0) \tag{33}$$

Otherwise, the previous value of α must be replaced by some smaller value in the range (17), for example, using a bisection process, until Ineq. (33) is met. This is guaranteed by the descent property (21)–(22).

Summary of the Algorithm. In the light of the previous discussion, we summarize the modified quasilinearization algorithm as follows:

(a) Assume a nominal point x. At this point, determine the vector ϕ and the matrix ϕ_x.

(b) Determine the vector A by solving Eq. (26).

(c) Consider the one-parameter family of solutions (27) and perform a one-dimensional search on the function (28); specifically, perform a bisection process on α (starting from $\alpha = 1$), and continue the process until Ineq. (33) is satisfied.

(d) With the stepsize α known, compute the varied point $\tilde{x}$ from (27).

(e) With $\tilde{x}$ known, the iteration is completed. The varied point $\tilde{x}$ becomes the nominal point x for the next iteration. That is, return to (a) and iterate the algorithm.

(f) The algorithm is terminated when the stopping condition (13) is satisfied.

C. Numerical Examples[4]

In order to illustrate the theory, several numerical examples were developed using a Burroughs B-5500 computer and double-precision arithmetic. The algorithm was programmed in FORTRAN IV. *Convergence* was defined as follows:

$$P \leqslant 10^{-20} \tag{34}$$

and the number of iterations at convergence N_* was recorded. Conversely, *nonconvergence* was defined by means of the inequalities

(a) $$N \geqslant 100 \tag{35}$$

[4] The symbols employed in this section denote scalar quantities.

or

(b)
$$N_S \geqslant 20 \tag{36}$$

or

(c)
$$M \geqslant 0.4 \times 10^{69} \tag{37}$$

Here, N is the iteration number, N_S is the number of bisections of the stepsize α (starting from $\alpha = 1$) required to satisfy Ineq. (33), and M is the modulus of any of the quantities employed in the algorithm. Satisfaction of Ineq. (35) indicates divergence or extreme slowness of convergence; in turn, satisfaction of Ineq. (36) indicates extreme smallness of the displacement Δx; finally, satisfaction of Ineq. (37) indicates exponential overflow for the Burroughs B-5500 computer: the computer program is automatically stopped.

EXAMPLE C-1. Consider the nonlinear system

$$x^2 - y - 8 = 0, \qquad x^4 - y^2 = 0 \tag{38}$$

which has solutions

$$x = 2, \qquad y = -4 \tag{39}$$

and

$$x = -2, \qquad y = -4 \tag{40}$$

Assume the following nominal coordinates:

$$x = y = \tfrac{1}{2} \tag{41}$$

which do not satisfy the system (38). Starting with these nominal coordinates, we employ the algorithm of Section II,B. Convergence to the solution (39) is achieved in $N_* = 8$ iterations (see Table I). The converged coordinates are

$$x = 2.0000, \qquad y = -4.0000 \tag{42}$$

EXAMPLE C-2. Consider the nonlinear system

$$\begin{aligned} x^2 - x^3y^5z + z^3 - 1 &= 0 \\ y\sin(\tfrac{1}{2}\pi x) - 1 &= 0 \\ 2xy^2z^3 + y\exp(1 - x) - 3 &= 0 \end{aligned} \tag{43}$$

a known solution of which is

$$x = y = z = 1 \tag{44}$$

TABLE I

RESULTS PERTAINING TO EXAMPLE C-1

N	α	P
0	—	0.6×10^{2}
1	$\frac{1}{16}$	0.6×10^{2}
2	$\frac{1}{4}$	0.4×10^{2}
3	$\frac{1}{4}$	0.1×10^{2}
4	$\frac{1}{2}$	0.2×10^{1}
5	1	0.5×10^{-1}
6	1	0.3×10^{-5}
7	1	0.7×10^{-15}
8	1	0.5×10^{-34}

Assume the following nominal coordinates:

$$x = y = z = \tfrac{1}{4} \tag{45}$$

which do not satisfy the system (43). Starting with these nominal coordinates, we employ the algorithm of Section II,B. Convergence to the solution (44) is achieved in $N_* = 7$ iterations (see Table II). The converged coordinates are

$$x = 1.0000, \qquad y = 1.0000, \qquad z = 1.0000 \tag{46}$$

TABLE II

RESULTS PERTAINING TO EXAMPLE C-2

N	α	P
0	—	0.7×10^{1}
1	$\frac{1}{2}$	0.5×10^{1}
2	1	0.1×10^{0}
3	1	0.1×10^{-2}
4	1	0.1×10^{-6}
5	1	0.9×10^{-11}
6	1	0.4×10^{-19}
7	1	0.9×10^{-36}

EXAMPLE C-3. Consider the nonlinear system

$$\begin{aligned} (x-u)^2 + (y-w)^2 + (x+y+u+w)^2 - 16 &= 0 \\ x \sin(\tfrac{1}{2}\pi u) + y \cos(\tfrac{1}{2}\pi w) - 1 &= 0 \\ x + y^2 + u^3 + w^4 - 4 &= 0 \\ x + 2y + 3u + 4w - 10 &= 0 \end{aligned} \tag{47}$$

a known solution of which is

$$x = y = u = w = 1 \tag{48}$$

Assume the following nominal coordinates:

$$x = y = u = w = 3 \tag{49}$$

which do not satisfy the system (47). Starting with these nominal coordinates, we employ the algorithm of Section II,B. Convergence to the solution (48) is achieved in $N_* = 25$ iterations (see Table III). The converged coordinates are

$$x = 0.9999, \quad y = 1.0000, \quad u = 1.0000, \quad w = 0.9999 \tag{50}$$

TABLE III

RESULTS PERTAINING TO EXAMPLE C-3

N	α	P	N	α	P
0	—	0.3×10^{5}	13	1	0.2×10^{-6}
1	$\frac{1}{4}$	0.2×10^{5}	14	1	0.1×10^{-7}
2	1	0.1×10^{5}	15	1	0.9×10^{-9}
3	1	0.2×10^{4}	16	1	0.6×10^{-10}
4	$\frac{1}{2}$	0.1×10^{4}	17	1	0.3×10^{-11}
5	$\frac{1}{4}$	0.8×10^{3}	18	1	0.2×10^{-12}
6	1	0.1×10^{3}	19	1	0.1×10^{-13}
7	1	0.4×10^{1}	20	1	0.9×10^{-15}
8	1	0.1×10^{0}	21	1	0.5×10^{-16}
9	1	0.8×10^{-2}	22	1	0.3×10^{-17}
10	1	0.1×10^{-2}	23	1	0.2×10^{-18}
11	1	0.6×10^{-4}	24	1	0.1×10^{-19}
12	1	0.4×10^{-5}	25	1	0.9×10^{-21}

EXAMPLE C-4. Consider the nonlinear system

$$\begin{aligned}
&(x - y)^2 + (y - z)^2 + (2z - u - w)^2 = 0\\
&x^2 + y^2 + z^2 + u^2 + w^2 - 5 = 0\\
&(x - 1)^2 + (y - 2)^2 + w^4 - 2 = 0\\
&x + 2y^2 + 3z^3 + 4u^4 + 5w^5 - 15 = 0\\
&x^2 + xyz - u^3 - 1 = 0
\end{aligned} \tag{51}$$

a known solution of which is

$$x = y = z = u = w = 1 \tag{52}$$

Assume the following nominal coordinates:

$$x = y = z = 2, \qquad u = w = 3 \tag{53}$$

which do not satisfy the system (51). Starting with these nominal coordinates, we employ the algorithm of Section II,B. Convergence to the solution (52) is achieved in $N_* = 25$ iterations (see Table IV). The converged coordinates are

$$x = 1.0000, \quad y = 1.0000, \quad z = 0.9999, \quad u = 1.0000, \quad w = 1.0000 \tag{54}$$

TABLE IV

RESULTS PERTAINING TO EXAMPLE C-4

N	α	P	N	α	P
0	—	0.2×10^{7}	13	1	0.2×10^{-6}
1	$\frac{1}{16}$	0.2×10^{7}	14	1	0.1×10^{-7}
2	1	0.3×10^{6}	15	1	0.1×10^{-8}
3	1	0.8×10^{5}	16	1	0.7×10^{-10}
4	1	0.1×10^{5}	17	1	0.4×10^{-11}
5	1	0.1×10^{4}	18	1	0.2×10^{-12}
6	1	0.8×10^{2}	19	1	0.1×10^{-13}
7	1	0.4×10^{1}	20	1	0.1×10^{-14}
8	1	0.2×10^{0}	21	1	0.6×10^{-16}
9	1	0.1×10^{-1}	22	1	0.4×10^{-17}
10	1	0.1×10^{-2}	23	1	0.2×10^{-18}
11	1	0.7×10^{-4}	24	1	0.1×10^{-19}
12	1	0.4×10^{-5}	25	1	0.1×10^{-20}

D. Remarks

The following remarks are pertinent to the previous theoretical development.

(1) If the stepsize is set at the constant value $\alpha = 1$, the modified quasilinearization algorithm of Section II,B reduces to the ordinary quasilinearization algorithm. While modified quasilinearization exhibits the descent property (21)–(22), this is not necessarily the case with ordinary quasilinearization. Therefore, in ordinary quasilinearization, the performance index P may actually increase when passing from the nominal point x to the varied point $\tilde{x}$.

With reference to the examples of Section II,C, computer runs were made employing both modified quasilinearization and ordinary quasilinearization. In Table V, the number of iterations at convergence N_* is

TABLE V
NUMBER OF ITERATIONS AT CONVERGENCE

	N_*	
	$\alpha \leqslant 1$	$\alpha = 1$
Example C-1	8	12
Example C-2	7	11
Example C-3	25	66
Example C-4	25	Nonconvergence (*a*)

indicated and, as the table shows, the experimental evidence is in favor of modified quasilinearization. It is emphasized that the above conclusion was obtained through particular examples and that, consequently, the subject requires further investigation.

(2) The fundamental property of the modified quasilinearization algorithm is the descent property (21)–(22). This local property guarantees the decrease of the performance index P when passing from the nominal point x to the varied point $\tilde{x}$. However, it does not guarantee convergence; that is, it does not guarantee that $P \to 0$ as $N \to \infty$. This is due to the fact that convergence depends on the analytical nature of the function ϕ and on the nominal point x chosen to start the algorithm.

The above point can be illustrated with reference to Example C-4 and the following nominal coordinates:

$$x = 1, \qquad y = 2, \qquad z = 3, \qquad u = 4, \qquad w = 5 \tag{55}$$

Ordinary quasilinearization fails to converge because of exponential overflow [nonconvergence (c)]. Modified quasilinearization fails to converge because of excessive number of stepsize bisections [nonconvergence (b)].

E. Discussion and Conclusions

In Section II, a general method for solving nonlinear equations of the form $\phi(x) = 0$ is presented, where x and ϕ are n-vectors. The method is based on the consideration of the performance index P, the cumulative error in the equations.

A modified quasilinearization algorithm is generated by requiring the first variation of the performance index δP to be negative. The algorithm has the form $\tilde{x} = x + \alpha A$. Here, α, $0 \leqslant \alpha \leqslant 1$, is the stepsize and A is obtained by solving a system of n linear equations by Gaussian elimination.

The main property of the modified quasilinearization algorithm is the descent property: if the stepsize α is sufficiently small, the reduction in P is guaranteed. Not only is P employed as a guide during progression of the algorithm, but also as a convergence criterion: the algorithm is terminated when the performance index P becomes smaller than some preselected value.

Several numerical examples are presented. They illustrate (i) the simplicity as well as the rapidity of convergence of the algorithm and (ii) the importance of stepsize control.

III. Solution of Nonlinear, Two-Point Boundary-Value Problems

A. Introduction

In recent years, considerable attention has been devoted to the solution of the two-point boundary-value problem for nonhomogeneous, linear differential systems. Among the techniques available, we mention (a) the method of *adjoint variables* and (b) the method of *complementary functions* (*13*). These two methods have one common characteristic: each requires the solution of two differential systems, namely, the original system plus the derived system; this derived system is the adjoint system for (a) and the homogeneous system for (b).

With particular regard to high-speed digital computing, programming can be made simpler if one employs the original system only. This technique, a modification of (b), consists of combining linearly several particular solutions of the original, nonhomogeneous system. For this reason, it has been called the method of particular solutions (*14*). It has the following advantages with respect to the previous techniques: (1) it makes use of only one differential system, namely, the original, nonhomogeneous system; (2) each particular solution satisfies the same prescribed initial conditions; and (3) in a physical problem, each particular solution represents a physically possible trajectory, even though it satisfies only the initial conditions and not the final conditions.

While the method of particular solutions has been developed for linear systems, it can also be used to solve nonlinear systems. First, quasilinearization must be employed, and the nonlinear system must be replaced by one that is linear in the perturbation about a nominal function [see, for example, refs. (*15–18*)]; to this linear system, the method of particular solutions can be applied to find the perturbation leading to a new nominal function; then, the procedure is employed iteratively (*19*).

The main advantage of the ordinary quasilinearization algorithm is simplicity and rapidity of convergence if the nominal function is a fair approximation to the solution. There are cases, however, where ordinary quasilinearization diverges due to excessive magnitude of the variations. This is why it is convenient to imbed the linearized system into a more general system by means of the scaling factor α, $0 \leqslant \alpha \leqslant 1$, applied to each forcing term. The resulting algorithm is called modified quasilinearization algorithm.

At first glance, the above imbedding procedure may seem arbitrary. However, a rigorous conceptual justification can be given through the consideration of the performance index P: this is the cumulative error in the differential equations and the boundary conditions. By computing the first variation of the functional P and requiring δP to be negative, one generates the modified quasilinearization algorithm. The main property of this algorithm is the descent property: if the stepsize α is sufficiently small, the reduction in P is guaranteed. In addition, the performance index P can also be employed as a convergence criterion: the algorithm is terminated when P becomes smaller than some preselected value.

B. Modified Quasilinearization

Consider a system described by the differential equation

$$\dot{x} - \phi(x, t) = 0, \qquad 0 \leqslant t \leqslant 1 \tag{56}$$

subject to the boundary conditions

$$f[x(0)] = 0, \qquad g[x(1)] = 0, \qquad h[x(0), x(1)] = 0 \tag{57}$$

Here, x and ϕ are n-vectors, f is a p-vector, g a q-vector, and h an r-vector, with $p + q + r = n$. The time t, a scalar, is the independent variable; without loss of generality, the prescribed initial time is $t = 0$ and the prescribed final time is $t = 1$. The dot denotes a derivative with respect to t.

It is assumed that (a) the first derivative of the function ϕ with respect to the vector x exists and is continuous and (*b*) the first derivatives of the functions f, g, h with respect to the vectors $x(0)$ and $x(1)$ exist and are continuous. It is also assumed that a solution to Eqs. (56) and (57) exists. The problem is to find the continuous vector function $x(t)$ which solves Eqs. (56) and (57).

Performance Index. In general, the system (56)–(57) is nonlinear, so that approximate methods must be employed. In this connection, consider the class of continuous functions $x(t)$ not necessarily satisfying Eqs. (56) and (57). For these functions, let the performance index P be defined as

$$P = \int_0^1 (\dot{x} - \phi)^T(\dot{x} - \phi)\, dt + f^T f + g^T g + h^T h \tag{58}$$

The scalar functional P measures the cumulative error in the differential equation (56) and the boundary conditions (57); therefore, $P = 0$ for any $x(t)$ satisfying Eqs. (56) and (57), and $P > 0$ otherwise. When approximate methods are used, they must ultimately lead to a state $x(t)$ such that

$$P \leqslant \varepsilon \tag{59}$$

where ε is a small, preselected number.

Modified Quasilinearization. Here, we present a modification of the quasilinearization algorithm which has a descent property in the performance index P. Consider a nominal function $x(t)$ and a varied function $\tilde{x}(t)$ such that

$$\tilde{x}(t) = x(t) + \Delta x(t) \tag{60}$$

where $\Delta x(t)$ denotes the perturbation of x at a constant station t. The passage from the nominal function to the varied function causes the performance index P to change. To first order, we see that

$$\delta P = 2 \int_0^1 (\dot{x} - \phi)^T \delta(\dot{x} - \phi)\, dt + 2(f^T \delta f + g^T \delta g + h^T \delta h) \tag{61}$$

where the symbol $\delta(\ldots)$ denotes the first variation.

Next, consider the system of variations defined by

$$\delta(\dot{x} - \phi) = -\alpha(\dot{x} - \phi) \tag{62}$$

and

$$\delta f = -\alpha f, \qquad \delta g = -\alpha g, \qquad \delta h = -\alpha h \tag{63}$$

where α is a scaling factor (or stepsize) in the range

$$0 \leqslant \alpha \leqslant 1 \tag{64}$$

Consequently, the first variation of the performance index P becomes

$$\delta P = -2\alpha \int_0^1 (\dot{x} - \phi)^T(\dot{x} - \phi)\, dt - 2\alpha(f^T f + g^T g + h^T h) \tag{65}$$

and, in the light of the definition (58), is equivalent to

$$\delta P = -2\alpha P \tag{66}$$

Note that, for any nominal curve $x(t)$ not satisfying Eqs. (56) and (57),

$$P > 0 \tag{67}$$

Therefore, for α positive, one has

$$\delta P < 0 \tag{68}$$

This is the basic descent property of the algorithm defined by Eqs. (62) and (63): it guarantees that, if α is sufficiently small,

$$\tilde{P} < P \tag{69}$$

System of Variations. To first order, the changes of the functions appearing in Eqs. (62) and (63) are related to the change $\Delta x(t)$ as follows:[5]

$$\delta(\dot{x} - \phi) = \Delta\dot{x} - \phi_x{}^T \Delta x, \qquad 0 \leqslant t \leqslant 1 \tag{70}$$

and

$$\delta f = f_{x(0)}^T \Delta x(0), \qquad \delta g = g_{x(1)}^T \Delta x(1), \qquad \delta h = h_{x(0)}^T \Delta x(0) + h_{x(1)}^T \Delta x(1) \tag{71}$$

where the matrix ϕ_x is $n \times n$, the matrix $f_{x(0)}$ is $n \times p$, the matrix $g_{x(1)}$ is $n \times q$, and the matrices $h_{x(0)}$ and $h_{x(1)}$ are $n \times r$. Consequently, Eqs. (62)–(63) can be rewritten as

$$\Delta\dot{x} - \phi_x{}^T \Delta x + \alpha(\dot{x} - \phi) = 0, \qquad 0 \leqslant \alpha \leqslant 1 \tag{72}$$

and

$$f_{x(0)}^T \Delta x(0) + \alpha f = 0, \quad g_{x(1)}^T \Delta x(1) + \alpha g = 0, \quad h_{x(0)}^T \Delta x(0) + h_{(x)1}^T \Delta x(1) + \alpha h = 0 \tag{73}$$

For a given value of α, Eq. (72) is equivalent to n scalar differential equations and Eqs. (73) are equivalent to $p + q + r = n$ scalar boundary conditions. These equations and boundary conditions are linear and nonhomogeneous in the n components of the vector $\Delta x(t)$. The resulting algorithm is called modified quasilinearization algorithm.

For $\alpha = 1$, Eqs. (72) and (73) become identical with those of ordinary quasilinearization (*15–18*), that is, the equations obtained by linearizing Eqs. (56) and (57) about the nominal function $x(t)$. While modified quasilinearization exhibits the descent property (68)–(69), this is not necessarily the case with ordinary quasilinearization. This means that, if Eqs. (72) and (73) are employed with $\alpha = 1$, the performance index P may actually increase when passing from the nominal functoin $x(t)$ to the varied function $\tilde{x}(t)$.

[5] The matrix φ_x appearing in Eq. (70) is defined so that its ith column is the gradient of the ith scalar component of φ with respect to the vector x. Analogous definitions hold for the matrices appearing in Eqs. (71).

Coordinate Transformation. To simplify the problem, we introduce the auxiliary variable

$$A(t) = \Delta x(t)/\alpha \tag{74}$$

and rewrite Eqs. (72) and (73) in the form

$$\dot{A} - \phi_x{}^T A + \dot{x} - \phi = 0, \qquad 0 \leqslant t \leqslant 1 \tag{75}$$

and

$$f_{x(0)}^T A(0) + f = 0 \tag{76a}$$

$$g_{x(1)}^T A(1) + g = 0 \tag{76b}$$

$$h_{x(0)}^T A(0) + h_{x(1)}^T A(1) + h = 0 \tag{76c}$$

The differential system (75)–(76) is linear and nonhomogeneous in the function $A(t)$ and can be solved without assigning a value to the stepsize α. With $A(t)$ known and the stepsize α specified, the correction $\Delta x(t)$ is obtained from (74), and the varied function $\tilde{x}(t)$ is computed from (60).

Integration Technique. Assuming that $p \geqslant q$, we integrate the previous differential system $q + r + 1$ times using a forward integration scheme in combination with the method of particular solutions (*14*). In each integration, we specify the initial conditions[6]

$$A_i^j(0) = \delta_{ij}, \qquad i = 1, 2, \ldots, q + r + 1, \qquad j = 1, 2, \ldots, q + r \tag{77}$$

where the Kronecker delta δ_{ij} is such that

$$\begin{aligned} \delta_{ij} &= 1, \qquad i = j \\ \delta_{ij} &= 0, \qquad i \neq j \end{aligned} \tag{78}$$

Then, we compute the missing initial conditions[7]

$$A_i^j(0), \qquad i = 1, 2, \ldots, q + r + 1, \qquad j = q + r + 1, q + r + 2, \ldots, n \tag{79}$$

by solving Eq. (76a). After performing the forward integrations, we obtain the functions

$$A_i = A_i(t), \qquad i = 1, 2, \ldots, q + r + 1 \tag{80}$$

each of which satisfies (75) and (76a) but not necessarily (76b) and (76c).

[6] The subscript i denotes a particular integration. The superscript j denotes a particular component of the vector A.

[7] The $q + r$ components of the vector $A_i(0)$ specified through Eq. (77) must be such that the Eq. (76a) can be solved in terms of the remaining p components (79) of the vector $A_i(0)$.

Next, we introduce the $q + r + 1$ undetermined, scalar constants k_i and form the linear combination

$$A(t) = \sum_{i=1}^{q+r+1} k_i A_i(t) \tag{81}$$

Then, we inquire whether, by an appropriate choice of the constants k_i, this linear combination can satisfy Eqs. (75) and (76). By simple substitution, it can be verified that the linear combination (81) satisfies the differential equation (75) and the separated initial condition (76a) providing

$$\sum_{i=1}^{q+r+1} k_i = 1 \tag{82}$$

Finally, the function (81) satisfies the separated final condition (76b) and the mixed boundary condition (76c) providing

$$\begin{aligned} \sum_{i=1}^{q+r+1} k_i[g_{x(1)}^T A_i(1)] + g = 0 \\ \sum_{i=1}^{q+r+1} k_i[h_{x(0)}^T A_i(0) + h_{x(1)}^T A_i(1)] + h = 0 \end{aligned} \tag{83}$$

The linear system (82)–(83) is equivalent to $q + r + 1$ scalar equations, in which the unknowns are the $q + r + 1$ scalar constants k_i. After the constants k_i are known, the function $A(t)$ is computed with (81). In this way, the two-point boundary-value problem is solved.

Determination of the Stepsize. After combining Eqs. (60) and (74), we obtain the relation

$$\tilde{x}(t) = x(t) + \alpha A(t) \tag{84}$$

Since the function $x(t)$ is given and the function $A(t)$ is known by solving the linearized, two-point boundary-value problem, Eq. (84) yields a one-parameter family of solutions, the parameter being the stepsize α. For this one-parameter family, the performance index P becomes a function of the form

$$P = P(\alpha) \tag{85}$$

At $\alpha = 0$, the slope of this function is negative and is given by

$$P_\alpha(0) = -2P(0) \tag{86}$$

The function (85) exhibits a relative minimum with respect to α, that is, a point where

$$P_\alpha(\alpha) = 0 \tag{87}$$

This point can be determined by means of a one-dimensional search (for example, using quadratic interpolation, cubic interpolation, or quasilinearization). Ideally, this procedure should be used iteratively until the modulus of the slope satisfies the following inequality:

$$|P_\alpha(\alpha)| \leqslant \theta \tag{88}$$

where θ is a small, preselected number.

Since the rigorous determination of α takes time on a computer, one might renounce solving Eq. (87) with a particular degree of precision and determine the stepsize in a noniterative fashion. To this effect, we first assign the value

$$\alpha = 1 \tag{89}$$

to the stepsize; this corresponds to full quasilinearization of Eqs. (56) and (57) and is the value which would solve Eq. (87) exactly, should Eqs. (56) and (57) be linear. Of course, the stepsize (89) is acceptable only if

$$P(\alpha) < P(0) \tag{90}$$

Otherwise, the previous value of α must be replaced by some smaller value in the range (64), for example, using a bisection process, until Ineq. (90) is met. This is guaranteed by the descent property (68)–(69).

Summary of the Algorithm. In the light of the previous discussion, we summarize the modified quasilinearization algorithm as follows:

(a) Assume a nominal function $x(t)$.

(b) Along the interval of integration, compute the vector $\dot{x} - \phi$ and the matrix ϕ_x. On the boundary, compute the vectors f, g, h and the matrices $f_{x(0)}$, $g_{x(1)}$, $h_{x(0)}$, $h_{x(1)}$.

(c) Solve the linearized two-point boundary-value problem (75)–(76) using the forward integration scheme of Section III,B.

(d) Consider the one-parameter family of the solutions (84) and perform a one-dimensional search on the function (85); specifically, perform a bisection process on α (starting from $\alpha = 1$), and continue the process until Ineq. (90) is satisfied.

(e) Once the stepsize α is known, compute the varied function $\tilde{x}(t)$ from (84).

(f) With the varied function known, the iteration is completed. The varied function $\tilde{x}(t)$ becomes the nominal function $x(t)$ for the next iteration. That is, return to (a) and iterate the algorithm.

(g) The algorithm is terminated when the stopping condition (59) is satisfied.

C. Numerical Examples[8]

To illustrate the theory, several numerical examples were developed using a Burroughs B-5500 computer and double-precision arithmetic. The algorithm was programmed in FORTRAN IV. The interval of integration was divided into 100 steps for the first three examples and 200 steps for the fourth example. The differential system (75)–(76) was integrated using Hamming's modified predictor–corrector method with a special Runge–Kutta procedure to start the integration routine (*20*). The definite integral P was computed using Simpson's rule. Convergence was defined as follows:

$$P \leqslant 10^{-16} \tag{91}$$

and the number of iterations at convergence N_* was recorded. Conversely, nonconvergence was defined by means of the inequalities

(a)
$$N \geqslant 40 \tag{92}$$

or

(b)
$$N_S \geqslant 10 \tag{93}$$

or

(c)
$$M \geqslant 0.4 \times 10^{69} \tag{94}$$

Here, N is the iteration number, N_S is the number of bisections of the stepsize α (starting from $\alpha = 1$) required to satisfy Ineq. (90), and M is the modulus of any of the quantities employed in the algorithm. Satisfaction of Ineq. (92) indicates divergence or extreme slowness of convergence; in turn, satisfaction of Ineq. (93) indicates extreme smallness of the displacement Δx; finally, satisfaction of Ineq. (94) indicates exponential overflow for the Burroughs B-5500 computer: the computer program is automatically stopped.

EXAMPLE C-1. Consider the differential equations

$$\dot{x} = \tfrac{1}{2}x^2y, \qquad \dot{y} = -\tfrac{1}{2}xy^2 \tag{95}$$

subject to the boundary conditions

$$x(0) + x(1) - e - 1 = 0, \qquad y(0) - x(1)y(1) - 0 \tag{96}$$

where $e = 2.71828$. In this problem, $n = 2$, $p = 0$, $q = 0$, $r = 2$. Since $q + r + 1 = 3$, three particular solutions are needed per iteration.

Assume the nominal functions

$$x(t) = 2, \qquad y(t) = 1 \tag{97}$$

[8] The symbols employed in this section denote scalar quantities.

which are not consistent with (95) and (96). Starting with these nominal functions, we employ the algorithm of Section III,B. Convergence to the solution is achieved in $N_* = 5$ iterations. The numerical results are presented in Tables VI and VII, where N denotes the iteration number.[9]

TABLE VI

STEPSIZE AND PERFORMANCE INDEX (EXAMPLE C-1)

N	α	P
0	—	0.6×10^{1}
1	1	0.8×10^{0}
2	1	0.1×10^{-1}
3	1	0.1×10^{-6}
4	1	0.8×10^{-15}
5	1	0.5×10^{-32}

TABLE VII

CONVERGED SOLUTION (EXAMPLE C-1, $N = 5$)

t	x	y
0.0	0.1000×10^{1}	0.2000×10^{1}
0.1	0.1105×10^{1}	0.1809×10^{1}
0.2	0.1221×10^{1}	0.1637×10^{1}
0.3	0.1349×10^{1}	0.1481×10^{1}
0.4	0.1491×10^{1}	0.1340×10^{1}
0.5	0.1648×10^{1}	0.1213×10^{1}
0.6	0.1822×10^{1}	0.1097×10^{1}
0.7	0.2013×10^{1}	0.9931×10^{0}
0.8	0.2225×10^{1}	0.8986×10^{0}
0.9	0.2459×10^{1}	0.8131×10^{0}
1.0	0.2718×10^{1}	0.7357×10^{0}

EXAMPLE C-2. Consider the differential equations

$$\begin{aligned} \dot{x} &= y, \qquad \dot{y} = z, \qquad \dot{z} = -\tfrac{1}{6}z^2uw \\ \dot{u} &= w, \qquad \dot{w} = -\tfrac{1}{2}yw^3 \end{aligned} \tag{98}$$

subject to the boundary conditions

$$x(0) = 1, \qquad u(0) = 1, \qquad w(0) = -1, \qquad x(1) = 16, \qquad u(1) = \tfrac{1}{2} \tag{99}$$

[9] The solution of problem (95)–(96) is not unique. Another solution is characterized by constant values of x and y, specifically, $x(t) = \frac{1}{2}(e + 1)$, $y(t) = 0$.

In this problem, $n = 5$, $p = 3$, $q = 2$, $r = 0$. Since $q + r + 1 = 3$, three particular solutions are needed per iteration.

Assume the nominal functions

$$
\begin{gathered}
x(t) = 1 + 15t, \qquad y(t) = 0, \qquad z(t) = 0 \\
u(t) = 1 - \tfrac{1}{2}t, \qquad w(t) = -1
\end{gathered} \tag{100}
$$

which are consistent with the boundary conditions (99) but are not consistent with the differential equations (98). Starting with these nominal functions, we employ the algorithm of Section III,B. Convergence to the solution is achieved in $N_* = 11$ iterations. The numerical results are presented in Tables VIII and IX, where N denotes the iteration number.

TABLE VIII

STEPSIZE AND PERFORMANCE INDEX (EXAMPLE C-2)

N	α	P
0	—	0.2×10^{3}
1	$\frac{1}{16}$	0.2×10^{3}
1	$\frac{1}{8}$	0.1×10^{3}
3	$\frac{1}{4}$	0.1×10^{3}
4	$\frac{1}{2}$	0.4×10^{2}
5	$\frac{1}{2}$	0.2×10^{2}
6	1	0.1×10^{1}
7	$\frac{1}{2}$	0.3×10^{0}
8	$\frac{1}{2}$	0.1×10^{0}
9	1	0.2×10^{-1}
10	1	0.2×10^{-8}
11	1	0.1×10^{-21}

EXAMPLE C-3. Consider the differential equations

$$
\dot{x} = 10y, \qquad \dot{y} = 10z, \qquad \dot{z} = -5xz \tag{101}
$$

subject to the boundary conditions

$$
x(0) = 0, \qquad y(0) = 0, \qquad y(1) = 1 \tag{102}
$$

In this problem, $n = 3$, $p = 2$, $q = 1$, $r = 0$. Since $q + r + 1 = 2$, two particular solutions are needed per iteration.

Assume the nominal functions

$$
x(t) = 0, \qquad y(t) = t, \qquad z(t) = 0 \tag{103}
$$

which are consistent with the boundary conditions (102) but are not consistent with the differential equations (101). Starting with these nominal

TABLE IX

CONVERGED SOLUTION (EXAMPLE C-2, $N = 11$)

t	x	y	z	u	w
0.0	0.1000×10^1	0.4000×10^1	0.1200×10^2	0.1000×10^1	-0.1000×10^1
0.1	0.1464×10^1	0.5324×10^1	0.1452×10^2	0.9090×10^0	-0.8264×10^0
0.2	0.2073×10^1	0.6912×10^1	0.1728×10^2	0.8333×10^0	-0.6944×10^0
0.3	0.2856×10^1	0.8788×10^1	0.2028×10^2	0.7692×10^0	-0.5917×10^0
0.4	0.3841×10^1	0.1097×10^2	0.2352×10^2	0.7142×10^0	-0.5102×10^0
0.5	0.5062×10^1	0.1350×10^2	0.2700×10^2	0.6666×10^0	-0.4444×10^0
0.6	0.6553×10^1	0.1638×10^2	0.3072×10^2	0.6250×10^0	-0.3906×10^0
0.7	0.8352×10^1	0.1965×10^2	0.3468×10^2	0.5882×10^0	-0.3460×10^0
0.8	0.1049×10^2	0.2332×10^2	0.3888×10^2	0.5555×10^0	-0.3086×10^0
0.9	0.1303×10^2	0.2743×10^2	0.4332×10^2	0.5263×10^0	-0.2770×10^0
1.0	0.1600×10^2	0.3200×10^2	0.4800×10^2	0.5000×10^0	-0.2500×10^0

functions, we employ the algorithm of Section III,B. Convergence to the solution is achieved in $N_* = 6$ iterations. The numerical results are presented in Tables X and XI, where N denotes the iteration number.

TABLE X

STEPSIZE AND PERFORMANCE INDEX (EXAMPLE C-3)

N	α	P
0	—	0.3×10^2
1	1	0.1×10^1
2	$\frac{1}{8}$	0.2×10^0
3	1	0.3×10^{-1}
4	1	0.5×10^{-4}
5	1	0.2×10^{-9}
6	1	0.2×10^{-20}

EXAMPLE C-4. Consider the differential equations[10]

$$\begin{aligned} &\dot{x} = 13y, \quad \dot{y} = 13z, \quad \dot{z} = -20.15xz + 1.3y^2 - 13u^2 + 2.6y + 13 \\ &\dot{u} = 13w, \quad \dot{w} = -20.15xw + 14.3yu + 2.6u - 2.6 \end{aligned} \tag{104}$$

subject to the boundary conditions

$$x(0) = 0, \quad y(0) = 0, \quad u(0) = 0, \quad y(1) = 0, \quad u(1) = 1 \tag{105}$$

[10] This example, which involves unstable differential equations, was considered by Roberts *et al.* (*21*).

TABLE XI

CONVERGED SOLUTION (EXAMPLE C-3, $N = 6$)

t	x	y	z
0.0	0.0000×10^{0}	0.0000×10^{0}	0.3320×10^{0}
0.1	0.1655×10^{0}	0.3297×10^{0}	0.3230×10^{0}
0.2	0.6500×10^{0}	0.6297×10^{0}	0.2667×10^{0}
0.3	0.1396×10^{1}	0.8460×10^{0}	0.1613×10^{0}
0.4	0.2305×10^{1}	0.9555×10^{0}	0.6423×10^{-1}
0.5	0.3283×10^{1}	0.9915×10^{0}	0.1590×10^{-1}
0.6	0.4279×10^{1}	0.9989×10^{0}	0.2402×10^{-2}
0.7	0.5279×10^{1}	0.9999×10^{0}	0.2201×10^{-3}
0.8	0.6279×10^{1}	0.9999×10^{0}	0.1224×10^{-4}
0.9	0.7279×10^{1}	0.9999×10^{0}	0.4130×10^{-6}
1.0	0.8279×10^{1}	0.1000×10^{1}	0.8413×10^{-8}

In this problem $n = 5$, $p = 3$, $q = 2$, $r = 0$. Since $q + r + 1 = 3$, three particular solutions are needed per iteration.

Assume the nominal functions

$$x(t) = 0, \qquad y(t) = 0, \qquad z(t) = 0, \qquad u(t) = t, \qquad w(t) = 0 \tag{106}$$

which are consistent with the boundary conditions (105) but are not consistent with the differential equations (104). Starting with these nominal functions, we employ the algorithm of Section III,B. Convergence to the solution is achieved in $N_* = 6$ iterations. The numerical results are presented in Tables XII and XIII, where N denotes the iteration number.

TABLE XII

STEPSIZE AND PERFORMANCE INDEX (EXAMPLE C-4)

N	α	P
0	—	0.9×10^{2}
1	$\frac{1}{2}$	0.3×10^{2}
2	$\frac{1}{2}$	0.8×10^{1}
3	1	0.4×10^{-1}
4	1	0.6×10^{-4}
5	1	0.5×10^{-10}
6	1	0.3×10^{-22}

TABLE XIII

CONVERGED SOLUTION (EXAMPLE C-4, $N = 6$)

t	x	y	z	u	w
0.0	0.0000×10^{0}	0.0000×10^{0}	-0.9663×10^{0}	0.0000×10^{0}	0.6529×10^{0}
0.1	-0.5028×10^{0}	-0.5802×10^{0}	-0.7188×10^{-1}	0.6971×10^{0}	0.4220×10^{0}
0.2	-0.1215×10^{1}	-0.4603×10^{0}	0.1945×10^{0}	0.1100×10^{1}	0.2036×10^{0}
0.3	-0.1631×10^{1}	-0.1744×10^{0}	0.2210×10^{0}	0.1247×10^{1}	0.3249×10^{-1}
0.4	-0.1688×10^{1}	0.7033×10^{-1}	0.1443×10^{0}	0.1213×10^{1}	-0.7189×10^{-1}
0.5	-0.1506×10^{1}	0.1844×10^{0}	0.3000×10^{-1}	0.1093×10^{1}	-0.1002×10^{0}
0.6	-0.1270×10^{1}	0.1602×10^{0}	-0.5755×10^{-1}	0.9815×10^{0}	-0.6490×10^{-1}
0.7	-0.1120×10^{1}	0.6614×10^{-1}	-0.7534×10^{-1}	0.9334×10^{0}	-0.1024×10^{-1}
0.8	-0.1091×10^{1}	-0.1365×10^{-1}	-0.4303×10^{-1}	0.9447×10^{0}	0.2223×10^{-1}
0.9	-0.1133×10^{1}	-0.4258×10^{-1}	-0.1453×10^{-2}	0.9774×10^{0}	0.2352×10^{-1}
1.0	-0.1173×10^{1}	-0.1508×10^{-20}	0.9405×10^{-1}	0.1000×10^{1}	0.1765×10^{-1}

D. Remarks

The following remarks are pertinent to the previous theoretical development.

(1) If the stepsize is set at the constant value $\alpha = 1$, the modified quasilinearization algorithm of Section III,B reduces to the ordinary quasilinearization algorithm. While modified quasilinearization exhibits the descent property (68)–(69), this is not necessarily the case with ordinary quasilinearization. Therefore, in ordinary quasilinearization, the performance index P may actually increase when passing from the nominal function $x(t)$ to the varied function $\tilde{x}(t)$.

With reference to the examples of Section III,C, computer runs were made employing both modified quasilinearization and ordinary quasilinearization. In Table XIV, the number of iterations at convergence N_* is indicated and, as the table shows, the experimental evidence is in favor of modified quasilinearization. It is emphasized that the above conclusion was obtained through particular examples and that, consequently, the subject requires further investigation.

(2) The fundamental property of the modified quasilinearization algorithm is the descent property (68)–(69). This local property guarantees the decrease of the performance index P when passing from the nominal function $x(t)$ to the varied function $\tilde{x}(t)$. However, it does not guarantee convergence; that is, it does not guarantee that $P \to 0$ as $N \to \infty$. This is due to the fact that convergence depends on the analytical nature of the functions ϕ, f, g, h and on the nominal function $x(t)$ chosen to start the algorithm.

TABLE XIV

NUMBER OF ITERATIONS AT CONVERGENCE

	N_*	
	$\alpha \leqslant 1$	$\alpha = 1$
Example C-1	5	5
Example C-2	11	Nonconvergence (*c*)
Example C-3	6	8
Example C-4	6	Nonconvergence (*c*)

E. Discussion and Conclusions

In Section III, a general method for solving nonlinear, two-point boundary-value problems is presented; it is assumed that the differential system has order n and is subject to p separated initial conditions, q separated final conditions, and r mixed boundary conditions, with $p+q+r=n$. The method is based on the consideration of the performance index P, the cumulative error in the differential equations and the boundary conditions.

A modified quasilinearization algorithm is generated by requiring the first variation of the performance index δP to be negative. The algorithm has the form $\tilde{x}(t) = x(t) + \alpha A(t)$. Here, α, $0 \leqslant \alpha \leqslant 1$, is the stepsize and the function $A(t)$ is obtained by solving a system of n nonhomogeneous, linear differential equations subject to p separated initial conditions, q separated final conditions, and r mixed boundary conditions. This system is solved employing the method of particular solutions: $q+r+1$ independent solutions are combined linearly, and the coefficients of the combination are determined so that the linear system is satisfied.

The main property of the modified quasilinearization algorithm is the descent property: if the stepsize α is sufficiently small, the reduction in P is guaranteed. Not only is P employed as a guide during progression of the algorithm, but also as a convergence criterion: the algorithm is terminated when the performance index P becomes smaller than some preselected value.

Several numerical examples are presented; they illustrate (i) the simplicity as well as the rapidity of convergence of the algorithm and (ii) the importance of stepsize control.

References

1. A. MIELE, S. NAQVI, and A. V. LEVY, Modified quasilinearization method for solving nonlinear equations. Aero-Astronautics Rep. No. 78, Rice Univ., Houston, Texas, 1970.
2. A. MIELE and R. R. IYER, Modified quasilinearization method for solving nonlinear, two-point boundary-value problems. Aero-Astronautics Rep. No. 79, Rice Univ., Houston, Texas, 1970.
3. D. F. DAVIDENKO, On a new method of numerical solution of systems of nonlinear equations (in Russian). *Dokl. Akad. Nauk SSSR* **88**, No. 4, 601–602 (1953).
4. H. H. ROSENBROCK, An automatic method for finding the greatest or least value of a function. *Computer J.* **3**, No. 3, 175–184 (1960).
5. F. FREUDENSTEIN and B. ROTH, Numerical solution of systems of nonlinear equations. *J. Assoc. Computing Machinery* **10**, No. 4, 550–556 (1963).
6. W. KIZNER, A numerical method for finding solutions of nonlinear equations, *SIAM J. Appl. Math.* **12**, No. 2, 424–428 (1964).
7. M. J. D. POWELL, A method for minimizing a sum of squares of nonlinear functions without calculating derivatives. *Computer J.* **7**, No. 4, 303–307 (1965).
8. J. G. P. BARNES, An algorithm for solving nonlinear equations on the secant method. *Computer J.* **8**, No. 1, 66–72 (1965).
9. C. G. BROYDEN, A class of methods for solving nonlinear simultaneous equations. *Math. Computation* **19**, No. 92, 577–593 (1965).
10. F. H. DEIST and L. SEFOR, Solution of systems of nonlinear equations by parameter variation. *Computer J.* **10**, No. 1, 78–82 (1967).
11. C. G. BROYDEN, Quasi-Newton methods and their application to function minimization. *Math. Computation* **21**, No. 99, 368–381 (1967).
12. C. G. BROYDEN, A new method of solving nonlinear simultaneous equations. *Computer J.* **12**, No. 1, 94–99 (1969).
13. T. R. GOODMAN and C. N. LANCE, The numerical integration of two-point boundary-value problems. *Math. Tables Other Aids Computation* **10**, No. 54, 82–86 (1956).
14. A. MIELE, Method of particular solutions for linear, two-point boundary-value problems. *J. Optimization Theory Applications* **2**, No. 4, 260–273 (1968).
15. R. E. BELLMAN and R. E. KALABA, Quasilinearization and nonlinear boundary-value problems. Rep. No. R-438-PR, RAND Corp., Santa Monica, Calif., 1965.
16. E. S. LEE, "Quasilinearization and Invariant Imbedding." Academic Press, New York, 1968.
17. H. B. KELLER, "Numerical Methods for Two-Point Boundary-Value Problems." Blaisdell, Waltham, Massachusetts, 1968.
18. P. B. BAILEY, L. F. SHAMPINE, and P. E. WALTMAN, "Nonlinear, Two-Point Boundary-Value Problems." Academic Press, New York, 1968.
19. A. MIELE and R. R. IYER, General technique for solving nonlinear, two-point boundary-value problems via the method of particular solutions. *J. Optimization Theory Applications* **5**, No. 5, 382–399 (1970).
20. A. RALSTON, Numerical integration methods for the solution of ordinary differential equations. "Mathematical Methods for Digital Computers" (A. Ralston and H. S. Wilf, eds.), Vol. 1. Wiley, New York, 1960.
21. S. M. ROBERTS, J. S. SHIPMAN, and C. D. ROTH, Continuation in quasilinearization. *J. Optimization Theory Applications* *2*, No. 3, 164–178 (1968).

Advances in Process Control Applications

C. H. WELLS AND D. A. WISMER

Systems Control, Inc.
Palo Alto, California

I. Introduction

If we had chosen an alternative title for this chapter, it would have been Applications of Modern Systems Theory to Process Control. In this case in order to begin on a controversial note we would be tempted to make the statement that there have not been any such applications. To be sure, there have been logging, operator guide, open-loop control, and single-loop feedback control applications, but there have been few, if any, applications of dynamic optimal control in the modern sense. Why have these applications been so elusive in the process industries?

The normal approach to process control applications has been to start with a model development and simulation approach. All too often this simulation is never completed because an attempt is made to represent the physical system too perfectly. In case a successful simulation is obtained, the model is usually too complex and too detailed by this time to be amenable to the application of modern control theoretical techniques. The approach proposed in this paper is to dispense with the initial phase of performing a detailed simulation and to let the control techniques and identification methods compensate for the inability to model the system perfectly. It is well documented historically by many process control budgetary overruns that the cost of obtaining simulation models and programming control systems has often outweighed the economic advantages obtained. In the remaining sections of this article we shall put the current situation for process control applications in some historical perspective and discuss several types of computer applications. We then formulate a modern approach to applying optimal control theory in the process industries in a general framework. This is followed by a detailed analysis of a specific application to the basic oxygen steelmaking process. This process represents one of the most complex and difficult-to-model of all industrial systems.

II. Historical Perspective

A. Early Applications

Process control was long overdue for some innovation by the middle 1950s. The carryover from earlier servomechanism work was more limited than first expected. Instead of dealing with completely measurable outputs, process industries have had to contend with situations where it was difficult to know what to measure and even more difficult to obtain a measurement. Clearly, some new approach was necessary if the technology was ever going to advance.

The first industrial computer control application was an RW-300 computer installed on a catalytic polymerization unit at the Texaco Refinery in Port Arthur, Texas. This installation occurred early in 1959, and the system had as inputs 26 flows, 72 temperatures, 3 pressures, and 3 gas compositions. The four main functions performed by the computer were to, (1) maximize reactor pressure, (2) determine the best feed distribution over five parallel reactor pairs (optimal allocation), (3) control the water heat injection rate based on catalyst activity, and, (4) determine the best recycle rate. The computer was justified on increased conversion and improved catalyst life. In retrospect, this was a fairly sophisticated application that was successfully implemented on a very rudimentary first-generation process control computer. Note that the stated goal of this project was the implementation of a feedback control system including a static optimization.

In the early 1960s, it became very fashionable to tabulate the respective process computer installations by type of application and by vendor. The results of a number of surveys published in *Control Engineering* between 1961 and 1968 are shown in Table I. Initially these tabulations only included those applications that were reported to be on closed-loop control; however, in each year following the initial report, the type of application listed was expanded to include operating guide applications,[1] and then logging computers. Apparently the reason for expanding the tabulation was that only a relatively small number of applications were actually on closed-loop control. The early applications were concentrated in the areas of steel, chemical, petroleum, and utility industry systems. The number of innovative applications in the miscellaneous category was small compared with those in the basic industries. However, in later years the miscellaneous category grew very rapidly when compared with the basic industries. Some representative applications from this category include:

TABLE I

ON-LINE COMPUTER INSTALLATIONS (WORLDWIDE)[a]

Date	Gas, Chemical, Petroleum, Paper, Cement	Power	Metals	Miscellaneous	Total
Mar. 1961	16	11	10	0	37
May 1962	45	66	23	23	159
Sept. 1963	92	117	55	76	340
Aug. 1965	212	203	144	236	795
Sept. 1966	336	289	242	485	1352
Mar. 1967	386	324	260	601	1571
July 1968	—	—	—	—	2890

[a]Source: *Control Engineering*.

(1) antenna and telescope positioning, (2) industrial and military systems checkout, (3) pipeline control, (4) nuclear reactor control, (5) automotive, air, and traffic control, (6) biomedical data acquisition and processing, (7) broadcast program switching, (8) building environmental control, (9) newspaper typesetting, and (10) machine tool control.

In 1965, about 20 computers were employed in testing the application of direct digital control. These initial applications were among the first to depart from the large supervisory system concept and were eventually to revolutionize the economics of the computer control field.

[1]Those applications where the computer outputs instructions to be performed by a human operator.

B. Process Computer Development

The earliest process control computer, the RW-300, was a drum-type machine. This rudimentary machine was relatively slow and difficult to program. Initial applications were programmed in machine language, whereas later applications were programmed in assembly language. To safeguard a certain program, a "track plug" was provided that could be changed manually from one memory track position to another to prevent the overwriting of stored programs. By 1962, a total of 19 companies had entered the process computer field and were rapidly saturating the market. Although this market was seen to be large at that time, it proved to be not nearly as large as anticipated. Because of the intensive competition, computer vendors were prone to develop faster and more sophisticated hardware. From the early drum-type machines, subsequent computer models included drum and core and then all core computers with backup memory consisting of drums, tapes, and disks. Because of the special features required for process control, such as multiple levels of priority interrupt and peripheral equipment for real-time input and output, the development costs for these machines were substantial, especially in light of the fact that the number of sales for each model was minimal. Unfortunately, the development of such sophisticated computer hardware was largely unwarranted, since in most process control applications the process time constants were sufficiently large that a relatively long sampling rate or cycle time could be tolerated. Thus, the relatively sophisticated computers and expensive prices for second- and third-generation process control computers could not be justified for most process applications. This situation contributed heavily to the disappointing number of sales of these systems and led inevitably to the demise of all but a few of the early process computer vendors.

In the latter 1960s the advent of the minicomputer and the applications for direct digital control tended to direct the process computer applications away from the large supervisory systems often costing one half million dollars and toward the smaller applications in the neighborhood of $50,000. By 1970 there was a surplus of vendors competing for this mini–computer market that was reminiscent of the situation 5 years earlier for larger computers. However, the trend now seems to be toward using many small-scale computers, perhaps tied together by a large central processor, rather than to centralize all computer control operations for an entire plant within a single large-scale process computer.

One additional factor worth noting is that throughout the development of the process computer market, computer control software has always lagged far behind the development of hardware systems. From the initial installations, which were programmed in machine language, through the assembly language programming and up until the development of high level compiler languages, the user has always been faced with delays in software; in fact, appreciable amounts of software development have often been done by the users themselves because of the unavailability of vendor-supplied software systems.

C. Economics (*1*)

Certain process characteristics are common to most industrial processes where computer control has been successful. These characteristics include (1) large size, (2) frequent disturbances, (3) high complexity, (4) adequate instrumentation, (5) continuing future importance, (6) favorable labor and management attitudes, and (7) availability of technical people. To make computer control economical for supervisory control applications, a plant should usually represent a product value of $4 million or more. Experience has shown that such computer systems usually range in cost from $200,000 to $400,000 and produce benefits of between 2 and 5%. To recover the cost of the control system in 2 years means that before taxes the improvement resulting from computer control must equal roughly its cost in each of the first 2 years. Thus the minimum product value on which the improvement must be calculated is $4 million for a 5% improvement and $20 million for a 2% improvement. Economic justification of this type presumes an unlimited production situation. If all the product produced cannot be sold, the problem of economic justification is more difficult.

D. Control Theory

During and following World War II much of the early servomechanism work was available for application in industrial process control. However, it was not until the development in the early 1950s of sampled data control theory that the application of these methods to industrial processes became feasible. A minor exception to this statement arises from the application of continuous servomechanism theory using analog computers; however, the number of these applications is very small. The field of process computer control as we know it today awaited the development of digital computers with input/output capability. Although sampled data control theory provided the basis for obtaining closed-loop control, it was seldom applied in industrial process applications. To speculate on the reasons for its absence may be pure conjecture but the following three factors almost certainly are involved: poor process models, poor or inadequate instrumentation, and a dearth of control systems engineers being employed by the process industries.

By the early 1960s modern control theory as we know it today was developed and highly refined. This body of knowledge based on dynamic optimization techniques using state space methods provided a framework for industrial process applications. Thus for the first time the theory was available to handle the large multi-input, multi-output systems actually encountered in practice. Unfortunately, these methods are computationally tractable only for linear systems, and this computational problem is further complicated by the operational requirement for real-time response in process applications. The limited size and speed for computers for on-line control further restricts the size and complexity of the control problems that can be solved. Other theoretical tools developed during this 10-year period and largely unused for process applications include optimal estimation and filtering, system identification techniques, and dynamic model adaptive methods.

E. Future Outlook

The relative lack of application of advanced control system methodology to process control is evident from even a brief screening of the literature. It might be well to ask why modern control theory has seen so little application to industrial process control. Certainly the answer would contain elements of each of the following: (1) poor dynamic process models, (2) nonlinear process phenomena, (3) partial observation of state variables, (4) observations contaminated with noise, (5) unknown performance criterion, and (6) high system dimensionality. The discussion in this article is not meant to imply that the future outlook for process computer applications of modern control theory is bleak because of the relatively slow beginning. Certainly, the reasons listed above for this stuttering start are formidable; however, the point to be made is that modern control theory itself can help to overcome many of these difficulties. In particular, by using fairly low-dimensional linear models that may be only crude approximations of the actual system behavior, it is often possible to model the system accurately enough to be controlled within a small operating region. The model coefficients can then be determined as functions of time in order to have the model follow the process (adaptive filtering). In addition, estimation techniques can be used to compensate for partial state observation and noise contamination in measurements. To demonstrate this approach, which we feel will have substantial application in the future, we have chosen as an example one of the most difficult-to-model industrial processes, the basic oxygen steelmaking process.

III. A Modern Approach to Process Control

A. Introduction

The approach to process control described in this section is oriented toward applications in complex industrial processes. Typical examples considered have included the fluid catalytic cracking processes, the basic oxygen furnace, distillation columns, rolling mills, paper machines, and anaerobic digesters. Conventional single loop control systems, such as flow, temperature, and level can be controlled accurately using standard algorithms such as a two-mode DDC algorithm or conventional three-mode pneumatic controllers.

The process systems considered here characteristically have multiple inputs and multiple outputs. The process equations are generally not known with high accuracy and random variations within the system cause unwanted oscillations in the product quality. Process observations such as temperatures and pressures are often excessively noisy as a result of both random instrumentation errors and random disturbances to the process itself. Most industrial processes cannot be pulse-tested or otherwise removed from production for identification, thus making the problem of process identification even more difficult.

The modern approach discussed in this section is as follows. First, the input and output variables are identified. Next, the predominant unsteady state material and energy balances are derived and the open-loop input–output data records are used to identify unknown parameters in the unsteady state conservation laws. The process performance criterion is identified and an optimizing algorithm is developed. A state estimation algorithm is then developed. A closed-loop controller is developed, and finally both the state estimator and the closed-loop controller are implemented in a digital computer.

B. Input/Output Selection

One of the most important steps in developing an optimal control strategy for an industrial process is to clearly identify those variables in the process that are independent, dependent, and parametric.

1. Control Variables. Control variables can be manipulated within upper and lower bounds without regard to other variables in the process, i.e., independently. As an example, the most common control variable in chemical processes is the air pressure signal to a control valve.

2. Observable Variables. The output or observable variables include those variables that respond to changes in the independent variables and that are measurable. These variables include measurements of the product quality, which could include temperature, pressure, volume, thickness, tension, or chemical analysis. The output variables, or the observables as they are often called in control theory, are normally contaminated with sensor noise. The observables are expressed in engineering units rather than in units of the primary signal (emf in the case of thermocouples).

3. Parametric Variables. Parameters in models of processes are those constant quantities in the conservation equations for the process. In chemical reactors, for example, rate constants, activation energy, and heat transfer coefficients are normally assumed to be known constants. In certain cases, flow rates can be considered as parameters also.

Some of the parameters in the process equations will be unknown, and it will be necessary to identify them using actual data. Other parameters may vary with time, in which case they are considered as state variables and identified on-line.

C. Mathematical Modeling

The first step in modeling the system is to derive the dynamic material and energy balances for the major chemical species in the system. An energy balance should be written for each distinct measurable phase within the system. For example, in a gas–liquid system, an energy balance on both the gas phase and the liquid phase should be derived. Dependent variables in energy balances generally contain observable variables since temperature is readily measurable.

Material balances on the major mass species in the system are also written. The dependent variables in equations of this type are generally not measurable. The conservation laws can be written in the convenient state space notation as described below.

Suppose the dependent variables in the conservation laws are denoted by the symbol x_i, where i denotes a particular dependent variable. The equations can be put into state variable form by writing them in the following notation:

$$\dot{x}_i = f_i(x_i, x_j, p_k, \ldots, p_e, u_\alpha \ldots, u_\gamma) \tag{1}$$

where x_j represents the set of dependent variables that also influence $\dot{x}_i$, $p_k, \ldots, p_e$ denote the parameters in the conservation law for the ith variable, and $u_\alpha, \ldots, u_\gamma$ denote those independent variables that influence

$\dot{x}_i$.[2] Conservation laws for each major dependent variable in the process can be written in the same notation.

Define the state vector

$$\mathbf{x} = \begin{bmatrix} x_1 \\ \vdots \\ x_i \\ \vdots \\ x_{n_x} \end{bmatrix} \tag{2}$$

where n_x denotes the number of "state" variables in the process equations. The term "state" is defined herein as the minimum set of numbers such that, if all of them are known at any one time, and if the values of future independent variables are known, then all future values of the state variables can be computed.

The process equations can be written in compact notation as follows:

$$\dot{x} = \mathbf{f}(\mathbf{x}, \mathbf{p}, \mathbf{u}) \tag{3}$$

where $\mathbf{p}$ is an n_p-dimensional vector representing the parameters, $\mathbf{u}$ is an n_u-dimensional vector representing the controls, and $\mathbf{x}$ is an n_x-dimensional vector representing the state of the system.

In typical applications, n_x is usually 10 or less. The real process, of course, is represented by an infinite number of states, and consequently Eq. (3) is an incomplete representation of the true state variables in the process. To account for this incompleteness or process uncertainty, a random vector is added to the right-hand side of Eq. (3). The process equations then become

$$\dot{x} = \mathbf{f}(\mathbf{x}, \mathbf{p}, \mathbf{u}) + \mathbf{w} \tag{4}$$

where $\mathbf{w}$ is a random n_x-dimensional vector. Alternatively, $\mathbf{w}$ may represent random input forcing functions.

Because not all state variables are measurable, a set of observation equations must be included in the process equations to define the control system completely, In the most general case, the observations are nonlinear combinations of the state variables. These equations can be written

$$\mathbf{z} = \mathbf{g}(\mathbf{x}, \mathbf{p}) + \mathbf{v} \tag{5}$$

where $\mathbf{z}$ is an n_z-dimensional vector representing the process observations, $\mathbf{g}$ is a nonlinear n_z-dimensional vector function, and $\mathbf{v}$ is a random n_z-dimensional vector that represents random sensor noise.

[2] $(\dot{\ })$over symbol denotes derivative with respect to time.

In summary, the system equations for process control can be written:

$$\dot{x} = \mathbf{f}(\mathbf{x}, \mathbf{p}, \mathbf{u}) + \mathbf{w}$$
$$\mathbf{z} = \mathbf{g}(\mathbf{x}, \mathbf{p}) + \mathbf{v} \tag{6}$$

A block diagram of this system is shown in Fig. 1.

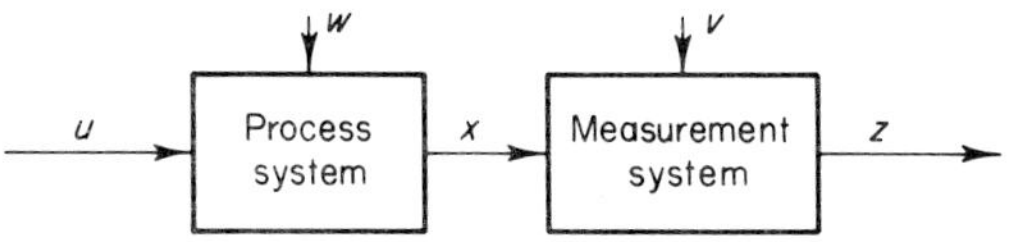

FIG. 1. Schematic diagram of a process system in state space notation.

The control variables **u** influence the state variable **x** through the system dynamics **f**(**x**, **p**, **u**), and the measurement system produces partial observations **z** of the system state.

D. Data Acquisition

Open-loop data can be obtained by simultaneously recording data from the control actuating mechanisms in the process and from the measuring instruments. This may require special recording equipment. If mobile equipment is used, it is desirable to record process data in digital format for subsequent off-line use.

A schematic diagram of a classical single loop process control system is shown in Fig. 2.

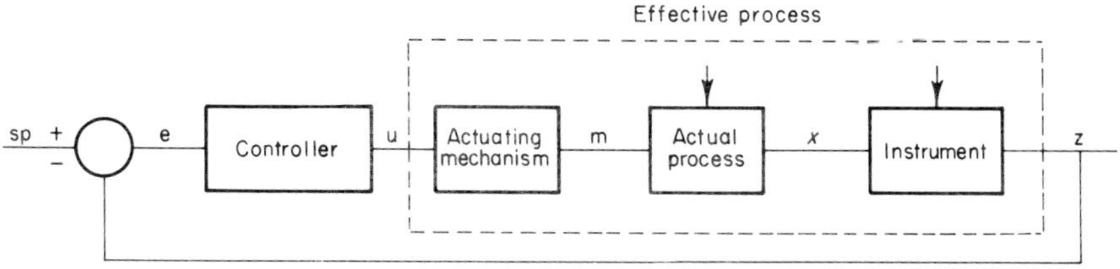

FIG. 2. Classical closed-loop diagram.

In this figure, sp represents the set point for the process. Note that the output z is being controlled and *not the state*. An error signal is generated and used as input to the controller. The controller output signal u is transmitted to the actuating mechanism, which in turn produces an input signal m directly to the process. The state variables are not directly observable, and consequently an instrumentation system produces an observation z which is used as a feedback signal.

Open-loop data can be obtained by simultaneously recording the signal u and z. Note here that the actuating mechanism has been included as part of the process.

It is important in any identification procedure to ensure that the system dynamics have been sufficiently excited. Systems under closed-loop control can often be approximated by linear differential equations; and consequently, if the nonlinear dynamics are not excited, only the linear terms in the conservation equations will be identified. For this reason, it is important to collect data over the operating intervals of interest.

E. Process Identification

As indicated in Section C, dynamic material and energy balances can be written for most unit processes. These mathematical models may vary in complexity from a single overall material balance in a chemical process to individual population balances for bacteria in a biological process. In most instances, some of the parameters in these equations are not accurately known.

Many schemes have been applied to the problem of identifying the values of unknown parameters in models of real systems from process data. The standard least squares or equation error technique produces unbiased estimates of parameters only if all state variables are measurable and if the independent variables contain no randomness. The criterion for optimization in the least squares or so-called equation error identification methods (*2*) is

$$J = \int_0^T \|\mathbf{x} - \hat{x}\|^2_{Q^{-1}}\, dt \tag{7}$$

where T is the period over which open-loop data are available and Q denotes the process noise covariance matrix $Q(t) = E[\mathbf{w}(t)\mathbf{w}(t-\tau)^T]$.

The least squares approach to identification of unknown parameters may be summarized mathematically as follows:

Given: Noisy measurements of the state variables $\mathbf{x}$ from $[0, T]$ and known process noise covariance matrix Q,

Find: $\hat{p}$ such that

$$J = \min_p \int_0^T \|\mathbf{x} - \hat{x}\|^2_{Q^{-1}}\, dt$$

Output error identification methods, on the other hand, produce unbiased estimates of the unknown parameters $\mathbf{p}$, only if no process noise is contained in the system equations and if the input variables are deterministic. The output error identification problem is summarized as follows:

Given: Noisy measurements of the system output $\mathbf{z}$ from $[0, T]$ and known observation noise covariance matrix R.

Find: $\hat{\mathbf{p}}$ such that

$$J = \min_{p} \int_0^T \|\mathbf{z} - \mathbf{g}(\hat{\mathbf{x}}_1, \hat{\mathbf{p}}, \mathbf{u})\|^2_{R^{-1}}\, dt \tag{8}$$

subject to the constraints

$$\dot{\mathbf{x}} = \mathbf{f}(\mathbf{x}, \mathbf{p}, \mathbf{u}) \tag{9}$$

The maximum likelihood (*2–4*) identification procedure applies to the general case in which both Q, R, and $\mathbf{x}_0$ are unknown and only $\mathbf{z}$ is observable. This is the most common situation in process control identification problems.

The likelihood function for this general case is very complicated and is given in terms of the optimal nonlinear filter for the system (*5*). The formulation and solution to this optimization problem is given by Mehra (*6*). It should be noted that the solution to the general problem is a formidable nonlinear programming problem and, in general, advanced optimization techniques are required to find the optimum solution.

F. Process Optimization

The next step in the control procedure consists of finding the optimum open-loop trajectories for the process. The identified model of the unit process is summarized in state-space notation as follows:

$$\dot{\mathbf{x}} = \mathbf{f}(\mathbf{x}, \mathbf{u}, \mathbf{p}), \qquad \mathbf{x}(0) \text{ given} \tag{10}$$

where only the identified deterministic portion of the problem has been retained. The stochastic part is considered in Sections III, G and H.

It is required to choose the control $\mathbf{u}(t)$ so that the total system performance is maximized. The system performance function may be written

$$J = \phi(\mathbf{x}(T)) + \int_0^T L(\mathbf{x}, \mathbf{u}, t)\, dt \tag{11}$$

subject to certain constraints on the control and the state variables

$$\mathbf{c}(\mathbf{x}, \mathbf{u}, t) \leqslant 0 \tag{12}$$

$$\boldsymbol{\psi}(\mathbf{x}(T)) = 0 \tag{13}$$

The system performance in industrial systems is related to the profitability of the process. Profit, operating cost, and throughput have been used as performance functionals in industrial systems.

The necessary conditions of optimality can be obtained by adjoining the constraints (10), (12), and (13) to the performance functional J and considering infinitesimal variations with respect to $\mathbf{u}(t)$ and $\mathbf{x}(t)$.

Let $\boldsymbol{\lambda}(t)$ be the adjoint multipliers for Eq. (10), $\boldsymbol{\mu}(t)$ be the multipliers for Eq. (12) and $\boldsymbol{\nu}(t)$ be the multipliers for Eq. (13). Then

$$J = \phi(\mathbf{x}(T)) + \boldsymbol{\nu}^T\boldsymbol{\psi}(x(T)) + \int_0^T [L(\mathbf{x}, \mathbf{u}, t) + \boldsymbol{\lambda}^T(\mathbf{f}(\mathbf{x}, \mathbf{u}, t) - \dot{\mathbf{x}}) + \boldsymbol{\mu}^T\mathbf{c}(\mathbf{x}, \mathbf{u}, t)]\, dt$$

$$= \phi(\mathbf{x}(T)) + \boldsymbol{\nu}^T\boldsymbol{\psi}(\mathbf{x}(T)) + \int_0^T [H(\mathbf{x}, \mathbf{u}, \lambda, t) - \boldsymbol{\lambda}^T\dot{\mathbf{x}}]\, dt \tag{14}$$

where

$$H(\mathbf{x}, \mathbf{u}, t) = L(\mathbf{x}, \mathbf{u}, t) + \boldsymbol{\lambda}^T\mathbf{f}(\mathbf{x}, \mathbf{u}, t) + \boldsymbol{\mu}^T\mathbf{c}(\mathbf{x}, \mathbf{u}, t) \tag{15}$$

denotes the *Hamiltonian* of the system. Notice that $\boldsymbol{\mu}$ is nonzero only if the constraint is violated, i.e., if $\mathbf{c}(\mathbf{x}, \mathbf{u}, t) > 0$. Considering variations

$$\overline{\delta J} = (\phi_x + \boldsymbol{\nu}^T\boldsymbol{\psi}_x)\boldsymbol{\delta}\mathbf{x}|_{t=T} \int_0^T (\mathbf{H}_x\, \boldsymbol{\delta}\mathbf{x} + \mathbf{H}_u\, \boldsymbol{\delta}\mathbf{u} - \boldsymbol{\lambda}^T\, \boldsymbol{\delta}\dot{\mathbf{x}})\, dt$$

$$= (\phi_x + \boldsymbol{\nu}^T\psi_x - \boldsymbol{\lambda}^T)\, \boldsymbol{\delta}\mathbf{x}|_{t-T} + \int_0^T [(\mathbf{H}_x + \dot{\boldsymbol{\lambda}}^T)\, \boldsymbol{\delta}\mathbf{x} + \mathbf{H}_u\, \boldsymbol{\delta}\mathbf{u}]\, dt$$

Setting

$$\dot{\boldsymbol{\lambda}} = -\mathbf{H}_x^T \tag{16}$$

and

$$\boldsymbol{\lambda}(T) = (\phi_x^T + \psi_x^T\nu)|_{t=T} \tag{17}$$

we obtain

$$\overline{\delta J} = \int_0^T \mathbf{H}_u\, \boldsymbol{\delta}\mathbf{u}\, dt$$

A necessary condition for optimality is that $\overline{\delta J}$ be zero for first order variations in $\mathbf{u}(t)$. Therefore

$$\mathbf{H}_u = 0 \tag{18}$$

Equations (16), (17), and (18) together with Eqs. (10), (12), and (13) are the necessary conditions of optimality. If Eq. (18) is solved for $\mathbf{u}$ in terms of $\mathbf{x}$, $\boldsymbol{\mu}$, and $\boldsymbol{\lambda}$, and the resulting expression for $\mathbf{u}$ is put into Eqs. (10) and (16), a two-point boundary-value problem results. A number of numerical methods are available for solving these problems. Some of them are:

1. Gradient or Steepest Descent Method
2. Quasilinearization
3. Newton–Raphson or Second Order Gradient (7)
4. Variational Reduced Gradient (*8*).

In the steepest descent methods, a control history $\mathbf{u}^0(t)$, for $0 \leqslant t \leqslant T$ is assumed and Eq. (10) is solved forward in time. Then Eqs. (16) and (17) are solved backward in time and the function $\mathbf{H}_u(t)$ is calculated. The control history is then modified as

$$\mathbf{u}^1(t) = \mathbf{u}^0(t) - \alpha \mathbf{H}_u(t) \tag{19}$$

The variational reduced gradient method works on the same principle, but chooses some of the state variables as the independent variables whenever they happen to lie on the constraint boundary. Moreover, it updates $\mathbf{u}(t)$ along a conjugate direction and converges faster than a steepest descent method.

The Newton–Raphson method requires calculation of the second variations. It has faster convergence than the steepest descent method. A comparison of these methods and their application to trajectory optimization problems is given in references (*8*)–(*11*).

G. State Estimation

The next step is to develop a state estimator, using the identified model for the system. The state estimator may be designed to operate around a nominal optimal trajectory. As indicated earlier, knowing the values of the state variables, one may compute the future behavior of the system for feasible values of the control variables. Estimates of the state variables will be used in determining the closed-loop optimal control law for the system.

The process equations are summarized in the form

$$\dot{\mathbf{x}} = \mathbf{f}(\mathbf{x}, \mathbf{u}) + \mathbf{w} \tag{20}$$

$$\mathbf{z} = \mathbf{g}(\mathbf{x}, \mathbf{u}) + \mathbf{v} \tag{21}$$

since all unknown parameters have been identified. The values of R and $\underset{\sim}{Q}$ have been identified also, and any biases in the observations equations have been removed. The problem now is to develop an algorithm for real-time use that will produce the "best" estimate of the state. Since industrial processes are generally nonlinear, and nonlinear estimation theory has not yet been developed to a point where it can be used in practice, a suboptimal approach to state estimation is described below. The approach described below is often referred to as extended Kalman estimation (*12*, *13*).

1. The Extended Kalman Filter. Since the state estimator will be used in real-time on a process control computer, the discretized nonlinear differential equations are used. The discretized process equations may be written

$$\mathbf{x}_{k+1} = \mathbf{f}(\mathbf{x}_k, \mathbf{u}_k) + \mathbf{w}_k \tag{22}$$

$$\mathbf{z}_k = \mathbf{g}(\mathbf{x}_k, \mathbf{u}_k) + \mathbf{v}_k \tag{23}$$

where k denotes discretized time, $t = k\Delta T$, and ΔT is the sampling interval.

Numerous successful applications of the extended Kalman estimator have been reported in literature (*13–16*).

The extended Kalman filter is represented by the following recursive equations:

Prediction

$$\hat{\mathbf{x}}_{k/k-1} = \mathbf{f}_{k-1}(\hat{\mathbf{x}}_{k-1/k-1}, \mathbf{u}_{k-1}) \tag{24}$$

$$\hat{\mathbf{z}}_{k/k-1} = \mathbf{g}_k(\hat{\mathbf{x}}_{k/k-1}) \tag{25}$$

$$P_{k/k-1} = \Phi_{k-1} P_{k-1/k-1} \Phi^T_{k=1} + Q_{k-1} \tag{26}$$

Correction

$$\hat{\mathbf{x}}_{k/k} = \hat{\mathbf{x}}_{k/k-1} + W_k(\mathbf{z}_k - \hat{\mathbf{z}}_{k/k-1}) \tag{27}$$

$$P_{k/k} = (I - W_k H_k) P_{k/k-1} \tag{28}$$

where

$$\Phi_{k-1} = (\mathbf{f}_{k-1})_{x_{k-1/k-1}} = \partial \mathbf{f}_{k-1}/\partial \mathbf{x}_{k-1}\big|_{\hat{\mathbf{x}}_{k-1/k-1}} \tag{29}$$

$$H_k = (\mathbf{g}_k)_{\hat{\mathbf{x}}_{k/k}} = \partial \mathbf{g}_k/\partial \mathbf{x}_k\big|_{\hat{\mathbf{x}}_{k/k}} \tag{30}$$

$$Q_k = E[w_k w_j^T] = Q_k \delta_{kj}; \qquad R_k = E[v_k v^T{}_j] = R_k \delta_{kj}$$

The *a priori* initial values for the recursive equations are

$$\hat{\mathbf{x}}_{0/-1} = E[\mathbf{x}_0] = \bar{\mathbf{x}}_0 \tag{31}$$

$$P_{0/-1} = E[(\mathbf{x}_0 - \bar{\mathbf{x}}_0)(\mathbf{x}_0 - \bar{\mathbf{x}}_0)^T] \tag{32}$$

where E denotes expected value operator, δ_{kj} the Kronecker delta function and the overbar denotes the mean value.

The filter weighting gain W_k is given by

$$W_k = P_{k/k-1} H_k^T (H_k P_{k/k-1} H_k^T + R_k)^{-1} \tag{33}$$

2. Bias Problems. For the case where $\mathbf{f}_k$ and $\mathbf{h}_k$ are linear functions, it can be shown that $(x_k - \hat{x}_{k/k}) = \tilde{x}_{k/k}$ is a Gaussian variable. Its expected value and covariance, therefore, are sufficient to describe its probability distribution.

When $\mathbf{f}_k$ and $\mathbf{h}_k$ are nonlinear functions, the equation error is no longer Gaussian. In such cases, it may be difficult to obtain a complete description of its probability distribution. However, the first two moments, $E[\tilde{x}_{k/k}]$ and $E[(\tilde{x}_{k/k} - \bar{\tilde{x}}_{k/k})(\tilde{x}_{k/k} - \bar{\tilde{x}}_{k/k})^T]$, give a good representation of the distribution. These moments can be approximated as shown in reference *13*, and used to eliminate the estimation bias up to second order.

H. Closing the Loop

1. Closed-Loop Control. The final step in the modern approach to process control is to design the closed-loop controller. Two basic approaches can be used. The first is the conventional perturbation controller used extensively in the aerospace industry. The second approach, which is called multipoint control, had been successfully applied to the control of missile interceptors (*17*).

2. Perturbation Controller. The perturbation controller is optimal to second order in stochastic linear systems. If the controller synthesis problem is formulated as an optimal regulator problem, the linear perturbation controller will drive the system along the normal optimal trajectory and consequently deviations from linear system behavior will be minimized. The perturbation controller for the continuous case is described below.

Given the identified mathematical model of the system

$$\dot{\mathbf{x}} = \mathbf{f}(\mathbf{x}, \mathbf{u}) \tag{34}$$

the system performance function

$$J = \int_0^T L(\mathbf{x}, \mathbf{u}, t)\, dt + \phi(\mathbf{x}(T)) \tag{35}$$

and the system constraints

$$\mathbf{C}(\mathbf{x}, \mathbf{u}, t) \leqslant 0 \tag{36}$$

$$\psi(\mathbf{x}(T)) = 0 \tag{37}$$

the optimal control $\mathbf{u}^0(t)$, $0 \leqslant t \leqslant T$ is found using the techniques described in Section III,F. The optimum open-loop trajectory is denoted by

$$\mathbf{x}^0(t), \qquad 0 \leqslant t \leqslant T$$

Define the perturbations

$$\mathbf{x} = \mathbf{x}^0 + \boldsymbol{\delta}\mathbf{x}, \qquad \mathbf{u} = \mathbf{u}^0 + \boldsymbol{\delta}\mathbf{u} \tag{38}$$

Substitution of Eq. (38) into the right-hand side of Eqs. (34) and (35) results in

$$\boldsymbol{\delta}\dot{\mathbf{x}} = F\,\boldsymbol{\delta}\mathbf{x} + G\,\boldsymbol{\delta}\mathbf{u} \tag{39}$$

$$\delta J = \int_0^T (\boldsymbol{\delta}\mathbf{x}^T A\,\boldsymbol{\delta}\mathbf{x} + \boldsymbol{\delta}\mathbf{u}^T B\,\boldsymbol{\delta}\boldsymbol{\mu})\,dt \tag{40}$$

where the linear terms in δJ have been omitted for simplicity and the terminal cost $\phi(\mathbf{x}(T))$ has been set at zero (regulator problem). The problem defined in Eqs. (39) and (40) is the conventional linear regulator problem and has the well-known solution

$$\boldsymbol{\delta}\mathbf{u} = -B^{-1}G^T K\,\boldsymbol{\delta}\mathbf{x} \tag{41}$$

where

$$\dot{K} = -KF - F^T K + KGB^{-1}G^T K - A \tag{42}$$

with $K(t_f) = 0$. The major drawback of the controller design is that the control gains K must be solved backward in time. This means that they must be computed off-line. Recently Rao (*18*) developed a method for computing the control gains forward in time by using the method of incremental coefficients. This procedure is useful for on-line applications.

In typical applications, only a portion of the state variables are measurable and consequently the state estimate is used. This procedure is not optimal, but in most cases it yields very good results. The control law then becomes

$$\boldsymbol{\delta}\mathbf{u} = -B^{-1}G^T K\,\boldsymbol{\delta}\hat{\mathbf{x}} \tag{43}$$

where $\boldsymbol{\delta}\hat{\mathbf{x}}$ is computed, using the nominal optimal trajectory and the system state estimate $\hat{\mathbf{x}}$. For linear systems with quadratic performances criterion, this controller structure is optimal to second order.

3. Multipoint Controller. The multipoint controller design technique (*17*) is a new method for designing nonlinear optimal controllers. A detailed discussion of the design process may be found in reference (*17*). This control technique may be useful in complex process control systems.

IV. Application of Modern Control Methods to the Basic Oxygen Furnace

A. Process Description

The Basic Oxygen Furnace (BOF) is a highly efficient method for making steel from molten blast furnace iron. Since its beginnings in Europe in the late 1940s, the process has become the most common method for making steel. Over 50% of crude steel is now produced by the BOF process, and very few new open-hearth furnaces have been built since 1965.

Nearly pure oxygen under high pressure is blown directly into a bath of molten iron through a water-cooled lance. A precomputed charge of burnt lime and fluorspar, which are used to form the slag, is added prior to the start of the blow. Carbon reacts with the lance oxygen to form carbon monoxide. Other impurities, such as phosphorous and silicon, react with oxygen to form compounds with the slag calcium.

The hot exhaust gases (3000°F) are released into a water-cooled exhaust hood. Combustion of CO to CO_2 is partially completed before the hot gases are quenched by water. The cooled gases are sent to a gas cleaning system which contains either a wet scrubber or an electrostatic precipitator. A schematic diagram of the process is shown in Fig. 3. The objective of the

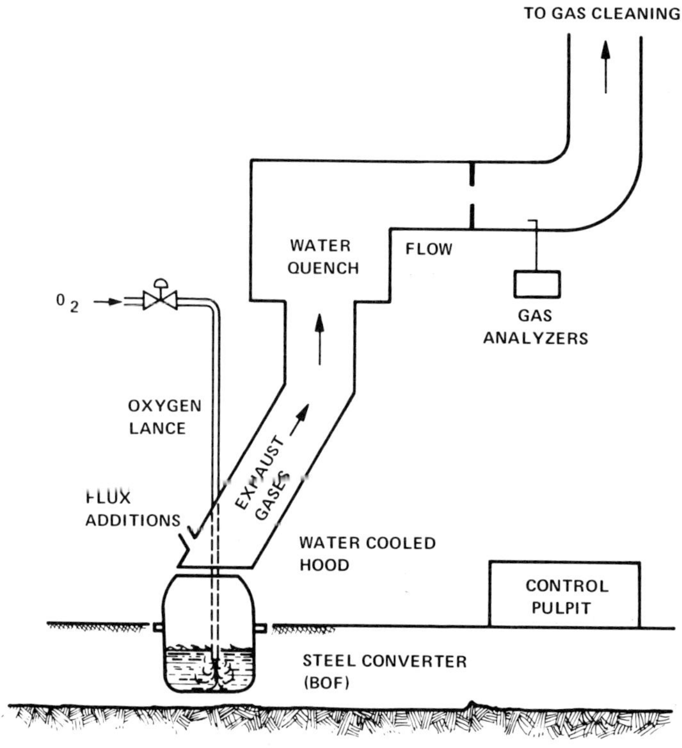

FIG. 3. Schematic diagram of the BOF and the exhaust gas measurement system.

process is to produce crude steel having a specific carbon concentration and temperature in minimum time.

Since the early 1950s, metallurgists have attempted to develop methods for estimating the percentage of carbon in the BOF. Europeans have traditionally attempted to use readings from indirect measurements in the process, such as flame color, sound, and oxygen calculations to determine carbon. These methods have been largely unsuccessful. American and Japanese metallurgists have attempted to model the process as a deterministic system and to use this model for control. These methods have had only limited success.

The process starts at high carbon percentage and relatively low temperature at the initial time T_0. Initially, carbon is removed faster than the rate at which the bath temperature increases; however, toward the end of the refining phase the rate of temperature rise increases and eventually overtakes the rate of decarburization. In the carbon/temperature plane the refining process can be represented by the curve shown in Fig. 4. As indicated above, the objective is to reach the terminal temperature and carbon concentration state in minimum time.

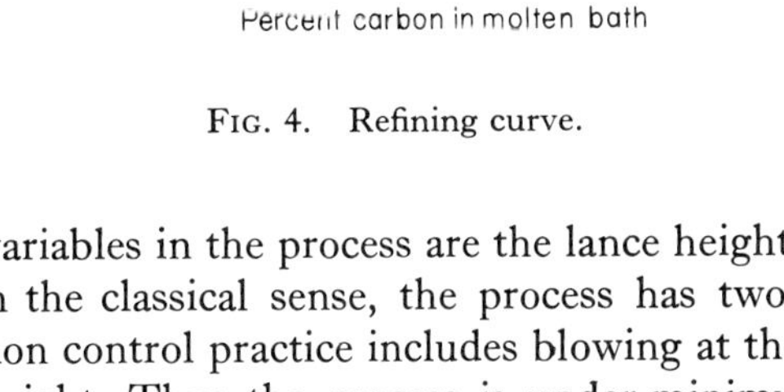

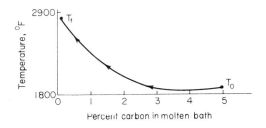

FIG. 4. Refining curve.

The control variables in the process are the lance height and the oxygen blowing rate. In the classical sense, the process has two states and two controls. Common control practice includes blowing at the maximum rate at fixed lance height. Thus the process is under minimum time control. The control objective is therefore to determine the best estimate of carbon and temperature in real time and to terminate the blow when the desired state is reached. Using this type of control, only one of the states can be controlled. Frequently, the temperature is controlled by the chemical makeup of the initial charge and is verified throughout the blow with bomb-type thermocouples. Carbon estimation is thus the key to optimum BOF control.

B. Data Acquisition and Modeling

In the early 1960s, continuous exhaust gas analysis systems were installed in new BOFs. However, the data were highly unreliable since CO_2 and O_2 instrumentation devices were in their infancy. By 1966 infrared CO_2 and CO analyzers had become fairly reliable, and the paramagnetic O_2 analyzer was commercially available.

A computer was required to determine the decarburization rate based on the waste gas data. The necessary additional data includes a mass flow measurement of the dirty wet gas, but an accurate mass flow measurement under these conditions is nearly impossible to obtain. In most cases, at least six measurements and several equations are needed to compute the decarburization rate. Furthermore, the signals are delayed by up to 30 seconds because of the gas transport lag in the exhaust gas system.

Early attempts at carbon estimation included numerically integrating the decarburization rate data to determine the percentage of carbon in the bath in real-time. This approach was unsuccessful because the initial conditions were known only to about an accuracy of 10%. Even if the initial condition is known perfectly, the mass flow computation is accurate to only about 15%.

C. State Estimation and Identification—A Case Study

In 1969, the authors began work on a project to develop a carbon estimation algorithm. The objective was to determine whether modern control techniques could be used to develop a practical carbon estimation algorithm.

The first task was to compute an estimate of the decarburization rate from raw measurements. The data were organized so that the decarburization rate was available with a total lag time of about 20 seconds, i.e., all estimates of carbon had to be predicted 20 seconds into the future to "catch up" with real-time.

A detailed literature search and internal research and development (*19*) showed that feasible mathematical models could not be derived because metallurgists could not agree on what chemical mechanisms limit the process reaction rate. Two alternatives were left:

1. To assume the process is completely stochastic, or
2. To assume the process contains deterministic and stochastic terms.

1. STOCHASTIC MODEL. It was decided to consider first the process as

purely random and to analyze the decarburization rate data, using correlation techniques. A correlation scheme developed by Mehra (*20*) was used to compute the correlation coefficients.

Let z = noisy observations of the decarburization rate $(-dc/dt)$ where $-dc/dt$ = pounds of carbon lost from molten bath per minute and t = time from start of blow.

Typical observations of dc/dt are shown in Fig. 5. In each of these heats, the lance height and lance oxygen flow rate control histories were identical.

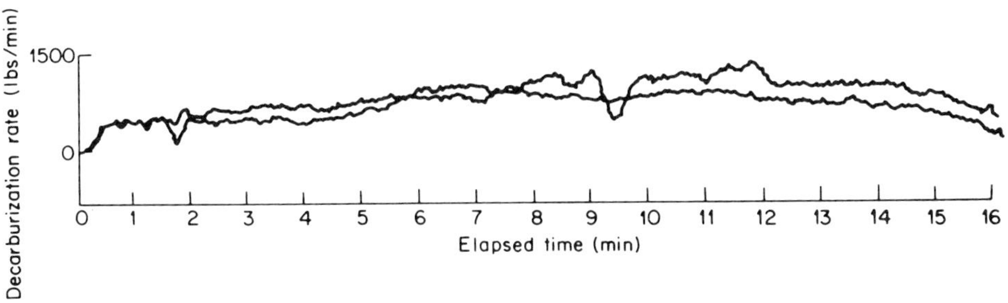

FIG. 5. Two typical observations of decarburization rate.

The correlation coefficients are defined as follows:

$$C_k^{(j)} = \frac{1}{N} \sum_{i=k+j}^{N} \nabla^j z_{i-k} \nabla^j z_i \tag{44}$$

where k denotes the lag, N denotes the number of data points, and superscript j denotes the order of the difference operator ∇ defined as

$$\nabla z_i = z_i - z_{i-1} \tag{45}$$

$$\begin{aligned} \nabla^2 z_i &= \nabla(\nabla z_i) = \nabla z_i - \nabla z_{i-1} \\ &= z_i - 2z_{i-1} + z_{i-2} \end{aligned} \tag{46}$$

and so on.

The following relations hold between correlations of different orders:

$$C_k^{(1)} = -(C_{k+1}^{(0)} - 2C_k^{(0)} + C_{k-1}^{(0)}) \tag{47}$$

$$C_k^{(2)} = C_{k+2}^{(0)} - 4C_{k+1}^{(0)} + 6C_k^{(0)} - 4C_{k-1}^{(0)} + C_{k-2}^{(0)} \tag{48}$$

The purpose of taking differences is to come up with a stationary random process whose correlation function dies out rapidly with lag k. All data points in the heat were used as the data base for the example shown below. The normalized correlations of the zeroth-, first-, and second-order differences of the decarburization rate $(-dc/dt)$ are shown in Figs. 6 through 8.

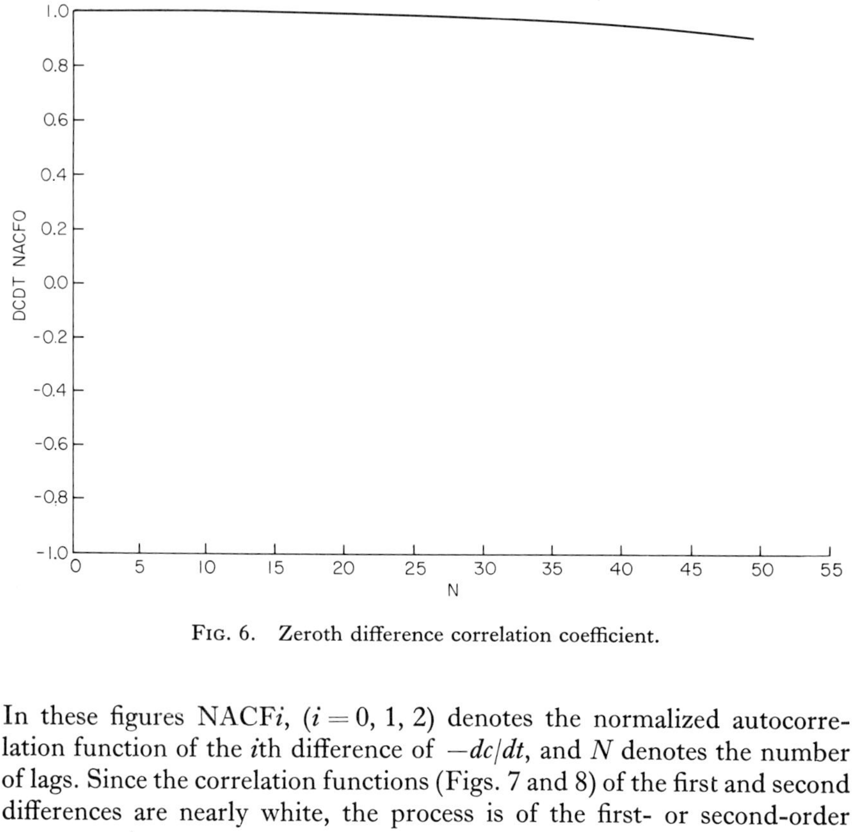

FIG. 6. Zeroth difference correlation coefficient.

In these figures NACFi, $(i = 0, 1, 2)$ denotes the normalized autocorrelation function of the ith difference of $-dc/dt$, and N denotes the number of lags. Since the correlation functions (Figs. 7 and 8) of the first and second differences are nearly white, the process is of the first- or second-order autoregressive type.

Based on a correlation analysis of the entire set of heats, a stochastic model of the following form was derived

$$\dot{C}_i = \dot{C}_{i-1} + w_{i-1} \tag{49}$$

$$w_i = \alpha w_{i-1} + n_{i-1} \tag{50}$$

$$C_i = C_{i-1} + \dot{C}_{i-1}\, \Delta t \tag{51}$$

$$z_i = \dot{C}_i + v_i \tag{52}$$

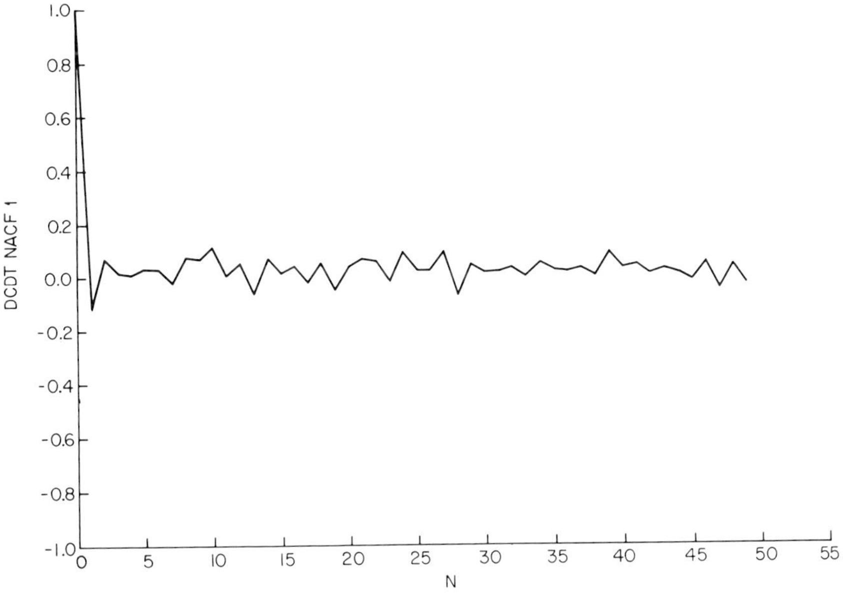

FIG. 7. First difference correlation coefficients.

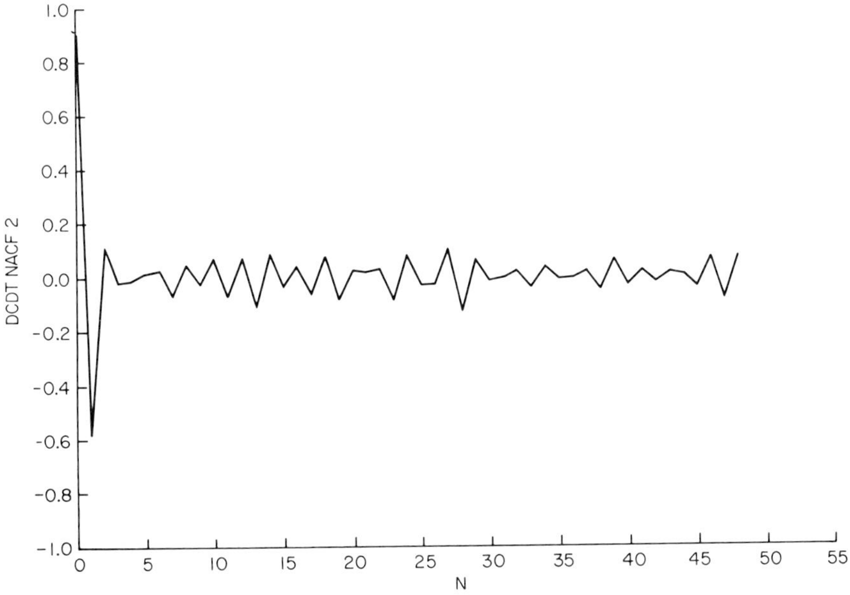

FIG. 8. Second difference correlation coefficients.

In these equations, $\dot{C}_i$ denotes carbon rate loss, w_i is a Markov process with a time constant $1/\alpha$ and n_i is a zero mean Gaussian process. The expected values are defined:

$$E[v_i v_i] = R \tag{53}$$

$$E[n_i n_i] = Q \tag{54}$$

$$E[w_i w_i] = q \tag{55}$$

$$E[v_i v_j] = E[n_i n_j] = 0 \qquad i \neq j \tag{56}$$

Let

$$\eta_i = z_i - z_{i-1} \tag{57}$$

The following relationships between the correlation coefficients and unknown parameters in the model are easily derived:

$$E[\eta_i^2] = 2R + q \tag{58}$$

$$E[\eta_i \eta_{i-1}] = -R + \alpha q \tag{59}$$

$$E[\eta_i \eta_{i-2}] = \alpha^2 q \tag{60}$$

$$Q = q(1 - \alpha^2) \tag{61}$$

Using these relations, α, q, Q, and R can be computed directly from the correlation coefficients.

Using the system of equations (49) through (54), the state-space model can be written

$$\mathbf{x}_{i+1} = \Phi \mathbf{x}_i + \mathbf{q}\mathbf{u}_i \tag{62}$$

$$z_i = H\mathbf{x}_i + v_i \tag{63}$$

where ΔT is the sampling interval and

$$\Phi = \begin{bmatrix} 1 & 0 & 1 \\ -\Delta T & 1 & 0 \\ 0 & 0 & \alpha \end{bmatrix}, \qquad \mathbf{g} = \begin{bmatrix} 0 \\ 0 \\ 1 \end{bmatrix} \tag{64}$$

$$\mathbf{x}_i = \begin{bmatrix} \dot{C}_i \\ C_i \\ w_i \end{bmatrix}, \qquad H = [1 \quad 0 \quad 0] \tag{65}$$

and

$$E[n_i n_i] = Q, \qquad E[v_i v_i] = R \tag{66}$$

2. Kalman Filter. Since the system equations are linear, the Kalman filter in its familiar form was used to process the raw data. Values for Q, R,

and α were obtained from the correlation analysis. An example of recursive identification of Q, R, and α is shown in Fig. 9.

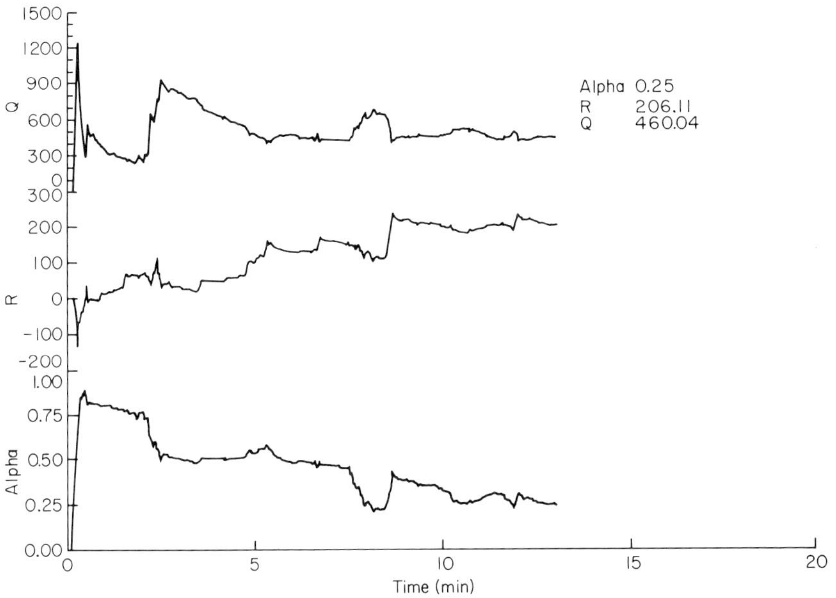

FIG. 9. On-line identification of Q, R, and α.

The Kalman filter was implemented to determine the percentage of carbon, using the mathematical model given by Eqs. (62) and (63).

For completeness, the Kalman filter algorithm is summarized below.

$$\hat{\mathbf{x}}_{k/k-1} = \Phi\hat{\mathbf{x}}_{k-1/k-1} \tag{67}$$

$$P_{k/k-1} = \Phi P_{k-1/k-1}\Phi^T + \mathbf{g}Q\mathbf{g}^T \tag{68}$$

$$W_k = P_{k/k-1}H_k^T[H_k P_{k/k-1}H_k^T + R_k]^{-1} \tag{69}$$

$$P_{k/k} = [I - W_k H_k]P_{k/k-1} \tag{70}$$

$$P_{k/k} = [P_{k/k} + P_{k/k}^T)^{1/2} \tag{71}$$

$$\hat{\mathbf{x}}_{k/k} = \hat{\mathbf{x}}_{k/k-1} + W_k[\mathbf{z}_k - H\hat{\mathbf{x}}_{k/k-1}] \tag{72}$$

where P denotes the state error covariance matrix.

The initial conditions for carbon were obtained from the initial hot metal charge data. The real-time estimate of carbon is computed by predicting seven data points in the future:

$$\hat{\mathbf{x}}_{k+7/k} = \Phi^7\hat{\mathbf{x}}_{k/k} \tag{73}$$

Average values for Q, R, and α were used in the Kalman filter for all heats. Each initial estimate of carbon was obtained from the charge data for that heat.

The algorithm was used in an attempt to calibrate the orifice coefficient used in the mass flow calculations. The orifice coefficient calibration resulted in coefficient values varying from 77,000 to 160,000 over a set of 131 heats. Since the initial percentage of carbon in the hot metal was used in orifice calibration calculations, and since the orifice plate remained clean and sharp for extended periods, it was concluded that the uncertainty associated with the initial carbon percentage was too great to yield accurate results for carbon prediction using integration.

The validity of the model was tested by correlating the innovation sequence $(\hat{z}_k - H_k \hat{\mathbf{x}}_{k/k-1})$ for each filter. In most of the cases, the innovation sequence was white with 95% confidence. An example of this carbon estimator is shown in Figs. 10 through 12.

In Fig. 10, the real-time estimate of carbon is plotted versus time. The carbon percentage is plotted in points, one point $= 0.01\%$. The asterisk denotes the true value of first turndown carbon. Note that the errors accumulate during integration of the measured decarburization rate. The actual innovations are shown in Fig. 11, and the correlation function for this sequence is shown in Fig. 12. The innovation process has units of lbs of

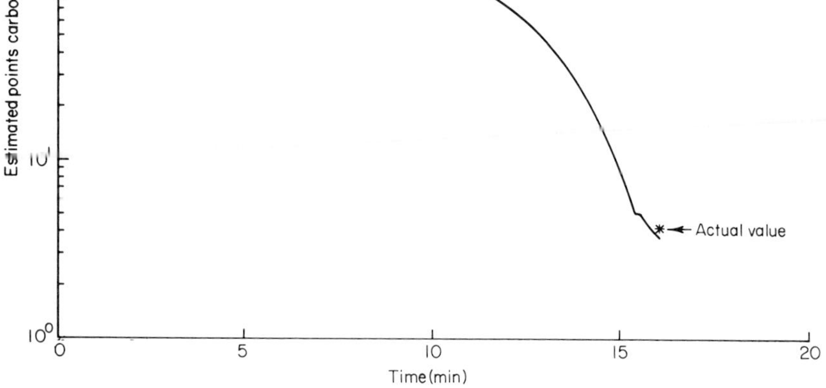

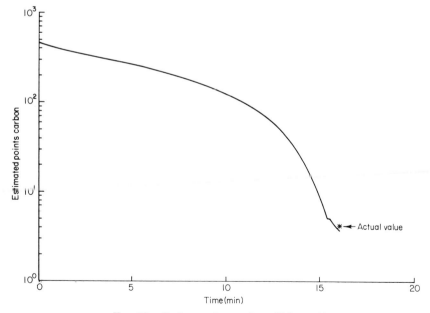

FIG. 10. Carbon estimates from Kalman filter.

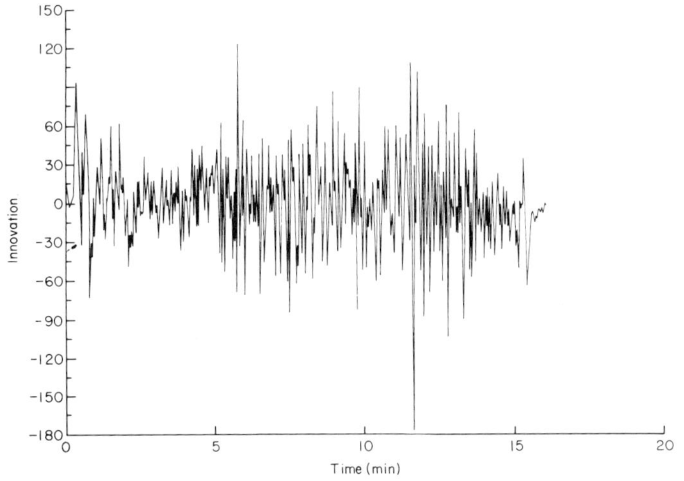

FIG. 11. Innovation sequence for the optimal filter.

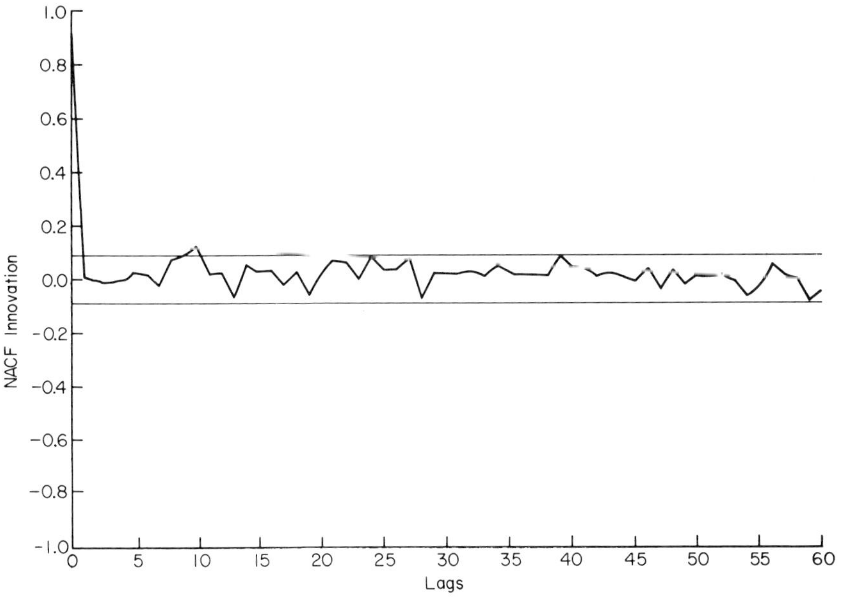

FIG. 12. Whiteness test for optimal filter.

carbon/min. The horizontal lines indicate the 95% confidence limits for the whiteness test.

The major reasons for the failure of this method are

1. Initial conditions are not known with sufficient accuracy.
2. Mass flow is randomly biased.
3. Wet gas is not saturated.

The initial conditions are determined for use in the static charge calculations by means of a load cell and a chemical analysis. Both measurements are, at best, accurate to only 5%.

The mass flow measurement requires the knowledge of an orifice coefficient. Since initial conditions contain substantial errors, the orifice calibration contains errors up to nearly 50%.

The wet gas was assumed to be saturated with water vapor. This may be true at times, but often the gas is not saturated. Furthermore, some of the CO_2 is absorbed by the water vapor, and this effect was not considered.

3. Optimal Smoothing. The optimal linear smoothing algorithm was applied to the filered data in the hope of providing a better estimate of the initial conditions on $\dot{C}$, C, and w. The smoothing algorithm selected for use was developed by Mehra (*21*). For completeness, the algorithm is summarized below:

Let $\boldsymbol{\lambda}_k = n_x$-vector representing the costate vector and $\hat{\mathbf{x}}_{k/N} = n_x$-vector representing the smoothed state estimate at time k given N data points.

The recursive lambda equations are solved backward in time:

$$\boldsymbol{\lambda}_N = 0 \tag{74}$$

$$\boldsymbol{\lambda}_{k-1} = (I - W_k H_k)^T \Phi_k^T \boldsymbol{\lambda}_k + H_k(H_k P_{k/k-1} H_k^T + R_k)^{-1}(\mathbf{z}_k - \mathbf{z}_{k/k-1}) \tag{75}$$

The smoothed state estimate is given by

$$\hat{\mathbf{x}}_{k/N} = \hat{\mathbf{x}}_{k/k} + P_{k/k} \Phi_k^T \boldsymbol{\lambda}_k \tag{76}$$

and the covariance matrices for the smoothed estimates are given by

$$\Lambda_N = 0 \tag{77}$$

$$\Lambda_{k-1} = (I - W_k H_k)^T \Phi_k^T \Lambda_k \Phi_k (I - W_k H_k) + H_k^T (H_k P_{k/k-1} H_k^T + R_k)^{-1} H_k \tag{78}$$

$$P_{k/N} = P_{k/k} - P_{k/k} \Phi_k^T \Lambda_k \Phi_k P_{k/k} \tag{79}$$

Note that $P_{k/N}$ is smaller than $P_{k/k}$. The algorithm provided improved estimates of the initial conditions on $\dot{C}$ and w; however, since there is no coupling between C and $\dot{C}$ or C and w from Eq. (64), the smoothed estimate of the initial condition on X_2 remained unchanged.

4. NONLINEAR CARBON ESTIMATOR. The decarburization curves reveal a sharp increase in decarburization after initiation of the blow, a relatively level decarburization rate, and finally a reduction in carbon loss rate. These three phases have been labeled the slag formation, carbon boil, and refining phases, respectively. Note that the inputs to the process (lance height and oxygen blowing rate) do not change throughout the process. In effect, the process is autonomous. Each phase has a model peculiar to that phase of the process. It was also clear that events occurring during the early phases of the process did not significantly influence the process behavior during the refining phase. It was decided to consider the refining phase separately.

A detailed literature search and internal research (*19*) showed that accurate mathematical models could not be derived, since metallurgists could not agree on what chemical mechanisms predominate the process. Therefore it was decided to model the refining phase of the blow with an empirically derived model. The derivation of this model may be found in reference (*22*). A variation of the model given in reference (*23*) was selected for online use. The model is given below:

$$\dot{x}_1 = -x_1 x_2 (k_1 u - x_1) + w_1 \tag{80}$$

$$\dot{x}_2 = w_2 \tag{81}$$

$$z = x_1 + v \tag{82}$$

where x_1 represents the decarburization rate, x_2 the refining factor, k_1 the average specific decarburization rate during the carbon boil phase, w_1 and w_2 represent random process noise components, and v represents instrumentation noise. The following variables are defined for this model.

$$\begin{aligned} E[vv] &= r \\ E[w_1 w_1] &= Q_1 \\ E[w_2 w_2] &= Q_2 \\ E[w_1 w_2] &= 0 \end{aligned} \tag{83}$$

The first-order extended Kalman filter, (*13*) for the system (80)–(82) is

Prediction Equation

$$\dot{\hat{x}}_1^- = -\hat{x}_1 \hat{x}_2 (k_1 u - \hat{x}_1) \tag{84}$$

$$\dot{\hat{x}}_2^- = 0 \tag{85}$$

$$\dot{P}^- = FP + PF^T + Q \tag{86}$$

Correction Equations

$$\hat{\mathbf{x}} = \hat{\mathbf{x}}^- + W(z - H\hat{\mathbf{x}}^-) \tag{87}$$

$$P = (I - WH)P^- \tag{88}$$

$$W = P^- H^T (HPH^T + R)^{-1} \tag{89}$$

where F denotes the Jacobian

$$F = \begin{bmatrix} \dfrac{\partial f_1}{\partial x_1} & \dfrac{\partial f_1}{\partial x_2} \\ \dfrac{\partial f_2}{\partial x_1} & \dfrac{\partial f_2}{\partial x_2} \end{bmatrix}, \qquad H = [1, 0] \tag{90}$$

The prediction equations are integrated forward to the next data point, and the results are used with the raw data at that time to compute an updated estimate of the state variables using the correction equations. The algorithm is initiated at any time after the start of the refining phase.

The above filter contains bias errors that can be corrected by adding the term

$$p_{11}\hat{x}_2 - (k_1 u - 2\hat{x}_1)p_{12} \tag{91}$$

to Eq. (83). The algorithm is then optimal to second order (13). Typical examples of the results of using this algorithm are shown in Figs. 13 through 16.

In Fig. 13 a plot of the real-time carbon estimate is shown. The carbon estimate is plotted in "points" of carbon, where 1 point $= 0.01\%$. The three-state linear filter described above is used during the slag formation

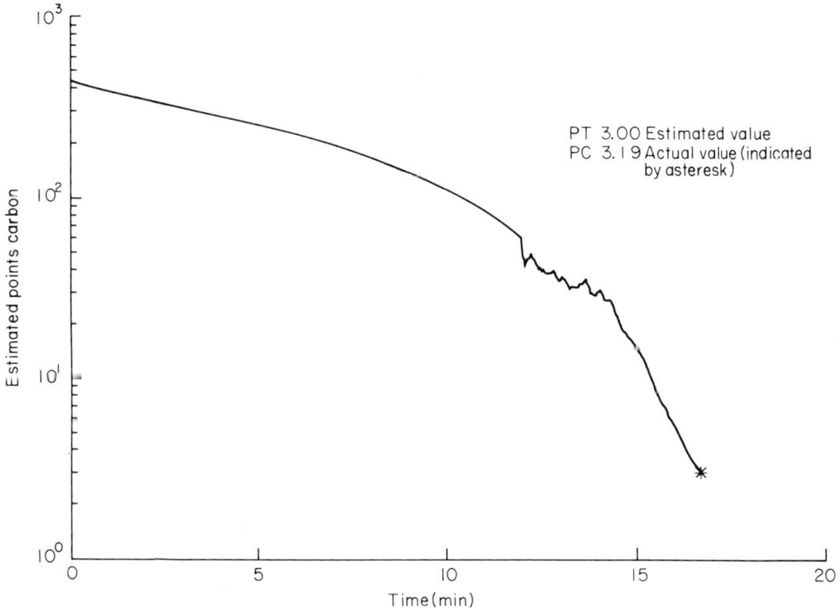

FIG. 13. Typical real-time estimated carbon curve.

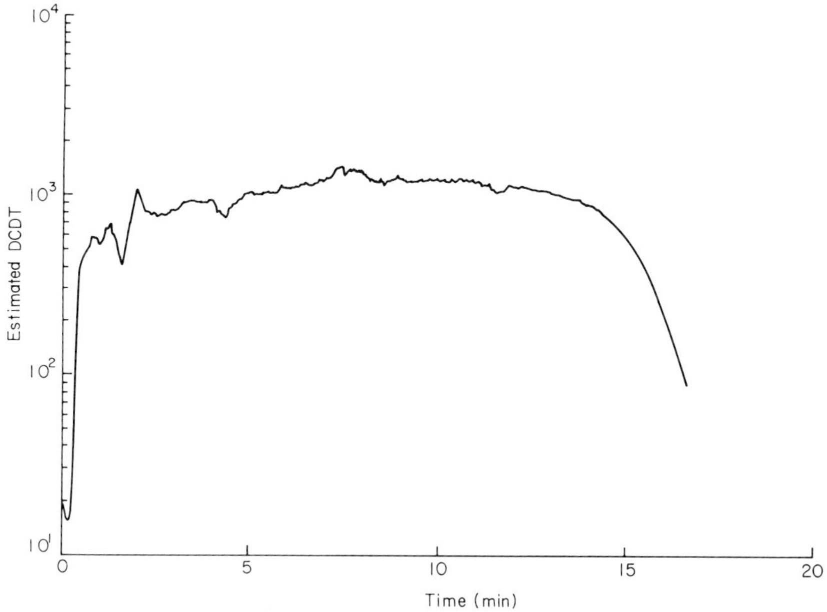

FIG. 14. Typical carbon loss rate curve.

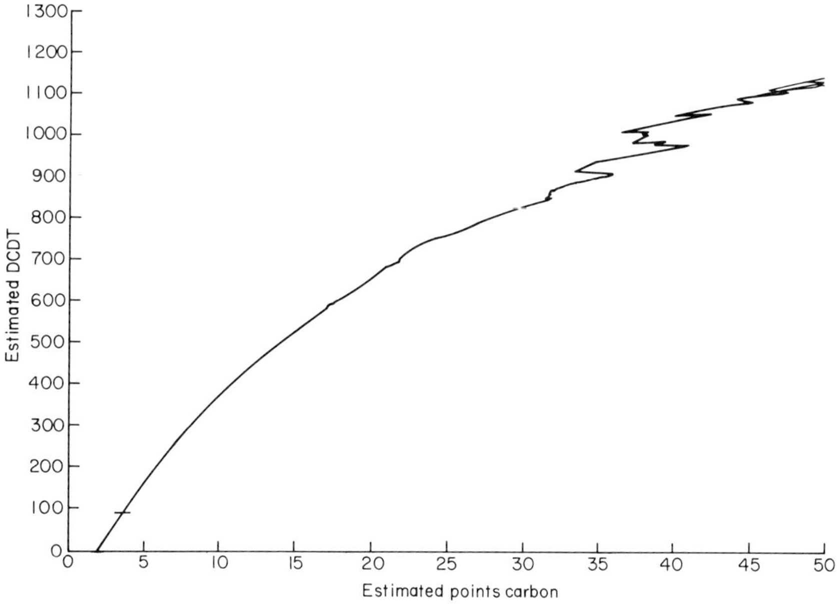

FIG. 15. Refining curve for typical heat.

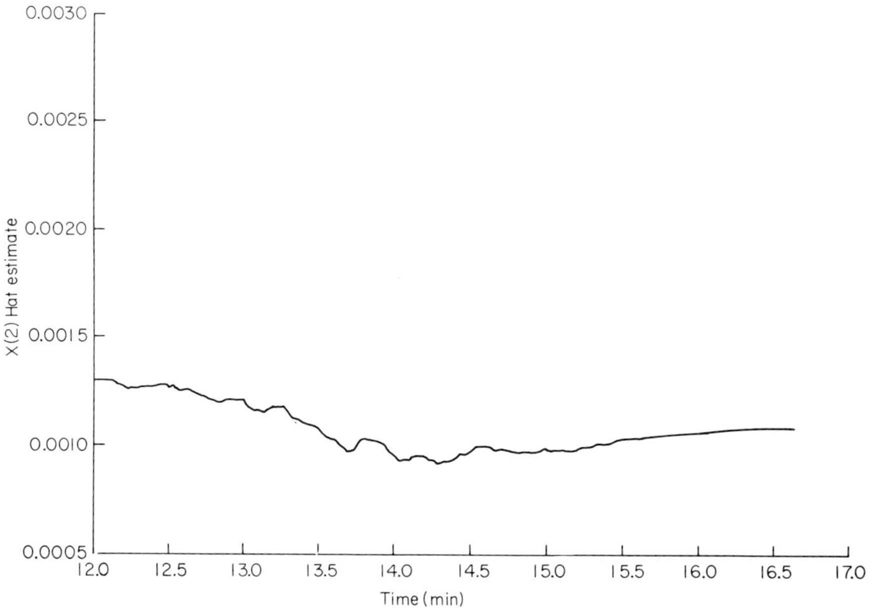

FIG. 16. Refining rate trajectory.

and carbon boil phases of the process. The initial conditions for the three state filter are obtained directly from the initial charge calculations. Twelve minutes into the blow, the nonlinear filter is initiated. Note the improvement in the estimate of the decarburization rate when the nonlinear filter is initialized. In Fig. 13, PT denotes true carbon, and PC denotes the real-time estimate of percentage carbon from the nonlinear filter.

In Fig. 14, a plot of estimated carbon loss rate is shown. Note that not much filtering is performed on the data until the refining phase begins. In Fig. 15, the phase plane diagram for the example heat is shown. In this figure the estimated decarburization rate is plotted versus estimated points of carbon. The refining curves are not smooth and vary throughout the refining phase.

In Fig. 16, the state variable x_2 is plotted. This variable has dimensions $(\text{lbs})^{-1}$ of carbon. The variable represents the refining rate in the exponential expression for decarburization rate. Note that it is not constant and changes with each new data point. The refining rate is estimated at each data point on the basis of observations of the decarburization rate. The nonlinear filter was insensitive to the initial conditions at $t = 12$ minutes and, during later stages of the study, only the nonlinear filter was used. The filter was initialized with the first observation of $(-dc/dt)$ and an initial estimate of $\hat{x}_2$. The overall performance of the filter was not degraded by this approximation. The sensitivity to variations in the orifice coefficient was examined, and it was decided to fix the coefficient at an arbitrary value.

5. Summary of Results. The algorithm described herein is substantially more efficient than those previously reported in the literature (*24*, *25*). A histogram of terminal errors obtained from actual data is summarized in Fig. 17. The computational requirements are negligible compared with

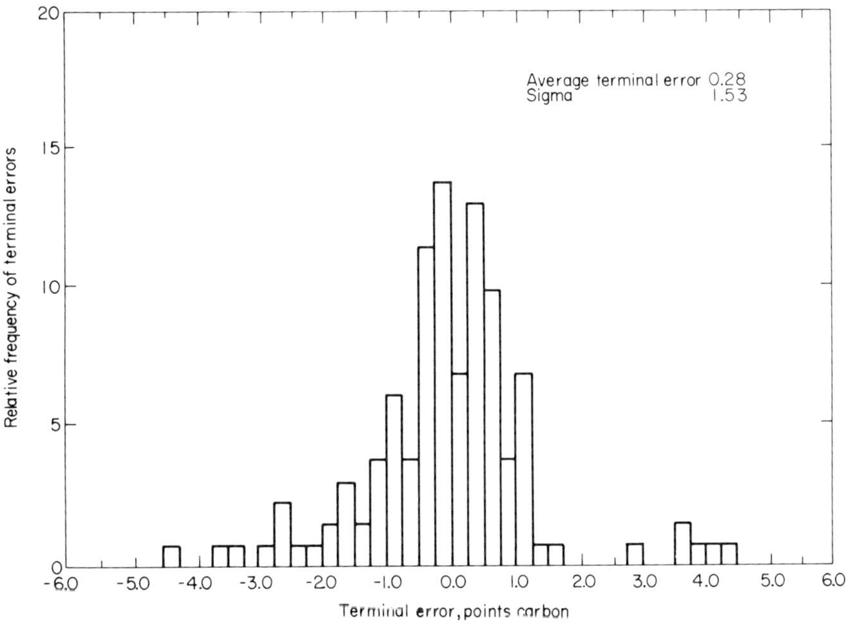

Fig. 17. Data analysis.

other techniques. The algorithm is general in form and can be modified easily for use on other BOF processes.

The performance reported above can be significantly improved by adjusting the starting times for the refining phase. The filter also provides an estimate of the state covariance matrix that could be used in the derivation of an optimal stochastic closed-loop controller for the BOF.

D. Feedback Controller

As indicated earlier in this section, the overall objective is to produce steel with a certain composition and temperature in minimum time.

Temperature and carbon are the major state variables to be controlled, and lance height and oxygen blowing rate are the control variables. At present, near optimal control is achieved by following an open-loop policy of lance height position control and a specified oxygen blowing rate schedule. In one basic oxygen shop, for example, the lance height and oxygen flow trajectories consist of three piecewise linear portions. The terminal state of temperature is achieved by proper blending of the raw material charge ingredients and the amount of carbon is controlled by turning off the oxygen at the appropriate time.

To design a true closed-loop control system, the effect of a certain control action on the state variables must be identified on-line. Since the controls are not manipulated during the refining stage of the blow, it is impossible to identify this relationship using present operating practices. In the opinion of the authors, the next step in achieving closed-loop control is to identify the dynamics of the process on-line. This step can be easily achieved by requesting that the operator "pulse" the oxygen blowing rate early in the refining phase. This would result in an improved dynamic model of the process that would subsequently improve the estimation accuracy and consequently improve the present method of terminal control. To date, no attempts at closed loop control of the BOF process have been reported.

V. Conclusions

In this paper, an application of nonlinear state estimation to a complex industrial process was described. The entire modern control methodology, which includes closing the loop, has not been implemented; however, in the near future closed-loop control of the type described above will almost certainly be achieved. The work described here on carbon estimation is really just the beginning of the development of successful closed-loop control of the BOF. However, this work does indicate that the techniques of modern control theory can be successfully applied to solving the difficult control problems of industrial processes.

This paper has traced the relatively slow progress towards achieving closed-loop control of industrial processes by using on line computers. After a 13 year history, it now begins to appear that the tools of modern control theory are going to be used at an increasing rate to compensate for the lack of understanding of the complex mechanism underlying many industrial processes. It is clear that the available modern techniques are capable of the task. What is not so clear is whether or not the process industries are ready to accept these modern approaches. A great deal of inertia must be overcome and it may require a new generation of industrial plant engineers before this potential will be fully realized.

References

1. T. M. Stout, Economics of computers in process control. *Automation* (Oct. 1966).
2. M. Cuenod and A. P. Sage, Comparison of some methods used for process identification in automatic control systems. *IFAC Symp., Prague, 1967.*
3. A. Wald, Note on the consistency of the maximum likelihood estimate. *Annu. Math. Statist.* **20**, 595 (1949).
4. J. Johnston, "Econometric Methods." McGraw-Hill, New York, 1964.
5. T. Kailath, A General Likelihood-Ratio Formula for Random Signals in Gaussian Noise. *IEEE Trans. Inform. Theory* **IT-14**, No. 3 (1969).
6. R. K. Mehra, Identification of stochastic linear dynamic systems. *IEEE 8th Symp. Adaptive Processes, 1969.*
7. R. K. Mehra, Maximum likelihood identification of aircraft parameters. Preprints of 1970 JACC (1970).
8. R. K. Mehra and R. Davis, "A Generalized Gradient Method for Optimal Control Problems with Inequality Constraints and Singular Area," Res. Rep. No. 2. Systems Control, Inc., Palo Alto, California, 1970.
9. A. E. Bryson and Y. C. Ho, "Applied Optimal Control." Blaisdell, Waltham, Massachusetts, 1969.
10. R. K. Mehra and A. E. Bryson, Conjugate gradient methods with an application to V/STOL flight path optimization. *AIAA J. Aircraft* **6**, No. 2 (1969).
11. S. R. McReynolds, "The Computation and Theory of Optimal Control." Academic Press, New York, 1970.
12. R. E. Larson, R. M. Dressler, and R. S. Ratner, Precomputation of the weighting matrix in an extended Kalman filter. Preprints of 1967 JACC, Philadelphia, Pennsylvania, pp. 634–645 (1967).
13. M. Athans, R. P. Wishner, and A. Bertolini, Suboptimal state estimation for continuous time nonlinear systems from discrete noisy measurements. *IEEE Trans. Autom. Control* **AC-13**, No. 5, 504–518 (1968).
14. K. J. Cox, Case study on Apollo lunar module digital autopilot. Joint Automatic Control Conference Case Studies in System Control, University of Colorado, Boulder, Colo., August 1969.
15. Aloise Braga-Illa, Case study on automatic orbit control of the Lincoln experimental satellite LES-6. Joint Automatic Control Conference Case Studies in System Control, University of Colorado, Boulder, Colo., August 1969.
16. K. J. Aström, Computer control of a paper machine—an application of linear stochastic control theory. Case Studies, Joint Automatic Control Conference, Georgia Tech., June 1970.
17. D. M. Salmon and P. V. Kokotovic, Design of feedback controllers for nonlinear plants. *IEEE Trans. Autom. Control* **AC-14**, No. 3, 289–292 (1969).
18. H. S. Rao and E. D. Denman, A forward integrating algorithm for the linear regulator problem. IEEE SWIEEECO Record of Technical Papers, Dallas, Texas, pp. 192–196, April 22, 24, 1970.

19. C. H. Wells, Optimum estimation of carbon and temperature in a BOF. Preprints of the 1970 JACC, Atlanta, Georgia (1970).
20. R. K. Mehra, On-line identification of linear dynamic systems with applications to Kalman filtering. Preprints of 1970 Joint Automatic Control Conference, Atlanta, Georgia, June 1970.
21. R. K. Mehra, On optimal and suboptimal linear smoothing. *Proc. Nat. Electron. Conf.*, **24** *1968.*
22. T. Isohe, Automatic control in the iron and steel industry. *Automatica* (1970).
23. W. E. Dennis *et al.*, Practical application of dynamic control to the BOF. *Rev. Met.* (*Paris*) **66**, 519–526 (1969).
24. D. W. Kern and P. D. Stelts, BOF control utilizing an in-furnace liquid vs. carbon and temperature sensor. 76th General Meeting of American Iron and Steel Institute, New York, May 23, 1968.
25. A. Shimada *et al.*, On computing control of a LD converter. TR No. 266. Yawata Iron and Steel Co., Japan, March, 1969.

Author Index

Numbers in parentheses are reference numbers and indicate that an author's work is referred to, although his name is not cited in the text. Numbers in italics show the page on which the complete reference is listed.

M

N

O

P

R

S

T

V

W

Subject Index

A

B

C

D

E

F

G